C000038122

GUIDE TO
TREES
OF BRITAIN & EUROPE

CHRIS HUMPHRIES • BOB PRESS • DAVID SUTTON

COMMISSIONING EDITOR *Frances Button*
EDITOR *Ingalo Thomson*
EXECUTIVE ART EDITOR *Mike Brown*
DESIGNERS *Chris Bell, Caroline Ohara*
PRODUCTION *Sally Banner*

Published in 2006 by Philip's,
a division of Octopus Publishing Group Ltd,
2–4 Heron Quays, London E14 4JP

ISBN-13 978-0-540-8734-1
ISBN-10 0-540-08734-3

A CIP catalogue record for this book is available
from the British Library.

First published as the *Hamlyn Guide to Trees
of Britain and Europe* 1981. Subsequent editions
1985, 1989, 1992, 2005.

Printed in China

FRONT COVER: *clockwise from top left Tilia x euchlora;*
legumes, *Acacia;* leaf, *Acer palmatum c.v. 'Atropurpureum';*
flower, *Corynabutilon vitifolium; Cedrus deodora;* acorn,
Quercus coccinea; female cone, *Picea sitchensis;* fruit,
Punica granatum (Philip's).
BACK COVER: *left fruit, Crataegus orientalis; right fruit,
Pyrus salvifolia* (Philip's).

Other titles from Philip's

Philip's publish a range of titles of
geographical interest in the same format
as this book, including:

Philip's Guide to Wetlands
Philip's Guide to Mountains
Philip's Guide to Oceans
Philip's Guide to Weather
Philip's Guide to Minerals, Rocks & Fossils
Philip's Guide to Gems
Philip's Guide to Fossils of the World
Philip's Guide to Global Hazards
Philip's Guide to the State of the World

For details of Philip's products
website: **www.philips-maps.co.uk**
email: **philips@philips-maps.co.uk**

tel: **020 7644 6940**
fax: **020 7644 6986**

CONTENTS

Preface	**4**
How to use this book	**5**
Introduction	**6**
What is a tree?	6
The morphology and growth of trees	6
Shoots	6
Habit and tree shape	7
Stem and wood structure	8
Leaves	9
Reproductive structures	9
Gymnosperms	10
Angiosperms	10
Distribution of trees	11
Systematics, taxonomy and nomenclature	12
Hybrids	14
Leaf shapes and inflorescences	**15**
Identification	**16**
Using keys	16
Key to genera	17
Keys to species	23
The trees of Britain and Europe	**34**
Gymnosperms	34
Angiosperms	90
Glossary	**310**
Bibliography	**313**
Acknowledgements	**313**
Index	**314**

PREFACE

This book, as with previous editions, is intended to provide the layman and the student with a simple guide to identifying the native, naturalised and more common exotic trees in Europe using a new pictorial key, descriptions and colour figures of the obvious features. Many genera have only one or two species and can be readily identified by the combined use of colour plates and photographs in popular works. There are, however, many other genera which are well represented in the European flora, and the accurate determination of species often depends on the correct use of keys and specialist monographs. Unfortunately, specialist literature is generally beyond the scope of the beginner and layman since it presupposes some detailed knowledge of the organisms in question. As an alternative, this book provides simple keys, illustrations and balanced, simplified accounts of the form, variation and distribution of most of the common European tree species, and aims to provide the currently accepted treatment of some 400 species.

The policy in selection has been to include all but the rarest of the native trees together with the most important exotics of silviculture and horticulture. Since more than a thousand introductions to Europe have been recorded at one time or another, many of them occurring only in gardens and private collections, it would be impossible to include them all in this book. The result is that exact identification in the culturally exploited groups cannot always be guaranteed. In an effort to keep things simple in these cases, and in those groups which involve complex forms of variation, the reader is directed to alternative sources.

The trees included are the same 400 or so species of the earlier editions, as experience tells us that little has changed despite the fears of global warming, the loss of some natives and the introduction of new exotics. It was hoped to include the new distributions to incorporate the new political boundaries in eastern Europe and Russia but our colleagues working on *Flora Europaea* tell us this is a task much larger than time available to revise this book. Therefore we have stuck to the only available edition of *Flora Europaea* as this is the chosen publication of specialists and botanists of many hues.

Chris Humphries
November 2005

The trees described in this book include nearly all native British species, most native European species, and many cultivated species if they are to be found in more than one European country. The geographical coverage follows the pattern adopted by *Flora Europaea*, which defines Europe according to its traditional boundaries. The area covered is shown in the map below. Sadly it has been impossible to update the distribution in the former Czechoslovakia, Soviet Union and Yugoslavia. These will therefore remain as published in *Flora Europaea*. Trees not included in this book are rarities from remote or restricted areas of Europe, and those only grown in private collections or Botanic Gardens. Since the equability of the European climate makes it possible to cultivate a wide range of introductions from China, Japan, America and Australia for timber, shade and decoration on a reasonably wide scale, the criteria used for inclusion are independent of native, cultivated or naturalized status.

This book consists of three main parts: keys to genera and species; the detailed species descriptions, with colour illustrations; and the index. These can be used independently or together in order to determine the name of a tree. If you wish to identify a tree for the first time, use the keys (which are all given together before the main part of the book, starting on page 16). If you believe you know the name of a tree already, it can be checked in the index and then found directly in the text. Almost all of the species described in the text are illustrated. The main plant groups, e.g. the oaks, the conifers, etc., are kept together so it is also possible just to thumb through the book to find the correct part.

Each description begins with the Latin name followed by the common English name, or the local European equivalent when an English name is not available.

In general, taxa below species level are only described when a variable species is represented in Europe by one particular subspecies or variety, or in the case of introduced trees represented only by artificially raised cultivars.

Key to country codes
Al Albania
Au Austria
Be Belgium
Bl Balearic Islands
Bu Bulgaria
Co Corsica
Cr Crete
De Denmark
FC Former Czechoslovakia
Fi Finland
Fr France
FS Former Soviet Union
FY Former Yugoslavia
GB Britain
Ge Germany
Gr Greece
Hu Hungary
Ic Iceland
Ir Ireland
It Italy
Ne Netherlands
No Norway
Pl Portugal
Po Poland
Ro Romania
Sa Sardinia
Si Sicily
Sp Spain
Sw Sweden
Sz Switzerland
Tu Turkey

INTRODUCTION

What is a tree?

The feature common to both shrubs and trees is that their main stems and branches increase in length each year by the outgrowth of buds (shoots) at the tips, and in diameter by the concentric growth of new internal layers, called secondary thickening. The difference is that a tree has a single main stem (a trunk or bole) between the roots and a diffusely branching crown, while a shrub has several stems arising from ground level. This book is about trees, but it must be remembered that the distinction between shrubs and trees is not always clear-cut. For example, the Common Hawthorn *Crataegus monogyna* is often seen as a hedge plant with many branches arising from ground level. However, because it can also occur as a tree with a distinct trunk up to 10m high it is included in this book. By the same token there are many shrub species, e.g. the Tree Heath *Erica arborea*, which can grow to 7m or more but which rarely if ever produce a regular single trunk, and are thus excluded. For the purposes of this book, a tree can be defined as a woody plant that commonly achieves a height of 3m or more on a single stem.

The morphology and growth of trees
Shoots

The shoot consists of stems which ultimately bear the leaves and flowers or cones. In most trees the shoot consists of a central axis or main stem with many side branches. The point where the leaf is attached to the stem is called the node. The angle which the leaf makes with the stem is called the axil, and borne in the axil there is frequently an axillary or lateral bud. The terminal bud is found at the apex of the stem or shoot. The bud can be considered as a specialized overwintering organ for the protection of the sensitive growing point, and can be best observed during the winter. Shown here is a three-year-old Horse Chestnut twig (*Aesculus hippocastanum*) presented to indicate the distribution of terminal and lateral buds. In addition to the buds, the scars from previous years' bud scales are also visible, as are the horseshoe leaf-scars with their distinctive vascular pattern. The other marks on the young twigs are lenticels; these are microscopic holes packed loosely with tiny particles of cork to give a porous breathing surface to the twig.

The terminal buds provide the points of growth extension to the main stems, whereas side branches are formed by the growth of some of the lateral buds on the second-year twigs. None of the

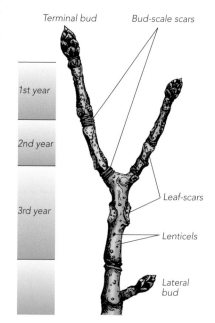

Terminal bud

Bud-scale scars

1st year

2nd year

3rd year

Leaf-scars

Lenticels

Lateral bud

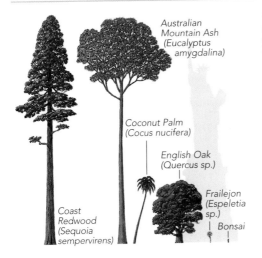

Australian
Mountain Ash
(Eucalyptus
   amygdalina)

Coconut Palm
(Cocus nucifera)

English Oak
(Quercus sp.)

Frailejon
(Espeletia
sp.)

Bonsai

Coast
Redwood
(Sequoia
sempervirens)

▲ *The range of sizes
in woody trees:
the tallest is Coast
Redwood* (Sequoia
sempervirens) *to the
smallest bonsai trees.*

lateral buds grow out into branches during the first year, except occasionally when the terminal bud becomes damaged. In the second spring the lateral buds of the second-year twigs can produce side branches. After three years of growth there is a main stem and two orders of side-branching.

Habit and tree shape

Trees are extremely variable in their overall shape due to a combination of growth characteristics and environmental influences. Most people know the difference in growth characteristics between a Christmas tree and an oak tree: one is pointed and conical while the other is rounded and bushy. To look at the difference in more detail, the Christmas tree has a very distinct central axis with rather short, more or less horizontal side branches emerging alternately from the main stem: the oak tree has several main branches, none of which dominates the others, and no main stem is distinguishable within the crown. That the main stem in Christmas trees grows upwards and the side branches horizontally is a manifestation of a control system called apical dominance. The apex is the fastest-growing point of the tree and the growth of the whole tree is controlled by hormones passing down from the main shoot into the side branches. Should the apex become damaged, one of the side branches bends upwards and assumes the role of the apical shoot.

By contrast, in mature flat-topped conifers, such as *Cedrus* and the Scots Pine *Pinus sylvestris,* there has been a gradual loss of apical dominance. With time, the side branches have grown up towards the same level as the apex, giving the tree a flat-topped appearance. All trees with regular growth at the main apex controlling the growth of lateral branches will be conical in shape with a tall crown at maturity. Poplar trees, wild cherries and several other broad-leaved trees grow in this way for many years, but the majority soon lose the central control of the main apex and quickly develop diffused branch systems. In regular, rounded, bushy-topped trees such as the oak, the lack of apical dominance is apparent from very early on in life.

The other factor affecting tree shape is the physical environment. The two principal physical influences on tree shape are light and wind. Trees grown in the open tend to retain massive old branches only a short distance from the ground. They appear to have short but stout trunks and very full crowns. Plantation trees, by contrast, which are grown close together, develop tall slender branch-free trunks and small overlapping crowns; the lower branches are crowded out by shading. Foresters grow the trees in this way for timber.

Wind is probably a more important environmental factor determining tree shape. Trees growing in sites with a continuous prevailing wind from one direction have longer, healthier branches on the leeward side, so that the crown appears to be blowing with the wind. This is due mainly to the fact that young buds exposed to prevailing winds are liable to be killed off. In addition, such trees regularly have their branches broken off as a result of strong winds, and those growing close to the seashore also become affected by salt spray on one side.

▲ *A section of a mature hardwood tree showing bark rays and central xylem hard wood.*

Stem and wood structure

The thickened main stem of a tree is the trunk; that part below the lowest branches is called the bole.

A transverse section or slice across a mature trunk will reveal three obvious layers: the inner heartwood, or xylem, the outer layer of corky bark, and a middle layer, the bast, or phloem. The xylem forms the main part of the thickened stem and can be seen to be composed of two parts: a central, dark coloured heartwood that contains no sap, and an outer, lighter coloured sapwood that is filled with water and dissolved substances passing from the soil. The heartwood in other words is dead and has ceased to function. With time it gradually fills with the hard, durable thickening material called lignin, the substance we call wood. Surrounding the wood cylinder is the phloem, through which pass the food products manufactured in the leaves. Outside the phloem is another layer, the cork layer, which varies in thickness according to the species of the tree. Bark and cork are both protective dead tissues.

Gymnosperm heartwood is called softwood and is made up of only two types of cells. The main conductive elements, called tracheids, are long, thickened fibres running end to end in the wood. The other cells, called parenchyma, consist of thin-walled brick-shaped cells arranged in radiating rows known as medullary rays, and it is these which give the characteristic grain to finished timbers.

Angiosperm heartwood is called hardwood and differs from gymnosperm wood in that it consists of three, rather than two, types of cells. Instead of having the fibrous support and the conducting tissues functionally combined into a tracheid, hardwoods have separate large, hollow, rather thin-walled conductive cells called vessels,

▼ *A transection of a monocotyledon wood showing the individual strands of xylem and phloem.*

— primary xylem
— primary phloem
— epidermis
— cortex

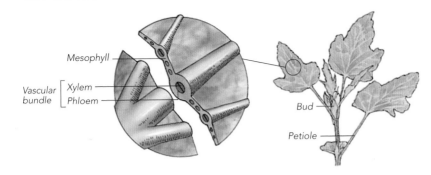

Mesophyll

Vascular bundle — Xylem
Vascular bundle — Phloem

Bud

Petiole

▲ *The detail on the left illustrates a sliced leaf showing the main conducting tissue (xylem and phloem), the parenchymatous mesophyl forming the bulk of the leaf structure, and the outer skin – epidermis. The illustration on the right shows the position detailed section and the positions of the bud and petiole (the leaf stalk).*

and rather more solid, thick-walled, sharp-pointed supportive cells called fibres. The parenchyma are arranged in medullary rays in much the same way as gymnosperm wood.

Leaves

The leaves are the food factories of plants. They are specialized organs which utilize water and dissolved minerals passed up by the roots and the stems from the soil, and carbon dioxide absorbed from the atmosphere through the stomata on the leaf surface, to manufacture complex food substances. They do this in the green part of the leaves, the chlorophyll, using sunlight as the energy source. The complex food substances, particularly carbohydrates, are redistributed around other organs of the plant by the phloem.

A typical leaf is composed of a leaf-stalk or **petiole** which attaches to the stem, and a **blade** (lamina) which is the functional part. In some cases the blade can be borne directly on the stem (in which case it is said to be sessile).

The leaf-blade is provided with a network of veins and the whole arrangement is called the venation pattern. The veins consist of xylem and phloem tissue, catering respectively for the transport of water and minerals into the leaf and the manufactured food substances out of the leaf. In some leaves there is one main vein which branches irregularly and further subdivides in a reticulate pattern – this is called net venation. Such a pattern is characteristic of elm, oak and maple leaves. In other species, particularly the monocotyledonous trees (the palms etc.) and conifers, instead of one main vein with branches there are several veins of equal size running parallel to each other, a pattern called parallel venation.

Reproductive structures

The sexual organs of gymnosperms and angiosperms are fundamentally quite different. The gymnosperm 'flowers' are almost always arranged in complex inflorescences called strobili or cones, and the two sexes are always borne in separate cones, although they may or may not be on the same tree. Angiosperm flowers by contrast are extremely variable.

9

▼ *The developmental stages of a conifer. The male cone gives rise to the pollen grains which fertilise the young ovules on the young female cone. The female cone develops with the ovules sitting on the ovuliferous scale.*

Male cone

Pollen grains

Young female cone

Mature female cone

They may or may not be arranged into inflorescences, the inflorescences themselves are very variable, and a single flower can be entirely male, entirely female, or hermaphrodite.

Gymnosperms

The young female cone consists of a central axis upon which the reproductive organs are arranged in a close spiral. One or more ovules are situated at the base of a leaf-like stalked structure, the ovuliferous scale, and enclosed by a lower and smaller scale known as the bract scale. The ovuliferous scale and bract scales vary in their relative proportions and their degree of fusion, so that in some genera, such as *Abies*, the bract and scale are always distinguishable; in others, such as *Cupressus*, the two are fused at maturity so as to be indistinguishable to the naked eye. The young cones are green and soft, and at the time of pollination the two scales are slightly separated to give the pollen access to the ovule. After pollen grains have been drawn into the ovules, the female cone closes up again and sometimes even becomes sealed by a resinous exudation. After several months, or even years in some taxa, the ovules become fertilized and seed development takes place. While all this is going on the female cone has become brown. Eventually the scales move apart to release the ripe seeds.

There is considerable variation in female morphology. The following are some of the more extreme examples. *Juniperus* has the scales fused into a berry. *Taxus* has a single ovule borne apically on a short shoot and surrounded by a fleshy aril. *Cephalotaxus* has female strobili composed of opposite pairs of cup-shaped bracts with two ovules at the base of each, usually only one of which develops into an olive-like 'fruit'.

The male strobilus consists of a number of microsporophylls or stamens, arranged in catkin-like clusters. Each sporophyll bears pollen sacs (microsporangia) which are usually coloured yellow, violet or crimson, and which contain the pollen grains.

Angiosperms

The flower of the angiosperms, like that of gymnosperms, is a modified leaf-bearing shoot, and propagates sexually by means of seeds. The ovules of angiosperms, however, unlike those of gymnosperms, are enclosed in an ovary. (The terms are derived from the Greek *angeion* meaning a case or vessel, *gymnos* meaning naked, and *sperma* meaning seed.) Another distinction is

Seeds on cone scale

Ripe seed

Seedling

the presence of a stigma at the tip of the ovary, specialized to catch pollen which can no longer reach the ovule directly, as it can in the gymnosperms. The pollen of gymnosperms is usually wind dispersed and therefore the cones are relatively inconspicuous. Although a number of the angiosperms are wind pollinated, e.g. the catkin-bearing genera (which also have inconspicuous flowers), the great majority are pollinated by animals. Flowers and animal pollination always occur together. A flower is a conspicuous organ consisting of four distinct groups of parts: **sepals** to protect the developing flower bud; fragrant or colourful **petals** to attract the pollinators; the **androecium**, consisting of the stamens (pollen sacs borne on filaments), and the **gynoecium**, consisting of an ovary containing the ovules, the stigma and the style. Most angiosperm flowers are hermaphrodite, but well-known dioecious exceptions include willow, birch, hazel, beech, oak and ash, which are generally catkin-bearing wind-pollinated plants.

There is considerable variation in the arrangement and structure of the flower parts. Each set of four parts is arranged in a whorl. The individual whorls differ in certain characters, namely the position of attachment to one another, the number of parts within each whorl and the degree of fusion between each of the parts, The picture is further confused by the fact that in some species various parts can be lost, for example the petals in *Eucalyptus* and in various catkin-bearing plants.

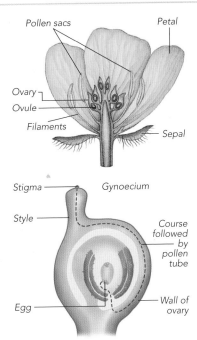

▲ The top illustration shows a section of a flower to show that angiosperms consist of four whorls; sepals subtending petals, subtending male filaments and pollen sacs and ovaries containing the ovules. The lower illustration shows the track of the pollen tube from the top of the stigma, through the wall of the ovary to eventually fertilise the ovule and endosperm (double fertilisation).

Distribution of trees

There are two main reasons for the considerable diversity in the European tree flora: the first is a combination of the wide range of ecological and climatic conditions, which have given rise to a rich native flora; the second is the centuries of man's activity which has brought exotic trees and extended the distribution of native trees into silviculture and horticulture.

The 190 native species included in this book are representative of several distinct distribution patterns. At the global level there are families such as the Fagaceae, the Ulmaceae and the Aquifoliaceae which span the continents on both sides of the equator. The Fagaceae family, for example, which is well represented in Europe by *Quercus*, *Castanea* and *Fagus*, is an extremely ancient one probably dating back to the early Cretaceous period. The closest relative of the northern beech genus *Betula*, so widespread in the northern hemisphere, is the southern beech genus *Nothofagus*,

11

equally widespread in the temperate areas of Australia, New Zealand, South America and the mountains of New Guinea and New Caledonia. The divergence of these two genera probably dates back to the break up of the ancient super-continent (Pangaea).

Within the northern hemisphere there is only one species of tree, the Common Juniper *Juniperus communis*, known to be widespread throughout Europe, Asia and North America. Nevertheless, there are quite a number of widely different genera which are represented by closely related species in the two separate continents. For example, the Eastern and Western Plane Trees, respectively *Plantanus orientalis* and *P. occidentalis*, are now widely separated on the two northern land masses, but probably formed continuous populations at a time before the continents drifted apart. Despite a long separation, a hybrid between the two species, the commonly cultivated London Plane *P. x hispanica* is a living testament to the genetic similarity of the parental species.

▲ *The shrub habit of* Juniperus communis.

In direct contrast to the intercontinental patterns are those genera strictly confined to either the New or the Old World. A classical Old World pattern for a relict distribution is seen in the Wing-nut genus *Pterocarya*, which has one species in the Caucasus, one in Japan and six in China. Another interesting example is the diverse genus *Cotoneaster*, which has some seventy species entirely restricted to the Old World mountain ranges. Much less diverse but showing another Old World distribution pattern is the genus *Laburnum*, which has three reasonably widespread species in southern Europe and western Asia.

Systematics, taxonomy and nomenclature

Systematics is the study of the relationships between organisms, and taxonomy is the process of making classification from that study. Most systems of classification are hierarchical, each level in the hierarchy being given a different name. Thus, a **species** is given a particular name, related species are put into the same **genus**, and in turn related genera are put into the same **family**. A **Taxon** (plural taxa) is a general term applied to any individual component or category within a classification; thus families, genera and species are all taxa, each at a different level.

▼ *The tree habit of a Plane tree.*

Man has always given names to different organisms in order to distinguish one from another. In the case of plants and animals the most familiar in everyday language are the common names. But although common names are convenient in everyday speech they have many disadvantages. They come into existence haphazardly with little direction from any one authority; they do not come within the control of any international body; the same name often refers to different organisms even in different parts of the same country, and, above all, common names are incommunicable to people of different tongues. It is true that many common names can be given qualifying names so that they apply to one particular species;

'Holm Oak', for example, refers to the evergreen species *Quercus ilex* L., but even this common English name is meaningless to, say, the Maltese and the French, who respectively call the same species 'Ballut' and 'Chîne-vert'.

Scientific naming is given precision by the adoption of Latin as a common language, since it is common to scientists, and can be understood by people of all nationalities. In botanical nomenclature a species is always given a binomial, so that a particular species can be identified together with the genus to which it belongs. All of the oaks are placed in the one genus *Quercus* and our chosen example, the 'Holm Oak', is called *Quercus ilex*. The full name of the Holm Oak is, however, *Quercus ilex* L. The 'L.' is an abbreviation of Linnaeus, the Latinized version of the name Carl von Linné, who first described the species in 1753. To give consistency to nomenclature, the name of the author of the first validly published name combination is always added (usually in an abbreviated form) to distinguish his use of the name. Occasionally a later author might use the same name for a different species. For example, Loureio gave a Burmese species the name *Quercus ilex* Lour. This later use is rejected.

With time, taxonomic concepts change due to increases in the amounts of material available for study and to changes in systematic philosophy. Furthermore, early botanists generally had wider species and generic concepts than we do today, so it has become necessary to create new genera for species removed from existing genera, to expand or contract species boundaries, or to reshuffle existing genera to accommodate new relationships. For example, Linnaeus first included the Common Alder in a broad genus of catkin-bearing trees, *Betula*, describing it as *Betula glutinosa* L. Another biologist, Phillip Miller, later considered that the name *Betula* should have a narrower range and be restricted to the Silver Birches. He described a new genus *Alnus* to accommodate the alders. It was left to a third author, Gaertner, to transfer the Common Alder to the genus *Alnus* Mill. The priority article in the *Botanical Code of Nomenclature*, the botanists' book of rules, insists that wherever possible the original specific epithet should be transferred to the new genus. The Common Alder thus became known as *Alnus glutinosa*. Since Linnaeus did not write the new combination but did coin the original specific epithet, his authority name is enclosed in parentheses at the end of the name and before the author who made the new valid combination. Hence the correct citation of the Common Alder is *Alnus glutinosa* (L.) Gaertner.

▼ Alnus glutinosa (L.), Gaertner. Also known as the European Alder.

There are three infra-specific categories used in general tree taxonomy which cater for variation within species. The **subspecies** category

13

caters for regionally distinct taxa which show some degree of intergradation with other regional variants of the same species. The **variety** category tends to cater for regional or sporadic variation on a smaller scale and at a level lower or less distinct than the subspecies. The application of names for both subspecies and varieties follow rules similar to those for species. The **cultivar** category caters for those variants which arise by deliberate selection, by cloning, or by mutation in trees raised in gardens and nurseries. Cultivars are given names according to the *International code of nomenclature of cultivated plants*, which differs from the botanical code in that authority names are not required. For example, the most commonly cultivated form of the Atlas Cedar, *Cedrus atlantica* (Endl.) Carrière, is the Blue Atlas Cedar cv. 'glauca', which has a glaucous blue waxy covering to the foliage.

Hybrids

A hybrid may be defined as the offspring of two dissimilar individuals, Since this book is concerned with different taxa (genera, species, subspecies, varieties and cultivars) the term can be restricted here to taxonomic hybrids, i.e. those involving crosses between individuals of different taxa. Thus hybrids can be intergeneric, interspecific, intervarietal, and so on.

Most of the hybrids described in this book are interspecific hybrids; in other words the parents belong to different species of the same genus. For example, the Hybrid Poplar is found in areas where its two parent species, the Grey Poplar, *Populus canescens* (Aiton) Sm., and the Aspen, *P. tremula* L., grow together. In Latin nomenclature, interspecific hybrids can be denoted in a variety of ways. When the male (pollen) and the female (ovule) parents are known it is conventional to put the female parent first. It is an unfortunate fact that the parental status of many hybrids is not really known, and that only the putative parents can be designated. Traditionally in such cases the names of the parents are given in alphabetical order with an 'x' between them, so that our example the Hybrid Poplar is given as *P. canescens x tremula*. Also, many of the hybrids which grow successfully in the wild are given single specific epithets in exactly the same way as conventional species, especially in the older taxonomic literature. In these cases an 'x' is given in front of the epithet to designate hybrid status, Thus the Hybrid Poplar can also be written as *P. x hybrida* Bieb.

The correct way to give the Latin name of an intergeneric hybrid (i.e. where the parents belong to species of different genera) is with a capital x in front of the hybrid name, However, these are extremely rare amongst trees and the only one in this book is the Leyland Cypress, *x Cupressocyparis leylandii* (Jackson & Dallim.) Dallim., an intergeneric hybrid between the Nootka Cypress, *Chamaecyparis nootkatensis* (Lamb.) Spach, and the Monterey Cypress, *Cupressus macrocarpa* Hartw.

▼ *A Leyland Cypress,* x Cupressocyparis leylandii *(Jackson & Dallim) Dallim.*

Ovate

Lanceolate, tip acute

Spathulate, tip obtuse

Orbicular

Linear, tip emarginate

Tip acuminate, margin double-toothed or biserrate, base truncate

Margin lobed, base auriculate

Margin dentate, base cordate

Palmate

Pinnate, leaflets elliptic

Twice-pinnate

Leaves rhombic, arrangement decussate

Arrangement whorled

Raceme

Panicle

Umbel

Cyme (pendent)

IDENTIFICATION

Using keys

The keys on the following pages can be used for the identification of all genera in the book and of species in genera containing more than six species. The genera with separate species keys are marked with an asterisk in the main key and two cross-references are given, the first to the page number of the text account and the second to the page number of the species key. The shorter genera simply have a cross-reference to the page on which the text starts. The keys given here are of the bracketed type and are dichotomous throughout, i.e. at every stage a choice must be made between two contrasting alternatives which together make up a couplet. They are designed to be practical, using as many field characters as possible, particularly those of leaf, bark etc., in order to facilitate identification throughout the year.

To find a genus, or species, to which a specimen belongs, start at couplet no. 1 and compare the specimen with the two alternative statements. For example, if it accords with the first line in couplet 1 of the generic key, proceed to couplet 2. However, if the specimen accords with the second line of couplet 1 then proceed to couplet 25. By continuing with the same process at each couplet, eventually the correct lead will be reached indicating the name of the genus, or species, to which the specimen belongs.

For most taxa the keys work reasonably well but sometimes they pose questions which appear to be entirely wrong for the specimen to hand. There can be a number of reasons for this, a common one being that the specimen to hand is an atypical plant – perhaps an obscure cultivar, or a rare species not actually included in the book. But perhaps the most likely reason is that there has been an error at one of the dichotomies in the key, probably due to misinterpretation of characters. The best remedy is to return to the first couplet and proceed through to the ambiguous dichotomy. If it is the case that a specimen does not exactly fit either lead one has to decide which of the two alternatives is the more relevant. In general the more reliable statement comes first. If, on the other hand, it is a case of total misjudgement at a particular couplet, the alternative lead must be taken and followed through to the appropriate part of the key.

Identification symbols	
P42	See this page number of main guide
⌁12	See this page number of Identification guide
▶	Illustration
*	Genera with separate species keys

Key to genera

1 Leaves dark green, hard, narrow and usually spine-tipped, scale-like or needle-like (except *Ginkgo*); veins parallel; usually annual growth in whorls; males and females always on separate trees; never with petals; fruit a cone, or berry-like
Ginkgo, conifers & taxads 2

Leaves lighter green, soft, leathery or hard, broad (rarely needle-like or linear); veins reticulate (except some monocotyledonous species); growth alternate or opposite, never in whorls; males and females hermaphrodite, monoecious or dioecious, with or without petals; fruit variable – a capsule, acorn, pod, nut, berry, winged or a pome etc.
Broadleaved angiosperm trees 25

2 Leaves fan-shaped, broadly 2-lobed, leathery, deciduous, fan-veined **Ginkgo** P34 ▶

Leaves scale-like, linear or lanceolate, but never fan-shaped **3**

3 Leaves appressed, opposite or whorled scales **4**

Leaves protruding scales, or not scale-like **9**

4 Foliage in flattened, fern-like sprays **5**

Foliage in multidimensional plumes **8**

5 Leaf scales 5mm or more wide, hard, glossy **Thujopsis** P49 ▶

Leaf scales less than 5mm wide, if glossy then soft **6**

6 Cones globose, woody when ripe **7**

Cones flask–shaped, leathery when ripe **Thuja** P48 ▶

7 Cones with 4 scales **Tetraclinis** P48 ▶

Cones with 6–12 scales x **Cupressocyparis** P38 **Chamaecyparis** P37 ▶

8 Free juvenile leaves at the base or the tip of the shoot *Juniperus* ☞23 P42 ▶

Leaves uniformly appressed scales **Cupressus** P39 ▶ x **Cupressocyparis** P38

9 Leaves mostly in rosettes on spurs from 2nd year shoots **10**

Leaves opposite or spirally arranged, neither in rosettes nor spurs **12**

10 Leaves soft, thin-textured, pale or bright green, deciduous **11**

Leaves hard, thick-textured, dark green, evergreen **Cedrus** P60 ▶

11 Spurs long and curved, leaves with pale margins **Pseudolarix** P65 ▶

Spurs short and straight; leaves uniformly coloured **Larix** P62 ▶

12 Fruits berry-like, without obvious scales **13**

Fruits cones, never berry-like, with obvious scales **15**

13 Fruits single-seeded surrounded by a bright red aril **Taxus** P35 ▶

Fruits several-seeded, blue, green or red **14**

14 Fruits globose; leaves needle-like or scale-like, in pairs or whorls of 3 *Juniperus* ☞23 P42 ▶

Fruits ovoid; leaves linear-lanceolate spirally arranged **Cephalotaxus** P35 ▶

15 Leaves arranged in 2 flat rows on either side of the shoots **16**

Leaves spirally arranged on the shoots **18**

16 Leaves and shoots alternate **17**

Leaves and shoots in opposite pairs **Metasequoia** P53 ▶

17 Female cone scales with short recurved spine **Taxodium** P52 ▶

Female cone scales without spines **Sequoia** P50 ▶

18 Leaves broadly triangular, 3–4cm long x 1cm wide at the base **Araucaria** P36 ▶

Leaves linear or linear-lanceolate, never more than 5mm wide **19**

19 Leaves with 2 obvious white bands on the lower surface **20**

Leaves without 2 obvious white bands on the lower surface **22**

20 Cones erect, leaves with sucker-like base *Abies* ♂24 P54 ►

Cones pendent, leaves not expanded at the base **21**

21 Leaves soft, but acute, cone bracts lobed **Pseudotsuga** P73 ►

Leaves hard, but ovoid, cone bracts not lobed **Tsuga** P72 ►

22 Leaves in bundles of 2, 3 or 5 *Pinus* ♂25 P74 ►

Leaves not in bundles **23**

23 Bark scaly, never fissured or fibrous, leaves sharp but never incurving *Picea* ♂24 P66 ►

Bark fissured, very fibrous, leaves sharp with long incurving spines **24**

24 Leaf-spine less than 1cm long, dull green or grey **Sequoiadendron** P51 ►

Leaf-spine more than 1cm long, bright green **Cryptomeria** P52 ►

25 Palm trees, with a single trunk and an unbranched crown of large compound leaves at the top **26**

Flowering trees, usually with a single trunk and a branched crown of small leaves **33**

26 Leaves pinnate 1–5m in length **30**

Leaves palmate 60–120cm in diameter **27**

27 Trunk covered by a 'petticoat' of dead leaves **Washingtonia** P309 ►

Trunk covered by leaf-bases or fibres, or smooth **28**

28 Leaves cut almost to the petiole with stiff straight segments **29**

Leaves cut two-thirds of the way to the petiole with soft, drooping segments **Livistona** P305 ►

29 Trunk densely covered with brown fibres, a moderate sized tree 3–12m high **Trachycarpus** P308 ►

Trunk smooth, a small tree 1–5m high **Chamaerops** P304 ►

30 Trunks very broad, studded with old leaf-bases **Phoenix** P306 ►

Trunks slender, smooth, ringed only by leaf-scars **31**

31 Leaflets less than 2.5cm wide **Arecastrum** P302 ►

Leaflets more than 2.5cm wide **32**

32 Leaflets divided at the apex, petiole short with stiff hairy filaments **Jubaea** P303 ►

Leaflets not divided at the apex, petiole up to almost 2m long **Howeia** P302 ►

33 Leaves compound **34**

Leaves simple **53**

34 Leaves with 3 leaflets or digitately lobed **35**

Leaves pinnate or twice-pinnate **36**

35 Leaves with 3 leaflets **Laburnum** P218 **Acer griseum** P231 ►

Leaves 5–7 digitately lobed **Aesculus** P243 ►

36 Leaves twice-pinnate **37**

Leaves pinnate **39**

37 Flowers lilac-coloured with 5 regular petals, leaflets toothed or lobed **Melia** P225 ►

Flowers pink or yellow with 5 irregular petals in a pea-like corolla, leaflets entire **38**

38 Flowers pink, leaves 30–45cm long with 6–12 pairs of main pinnae each with 20–30 pairs of pinnules **Albizia** P208 ►

Flowers yellow, leaves 6–15cm long with 15–20 pairs of pinnae each bearing up to 50 pairs of tiny pinnules *Acacia* ♂31 P212 ►

39 Flowers without petals **40**

Flowers with petals **43**

40 Leaves opposite *Fraxinus* ♂33 P286 ► **Acer negundo** P234

Leaves alternate **41**

41 Leaflets 3–9 *Carya* P110 ▶

  Leaflets 9–25 **42**

42 Bud without scales, fruit winged *Pterocarya* P112 ▶

  Bud with scales, fruit globose *Juglans* P112 ▶

43 Leaflet margins entire **47**

  Leaflet margins toothed or sometimes lobed **44**

44 Leaflet margins lobed *Koelreuteria* P242 ▶

  Leaflet margins toothed **45**

45 Leaflets linear-lanceolate *Schinus* P227 ▶

  Leaflets rounded, ovate to ovate-lanceolate **46**

46 Leaves pinnate with a terminal leaflet, flowers in flat panicle-like cymes *Sambucus* P298 ▶

  Leaves regularly pinnate, flowers in clustered racemes *Sorbus ⚘28 P170 ▶

47 Flowers zygomorphic, fruit a pod (Leguminosae) **48**

  Flowers radially symmetrical, fruit a samara or drupe **51**

48 Leaflets lanceolate to ovate-lanceolate, acuminate at the apex **49**

  Leaflets ovate, truncate-mucronate or notched mucronate at the apex **50**

49 Leaves with a terminal leaflet; lateral leaflets paired *Sophora* P220 ▶

  Leaves without a terminal leaflet; lateral leaflets alternate *Gleditsia* P211 ▶

50 Trees with spines; leaves with 13–15 pairs of leaflets *Robinia* P220 ▶

  Trees without spines; leaves with 4–10 pairs of leaflets *Ceratonia* P210 ▶

51 Fruit a drupe **52**

  Fruit a samara *Ailanthus* P224 ▶

52 Leaflets petiolate *Rhus* P226 ▶

  Leaflets sessile *Pistacia* P228 ▶

53 Leaves lobed **54**

  Leaves not lobed **65**

54 Leaves opposite **55**

  Leaves alternate **57**

55 Always a tree; flowers large, bell-shaped, blue, in profuse erect panicles *Paulownia* P296 ▶

  Usually a shrub or small tree; flowers small, white or yellow in flat panicles or loose clusters **56**

56 Fruits composed of 2 dry, winged seeds, borne in loose hanging clusters *Acer ⚘31 P230 ▶

  Fruits fleshy berries borne in flat panicles *Viburnum* P299 ▶

57 Flowers with obvious petals **58**

  Flowers without petals **60**

58 Leaves regularly lobed with a truncate apex and lateral lobes *Liriodendron* P148 ▶

  Leaves irregularly lobed with a pointed apex and a terminal lobe **59**

59 Shoots and leaves downy; stems not spiny, leaves slender, pointed with coarse teeth *Corynabutilon* P249 ▶

  Shoots and leaves not downy; stems spiny, leaves broadly pointed *Crataegus ⚘29 P184 ▶

60 Leaves with rounded lateral lobes **61**

  Leaves with pointed lateral lobes **62**

61 Evergreen tree with large, subshiny, dark green leaves c. 30 x 25cm *Ficus* P144 ▶

  Deciduous tree with leaves smooth, glossy green or light green above and pubescent below, c. 10 x 8cm *Morus* P142 ▶

62 Leaves somewhat palmate in outline with distinct wide-spreading lower lobes **63**

  Leaves oblong-ovate with small irregular lobes all around *Quercus ⚘27 P125 ▶

63 Leaves white-felted below
Populus ♂26 P104 ▶

Leaves glabrous or pubescent
below **64**

64 Bark pale to dark grey, fissured
Liquidambar P152

Bark dark grey or palish-brown,
flaking away to leave lighter
patches beneath *Platanus* P156 ▶

65 Leaves distinctly toothed or
crenate **103**

Leaves entire **66**

66 Leaves more than 60cm long **67**

Leaves less than 30cm long **69**

67 Leaves linear-lanceolate with
parallel longitudinal veins and
without a petiole **68**

Leaves ovate-oblong with a
central midrib and parallel right-
angled veins *Musa* P301 ▶

68 Inflorescence with 3 bracts; leaves
3–8cm wide *Cordyline* P300 ▶

Inflorescence without bracts;
leaves 3–4cm wide
Dracaena P301 ▶

69 Leaves scale-like or needle-
shaped *Tamarix* ♂33 P264 ▶

Leaves not as above **70**

70 Leaves with undulate or crinkled
margins **71**

Leaves with flat margins **81**

71 Leaves evergreen **72**

Leaves deciduous **74**

72 Leaves pale bright green with
strongly waved margins
Pittosporum P154 ▶

Leaves dark green or blackish
with only slightly waved or
crinkled margins **73**

73 Petiole red; leaf margins
crinkled, glabrous below
Laurus P150 ▶

Petiole brown or green;
leaf margin slightly undulate,
hairy below
Quercus ♂27 P125 ▶

74 Flowers with petals **75**

Flowers without petals **77**

75 Leaves dark glossy green above,
underside lighter, glabrous to
glabrescent **76**

Leaves pale yellow green, pale
and densely pubescent below
Mespilus P183 ▶

76 Bark black or dark pink-grey,
regularly cracked into thick,
small, square plates; flowers
urn-shaped, pendulous
Diospyros P284 ▶

Bark reddish-orange-brown,
deeply fissured into ridges;
flowers in globose heads
spreading from the base of new
shoots *Maclura* P144 ▶

77 Flowers surrounded by 4 large
white leafy bracts *Cornus* P281 ▶

Flowers not as above **78**

78 Petioles dark red *Nyssa* P260 ▶

Petioles green or brown **79**

79 Fruit an acorn
Quercus ♂27 P125 ▶

Fruit not as above **80**

80 Pubescence of stellate hairs
Hamamelis P153 ▶

Pubescence of simple hairs
Parrotia P153 ▶

81 Leaves blue-grey, leathery,
strongly aromatic **82**

Leaves light to dark green,
herbaceous to leathery, rarely
aromatic **83**

82 Fruit a conical cylindrical capsule,
opening by valves at the apex
Eucalyptus ♂33 P270 ▶

Fruit a flattened longitudinal
pod, opening by longitudinal
dehiscence *Acacia* ♂31 P212 ▶

83 Fruit an acorn
Quercus ♂27 P125 ▶

Fruit not as above **84**

84 Leaves deciduous **85**

Leaves evergreen **93**

85 Leaves opposite (sometimes
alternate at base) **86**

Leaves invariably alternate **89**

86 Leaves 2–12cm long **87**

Leaves 20–35cm long **88**

87 Flowers small, tubular, lilac or purple in terminal paired conical racemes; leaves long, acuminate, cordate *Syringa* P293 ▶

Flowers large, 3–4cm in diameter, solitary red with free petals; leaves acute, oblong lanceolate to obovate *Punica* P280 ▶

88 Bark dull pink and brown, scaling into flakes, or grey and fissured into flat ridges; lateral buds orange-brown *Catalpa* P294 ▶

Bark smooth, grey; lateral buds purplish *Paulownia* P296 ▶

89 Trees (or shrubs) with peltate or stellate scale-like hairs 90

Trees with simple hairs, or hairless 91

90 Dioecious; calyx 2-lobed *Hippophäe* P262 ▶

Polygamous; calyx 4-lobed *Elaeagnus* P263 ▶

91 Stipules absent; leaves orbicular *Cercis* P210 ▶

Stipules present; leaves ovate to obovate-elliptic, or ovate-deltoid to deltoid 92

92 Leaves ovate-deltoid to deltoid; flowers dioecious in long racemes *Phytolacca* P146 ▶

Leaves obovate to obovate-elliptic; flowers in umbel-like corymbs *Pyrus* ⚶28 P158 ▶

93 Leaves opposite 94

Leaves alternate 97

94 Leaves with scale-like hairs beneath *Olea* P291 ▶

Leaves glabrous or hairy below 95

95 Flowers tubular *Ligustrum* P290 ▶

Flowers with separate petals and sepals 96

96 Leaves aromatic when crushed; fruit a berry *Myrtus* P279 ▶

Leaves not aromatic when crushed; fruit a capsule *Buxus* P248 ▶

97 Leaves more than 5cm long 98

Leaves less than 5cm long *Cotoneaster* P183 ▶

98 Leaves elliptic-obovate to ovate-acuminate, dark green; flowers white, yellow or greenish 99

Leaves oblong-lanceolate, obtuse, light green; flowers bright red *Embothrium* P146 ▶

99 Flowers small, inconspicuous 100

Flowers large, petaloid 101

100 Inflorescence subsessile; perianth 4-lobed *Laurus* P150 ▶

Inflorescence long-pedunculate; perianth 6-lobed *Persea* P151 ▶

101 Fruit citrus-type; leaves sweetly and strongly aromatic when crushed *Citrus* P222 ▶

Fruit a cone, or a 2-bracted involucre; leaves not or only faintly aromatic when crushed 102

102 Fruit a cone; flower large, solitary, with 6–15 tepals *Magnolia* P149 ▶

Ovaries in a 2-bracted involucre; flowers in a loosely globose inflorescence with 7 recurved slender white petals *Drimys* P149 ▶

103 Leaves evergreen; usually dark green, leathery 104

Leaves deciduous; usually lighter green, herbaceous 112

104 Leaves opposite 105

Leaves alternate 106

105 Stipules present; petals absent *Rhamnus* P252 ▶

Stipules absent; petals present *Phillyrea* P292 ▶

106 Leaves with irregular spines and somewhat undulate margins *Ilex* P244 ▶

Leaves with serrate or crenate and flat or revolute margins 107

107 Leaf margins revolute *Myrica* P110 ▶

Leaf margins not revolute 108

21

108 Leaves usually more than 12cm long *Eriobotrya* P180 ▶

Leaves usually less than 10cm long **109**

109 Petals united **110**

Petals free **111**

110 Stamens as numerous as or less than the corolla lobes; fruit a drupe *Myoporum* P297 ▶

Stamens twice as numerous as the corolla lobes; fruit a globose berry *Arbutus* P282 ▶

111 Some leaves apparently with 3 leaflets *Eucryphia* P261 ▶

Leaves not as above *Frangula* P253 ▶

112 Leaves opposite **113**

Leaves alternate **115**

113 Leaves finely serrate or crenate, cordate-obovate or lanceolate **114**

Leaves with larger, irregular teeth, palmate *Acer* ♂31 P230 ▶

114 Petioles red; leaves cordate, crenate *Cercidiphyllum* P147 ▶

Petioles green; leaves lanceolate to ovate, serrate *Euonymus* P246 ▶

115 Trees with spiny stipules **116**

Trees with stipules not spiny, or stipules absent **117**

116 Young twigs minutely pubescent; fruit dry, winged *Paliurus* P250 ▶

Young twigs glabrous; fruit fleshy, unwinged *Zizyphus* P251 ▶

117 Fruit a pome or drupe; flowers with distinct free petals **118**

Fruit a nut, berry, acorn, samara or capsule; flowers without petals **125**

118 Carpels not joined to the flower tube; fruit a fleshy drupe **119**

Carpels joined to the flower tube; fruit a pome **120**

119 Indumentum of simple hairs *Prunus* ♂30 P192 ▶

Indumentum of stellate or scale-like hairs *Styrax* P285 ▶

120 Flowers solitary *Cydonia* P158 ▶

Flowers in 2- to many-flowered inflorescences **121**

121 Carpel wall becoming stony in fruit; leaves irregularly lobed *Crataegus* ♂29 P184 ▶

Carpel walls cartilaginous in fruit; leaves regular, serrate or crenate **122**

122 Flowers in compound corymbs; leaves densely lanate below *Sorbus* ♂28 P170 ▶

Flowers in umbels, racemes or few-flowered clusters **123**

123 Petals linear to oblong-ovate, not clawed *Amelanchier* P180 ▶

Petals obovate or orbicular, distinctly clawed **124**

124 Styles free; flesh of fruit with stone cells *Pyrus* ♂28 P159 ▶

Styles connected at base; flesh of fruit with few or no stone cells *Malus* P166 ▶

125 Flowers in catkins or dense heads **130**

Flowers not as above **126**

126 Perianth of 2 markedly different whorls **127**

Perianth not as above **128**

127 Inflorescence growing in the axil of a conspicuous bract partly joined to the peduncle *Tilia* ♂32 P254 ▶

Inflorescence not as above *Davidia* P261 ▶

128 Bark fissured; leaves double-toothed; flowers all hermaphrodite; fruit a samara *Ulmus* ♂27 P134 ▶

Bark not fissured; leaves simply serrate; flowers male and hermaphrodite; fruit a drupe **129**

129 Bark scaling; perianth segments joined; drupe dry **Zelkova** P138 ▶

Bark not scaling; perianth segments free; drupe fleshy **Celtis** P140 ▶

130 Latex present; fruit or false fruit fleshy **131**

Latex absent; fruit dry **132**

131 Buds with 3–6 scales; syncarp cylindrical or ovoid **Morus** P142 ▶

Buds with 2–3 scales; syncarp globose **Broussonetia** P145 ▶

132 Dioecious; perianth absent **133**

Monoecious; perianth present **134**

133 Buds with 1 outer scale; bracts entire; leaves linear-lanceolate *Salix* ♂26 P90 ▶

Buds with several outer scales; bracts dentate or fringed; leaves ovate to deltoid *Populus* ♂26 P104 ▶

134 Styles 3 or more; flowers of both sexes with a perianth **135**

Styles 2; perianth present in flowers of 1 sex only **138**

135 Male flowers in groups of 1–3 or pendent heads; buds spindle-shaped; nut sharply 3-sided **136**

Male flowers in long erect or pendent catkins; buds ovoid, nut ovoid to subglobose **137**

136 Male flowers solitary, in pairs or groups of 3, sessile or shortly stalk-ed; female flowers and nuts 3 in each involucre **Nothofagus** P123 ▶

Male flowers many-flowered; female flowers and nuts 2 in each involucre **Fagus** P122 ▶

137 Male catkins erect, with female flowers in lower part; cupule completely enclosing the nuts **Castanea** P124 ▶

Male catkins pendent; female flowers in separate inflorescences; cupule enclosing only lower half of nut *Quercus* ♂27 P125 ▶

138 Male flowers 3 to each bract; perianth present **139**

Male flowers 1 to each bract; perianth absent **140**

139 Fruiting catkin cylindrical or narrowly ovoid; scales 3-lobed, falling with fruit; stamens 2, bifid below the anthers **Betula** P114 ▶

Fruiting catkin ovoid, cone-like, scales 5-lobed, woody and persistent; stamens 4, entire though with shortly forked connective **Alnus** P116 ▶

140 Buds ovoid-obtuse; leaves usually with fewer than 8 pairs of veins; fruits in clusters of 1–4 **Corylus** P120 ▶

Buds fusiform, acute; leaves with 9 or more pairs of veins; fruits numerous, in pendent spikes **141**

141 Bark grey, smooth; male catkins appearing in spring; nut growing in the axil of a 3-lobed or serrate involucre **Carpinus** P118 ▶

Bark brown, rough, scaly; male catkins visible throughout winter; not enclosed in an entire, broadly pointed involucre **Ostrya** P119 ▶

Keys to species

Juniperus Junipers (p. 42)

1 Leaves all juvenile, needle-like, jointed at the base, in whorls of 3; cones in axils of leaves **2**

Leaves of two sorts: juvenile leaves needle-like, not jointed at the base; adult scale-like, closely appressed; cones at tips of shoots **3**

2 Leaves with a single white band above, cone 6–9mm long, blackish **communis** P42 ▶

Leaves with two white bands above, cone up to 1.5cm long, purplish **oxycedrus** P43 ▶

3 Juvenile leaves usually in whorls of 3; scale-leaves with a narrow, pale margin **4**

Juvenile leaves in pairs; scale-leaves green at the margin **5**

4 Juvenile leaves absent from adult shoots; scale-leaves blunt; cones dark red **phoenicea** P44 ▶

Juvenile leaves at the base of many adult shoots; scale-leaves pointed, cones bluish-white **chinensis** P47 ▶

5	Cones 4–6mm long *virginiana* P46 ▶
	Cones 0.7–1.2cm long **6**
6	Twigs 0.6–0.8mm thick, rounded in cross-section; scale-leaves up to 1.5mm long *excelsa* P44
	Twigs *c.* 1mm thick, squarish in cross-section; scale-leaves 1.5–2mm long **7**
7	Twigs arranged irregularly; cones blackish *foetidissima* P45 ▶
	Twigs arranged in two ranks, forming flattened sprays; cones dark purple *thurifera* P46

Abies Silver Firs (p. 54)

1	Leaves flexible, blunt or slightly notched at the tip, those at the side of the shoot pointing forwards **2**
	Leaves stiff, pointed, radiating at right-angles all round the shoot **9**
2	Twigs with reddish hairs; leaves bluish-grey above **3**
	Twigs with greyish or brownish hairs, or hairless; leaves usually green or rarely dull grey above **4**
3	Twigs grey; cones 5–10cm, the bracts not protruding beyond the cone scales *lasiocarpa* P57 ▶
	Twigs brown; cones 12–20cm, the bracts protruding beyond the cone scales *procera* P59 ▶
4	Buds without resin; cones 10–20cm long **5**
	Buds exuding resin; cones 5–10cm long **6**
5	Twigs densely hairy; cones 3–4cm in diameter *alba* P54 ▶
	Twigs almost hairless; cones 4–5cm in diameter *nordmanniana* P57 ▶
6	Leaves not parted beneath the shoot, some pointing downwards; the bracts protruding beyond the cone scales *delavayi* P55 ▶
	Leaves distinctly parted beneath the shoot; the bracts not protruding beyond the cone scales **7**
7	Twigs with conspicuous grey down; leaves 1.5–2cm x 1–1.3mm *sibirica* P59 ▶
	Twigs almost smooth, yellowish or brownish-green leaves 2–6cm x 1.5–2.5mm **8**

8	Young twigs brownish-green; leaves 2–4cm long *grandis* P56 ▶
	Young twigs yellowish-green; leaves 4–6cm long *concolor* P56
9	Leaves 1–1.5cm long with grey or whitish bands above and below; bracts not protruding beyond the cone scales *pinsapo* P 58 ▶
	Leaves 1.5–3.5cm long with grey bands below only; bracts protruding beyond the cone scales *cephalonica* P55 ▶

Picea Spruces (p. 66)

1	Leaves more or less 4-angled with whitish bands on all surfaces **2**
	Leaves flattened with 2 whitish bands on one surface only **7**
2	Leaves stiff with a spine-like tip, spreading, all round the shoot *pungens* P67 ▶
	Leaves flexible, the tip not spine-like, parted beneath the shoot **3**
3	Twigs covered with dense down **4**
	Twigs smooth or with scattered hairs **6**
4	Leaves 0.6–1cm long, blunt *orientalis* P68 ▶
	Leaves 1–2.5cm long, pointed
5	Twigs yellowish-brown; leaves 1.5–2.5cm long; cone scales narrowed into a squarish, irregularly toothed tip *engelmannii* P69 ▶
	Twigs brown; leaves 1–1.8cm long; cone scales rounded, sometimes slightly notched at the tip *abies* subsp. *obovata* P66 ▶
6	Leaves bluish-green, with fetid smell when crushed; cones 3.5–5cm long *glauca* P68 ▶
	Leaves dark, without fetid smell when crushed; cones 10–18cm long *abies* subsp. *abies* P66 ▶
7	Twigs long, slender and pendulous; cones 10–12cm long *breweriana* P67 ▶
	Twigs short and rather stiff; cones 5–10cm long **8**

8   Twigs downy; leaves 0.8–1.8cm long, blunt; cones 3–6cm long *omorika* P71 ▶

    Twigs smooth; leaves 1.5–2.5cm long, sharply pointed; cones 6–10cm long *sitchensis* P70 ▶

Pinus Pines (p. 74)

1   Leaves in groups of 3 or 5 **2**
    Leaves in pairs **13**

2   Leaves in groups of 5 **3**
    Leaves in groups of 3 **8**

3   Seeds not winged *cembra* P86 ▶
    Seeds winged **4**

4   Leaves 12–25cm long **5**
    Leaves 2–12cm long **6**

5   Cones 15–25 x 3cm; seeds 8–9mm long with a wing 1–2cm long *wallichiana* P87 ▶

    Cones 8–20 X 3–4cm; seeds 5–8mm long with a wing 1.5–2.5cm long *strobus* P88 ▶

6   Leaves 2–5cm long *aristata* P89
    Leaves 8–12cm long **7**

7   Shoots bright green, glabrous *peuce* P88 ▶

    Shoots brownish to pale green, with short hairs at the base of the leaves *strobus* P88 ▶

8   Leaves up to 15cm long **9**
    Leaves 15–30cm long **10**

9   Leaves very slender, bright green, lax; cone 12cm long *radiata* P76 ▶

    Leaves stout, stiff; cones 4cm long *rigida* P76 ▶

10 Winter buds ovoid, not resiniferous *canariensis* P84 ▶

    Winter buds cylindrical, resiniferous **11**

11 Shoots red-brown or grey-brown, not glaucous *ponderosa* P78 ▶

    Shoots blue-white or pale blue-grey to more or less glaucous violet **12**

12 Leaves 12–20cm long; cone boss with recurved spine *jeffreyi* P78 ▶

    Leaves 20–30cm long; cone boss with straight spine *sabiniana* P78 ▶

13 Shoots grey-glaucous in 1st year **14**
    Shoots yellow to green or dark red in 1st year **17**

14 Seeds with well-developed wings **15**
    Seeds wingless, or wings less than 1mm long *pinea* P85 ▶

15 Leaves more than 1mm wide; resin canals central **16**
    Leaves less than 1mm wide; resin canals submarginal *halepensis* P84 ▶

16 Shoots glaucous for 3 years; exposed part of scale pyramidal with a recurved spine *leucodermis* P82 ▶

    Shoots turning green-brown in 2nd year; exposed part of scale flat with a short, erect, pointed spine *heldreichii* P83 ▶

17 Buds resiniferous; scales erect at apex **18**
    Buds not resiniferous; scale recurved at apex **19**

18 Resin canals median; cone 8–20 x 5–8cm *pinaster* P75 ▶
    Resin canals marginal or submarginal; cone 5–11 x *c.* 4cm *brutia* P84 ▶

19 Resin canals median **20**
    Resin canals marginal or submarginal **21**

20 Cone asymmetrical; leaves twisted *contorta* P74 ▶

    Cone more or less symmetrical; leaves not, or scarcely twisted *nigra* P79 ▶

21 Leaves dark green; cones strongly curved *banksiana* P77 ▶

    Leaves light green or grey-glaucous; cones straight **22**

22 Shrub or small tree; leaves bright green, cone shining, patent *mugo* (incl. *uncinata*) P81 ▶

    Always a tree; leaves glaucous; cone dull, pendulous *sylvestris* P80 ▶

Salix Willows (p. 90)

1   Twigs long, slender, pendent (weeping) **2**

Twigs not pendent **3**

2   Twigs yellow; indumentum silky x *chrysocoma* P93

Twigs brown; leaves glabrous at maturity *babylonica* P93 ▶

3   Branches covered in a blue-white bloom, thinning to reveal purple bark with violet tinges *daphnoides* P103 ▶

Branches grey-brown or green **4**

4   Mature leaves glabrous **5**

Mature leaves at least pubescent below **7**

5   Leaves glossy above, finely and evenly serrate with yellow glands; stamens 4–12, usually 5 *pentandra* P91 ▶

Leaves not conspicuously glossy, rather coarsely serrate with white teeth; stamens 2–3 **6**

6   Stipules persistent; bark of old stems flaking off; twigs tough *triandra* P94 ▶

Stipules falling early; bark of old stems not flaking off; twigs easily breaking off *fragilis* P90 ▶

7   Leaves with rust-coloured hairs below *atrocinerea* P98 ▶

Leaves with white or grey hairs below **8**

8   Leaves with appressed silky white tomentum **9**

Leaves woolly or pubescent but not appressed **10**

9   Leaves glabrous above, narrowly linear, more or less entire, with revolute margins *viminalis* P101 ▶

Leaves silky-tomentose above, lanceolate, finely serrated, flat *alba* P92 ▶

10 Leaves 1.5–2 times as long as wide, ovate or obovate to ovate-oblong *caprea* P98 ▶

Leaves 2–14 times as long as wide, thin to lanceolate or oblanceolate **11**

11 Filaments joined for at least half their length *elaeagnos* P102 ▶

Filaments free **12**

12 Leaves turning black on drying, glabrous or more or less pubescent on both surfaces *borealis* P95 ▶

Leaves never turning black on drying, densely pubescent below **13**

13 Ovary and pedicel glabrous *pedicellata* P96 ▶

Ovary and pedicel pubescent **14**

14 2 to 4-year-old twigs without or with few inconspicuous ridges beneath the bark **15**

2 to 4-year-old twigs with numerous very prominent ridges beneath the bark *cinerea* P97 ▶

15 Stipules usually absent *xerophila* P100 ▶

Stipules well developed *appendiculata* P97 ▶

Populus Poplars (p. 104)

1   Margins of leaves translucent, leaves usually densely hairy or whitish beneath **2**

Margins of leaves not translucent, leaves usually glabrous and green beneath **5**

2   Petiole rounded in cross-section; crown columnar x *berolinensis* P109 ▶

Petiole flattened; crown usually broad **3**

3   Teeth of leaf margins callus-tipped and with 2–5 glands beneath; stamens 30–60 *deltoides* P109 ▶

Teeth of leaf margins without calluses or glands; stamens 20–30 **4**

4   Bole without bosses; leaves ciliate x *canadensis* P109 ▶

Bole with bosses; leaves not ciliate *nigra* P108 ▶

5   Mature leaves woolly beneath **6**

Mature leaves sometimes hairy but not woolly beneath **7**

6   Leaves with 3–5 lobes, hairy on the lower surface, white *alba* P104 ▶

	Leaves toothed, rarely lobed, hairs on lower surface grey *canescens* P105 ▶	
7	Petiole strongly flattened; buds and young leaves not fragrant *tremula* P106 ▶	
	Petiole rounded in cross-section; buds or young leaves fragrant 8	
8	Crown narrow, conical *balsamifera* P107 ▶	
	Crown somewhat broad, domed *trichocarpa* P107 ▶	

Quercus Oaks (p. 125)

1	Leaves deciduous or some remaining on the tree over winter, semi-evergreen soft or rarely leathery 2	
	Leaves evergreen, leathery 16	
2	Acorns ripening in the 2nd year on the leafless part of a twig 3	
	Acorns ripening in the 1st year among the leaves 8	
3	Tips of the involucre scales pressed closely together 4	
	Tips of the involucre scales spreading or reflexed 6	
4	Leaves divided to less than halfway to the midrib, the lobes pointing forwards *rubra* P125 ▶	
	Leaves divided to more than halfway to the midrib, the lobes spreading widely 5	
5	Underside of the leaf with conspicuous tufts of brown hairs in the vein axils *palustris* P126 ▶	
	Underside of the leaf with the tufts of hairs very small or absent *coccinea* P126 ▶	
6	Leaves smooth and shiny; petioles up to 5mm long *trojana* P129 ▶	
	Leaves dull with soft or stiff hairs; petioles usually 1cm or more 7	
7	Leaves smooth above, the lobes with long bristle-like tips *macrolepis* P129 ▶	
	Leaves rough above, the triangular lobes blunt or rarely with short points *cerris* P128 ▶	

8	Leaves semi-evergreen, glaucous beneath *canariensis* P133 ▶	
	Leaves not semi-evergreen, tomentose, pubescent or rarely smooth below, but not glaucous 9	
9	Scales of the involucre more or less fused; fruits on a long stalk 10	
	Scales of the involucre distinct and separate; fruits on a very short stalk, or stalkless 11	
10	Underside of leaves with grey down *pedunculiflora* P131 ▶	
	Underside of leaves smooth *robur* P131 ▶	
11	Young twigs smooth; the petioles grooved 12	
	Young twigs downy; the petioles not grooved 13	
12	Involucre more or less hairless; adult leaves smooth beneath *dalechampii* P130 ▶	
	Involucre with short down; adult leaves downy beneath *petraea* P130 ▶	
13	Leaves with more than 8 pairs of distinct side veins *frainetto* P132 ▶	
	Leaves with less than 8 pairs of distinct side veins 14	
14	Scales of involucre blunt, not pressed closely together *pyrenaica* P133 ▶	
	Scales of involucre pointed, pressed closely together 15	
15	Petiole 0.5–1.2cm long *pubescens* P132	
	Petiole 1.5–2.5cm long *virgiliana* P133 ▶	
16	Bark thick and corky, with orange under bark; midrib of leaf sinuous *suber* P128 ▶	
	Bark not thick and corky; midrib of leaf more or less straight 17	
17	Mature leaves hairy beneath; petiole 0.5–1.5cm long *ilex* P127 ▶	
	Mature leaves smooth beneath; petiole 1–4mm long *coccifera* P126 ▶	

Ulmus Elms (p. 134)

1 Pedicels much longer than the flowers; the fruits with the wings fringed with white hairs, pendulous on long stalks *laevis* P138 ▶

Pedicels shorter than the flowers; the fruits not fringed with hairs, or pendulous, almost stalkless 2

2 Base of the leaf with the longer half overlapping the petiole; seed in the centre of the fruit *glabra* P134 ▶

Base of the leaf with the longer half not overlapping the petiole; seed above the centre of the fruit 3

3 Leaves up to 15cm long, smooth above; the petiole 1–2cm long *x hollandica* P135 ▶

Leaves 6–10cm long, rough or smooth above; the petiole 1–5cm long 4

4 Leaves rounded, rough above; fruit about as long as wide *procera* P135 ▶

Leaves ovate, obovate or oblanceolate; fruit longer than wide 5

5 Twigs with dense white down; leaves with 12–16 pairs of veins, the underside with dense grey down *canescens* P137 ▶

Twigs almost smooth; leaves with 7–12 pairs of veins, the underside with tufts of hairs in the vein axils 6

6 Leaves with a very unequal base, the midrib curving towards the short side *coritana* P137 ▶

Leaves with the base almost equal or somewhat unequal, the midrib more or less straight 7

7 Young twigs short and rather stiff; leaves often concave *angustifolia* P137 ▶

Young twigs long and pendulous; the leaves flat 8

8 Leaves usually widest above the middle, the base of the longer half turning at right-angles towards the petiole *carpinifolia* P136 ▶

Leaves usually widest at the middle, the base of the longer half rounded 9

9 Crown dense, small branches ascending to a symmetrical tip *minor* P136 ▶

Crown slender, arching out a little and thinning out markedly below a slightly leaning, one-sided tip *plotii* P137 ▶

Pyrus Pears (p. 159)

1 Fruit with a deciduous calyx *cordata* P160 ▶

Fruit with a persistent calyx 2

2 Fruit 5–16cm, flesh sweet-tasting *communis* P165 ▶

Fruit not more than 5.5cm long, flesh hard, usually bitter 3

3 Leaves not more than 1.5 times as long as wide *pyraster* P160 ▶

Leaves more than 1.5 times as long as wide 4

4 Mature leaves glabrous or papillose beneath 5

Mature leaves hairy or woolly beneath 6

5 Leaves toothed, rounded at the base *bourgaeana* P161 ▶

Leaves entire to slightly toothed, wedge-shaped at the base *amygdaliformis* P163 ▶

6 Styles densely hairy at least at the base 7

Styles more or less glabrous 9

7 Styles hairy to the middle *elaeagrifolia* P162 ▶

Styles hairy only at the base 8

8 Fruit 2.5–3cm long *nivalis* P164 ▶

Fruit 3–5cm long *salicifolia* P159 ▶

9 Leaves usually less than 3.5cm wide, entire *salvifolia* P162 ▶

Leaves usually more than 3.5cm wide, toothed towards the apex *austriaca* P164 ▶

Sorbus Whitebeams, Rowans and Service Trees (p. 170)

1 Leaves all pinnate 2

At least most leaves simple 9

2	Leaves with terminal leaflet about the same size as the others, not deeply lobed **4**
	Leaves with terminal leaflet much larger than the others, usually deeply lobed **3**
3	Leaves with 2 pairs of free leaflets *hybrida* P179 ▶
	Leaves with 4–5 pairs of free leaflets *meinchii* P179 ▶
4	Ripe fruits orange or scarlet **7**
	Ripe fruits greenish, brownish, pink or white **5**
5	Ripe fruits greenish or brownish, ovoid or pear-shaped *domestica* P170 ▶
	Ripe fruits pink or white, globose **6**
6	Leaf-rachis grooved on the upper surface, reddish *hupehensis* P173 ▶
	Leaf-rachis not grooved on upper surface, green *vilmorinii* P171 ▶
7	Leaves with 5 or fewer pairs of leaflets, hairy on the lower surface; flowers opening in June *sargentiana* P173 ▶
	Leaves with 5 or more pairs of leaflets, glabrous or glabrescent on the lower surface; flowers opening in May **8**
8	Inflorescence 10–15cm in diameter; bud dark purple *aucuparia* P172 ▶
	Inflorescence less than 10cm in diameter; bud shiny red *commixta* P171 ▶
9	Leaves lobed **12**
	Leaves entire **10**
10	Leaves with teeth curved on the outer edge; fruit with numerous lenticels **11**
	Leaves with symmetrical teeth; fruit with few large lenticels *graeca* P175 ▶
11	Leaves with 10–14 pairs of veins; fruits more or less ovoid *aria* P174 ▶
	Leaves with 7–9 pairs of veins; fruits globose *rupicola* P175

12	Ripe fruits red **13**
	Ripe fruits brown or yellow **15**
13	Leaves yellowish-grey tomentose beneath *intermedia* P177 ▶
	Leaves whitish-grey-tomentose beneath **14**
14	Leaves 1.5–2 times as long as wide; fruit ovoid with few small lenticels *mougeotii* P176 ▶
	Leaves 1.25 times as long as wide; fruit globose with numerous large lenticels *austriaca* P176 ▶
15	Leaves lobed more than quarter way to the midrib, glabrous below *torminalis* P174 ▶
	Leaves lobed usually to less than quarter way (sometimes to halfway) to the midrib, tomentose below **16**
16	Leaves grey-hairy below; ripe fruit brown *latifolia* P178 ▶
	Leaves white-hairy below; ripe fruit yellow *umbellata* P176 ▶

Crataegus Hawthorns (p. 184)

1	Lateral veins of leaves ending only in the lobe apices or teeth **2**
	Lateral veins of leaves ending both in the apices and sinuses of the lobe or teeth **3**
2	Leaves unlobed, simply and acutely serrate above, entire at base *crus-galli* P184 ▶
	Leaves with 7–11 lobes, sharply and irregularly serrate to the base *nigra* P189 ▶
3	Styles 4–5 **4**
	Styles 1–3 **5**
4	Leaves sparsely villous with well-developed petioles; inflorescence lax; fruit black, more or less globose, rarely exceeding 1.1cm in diameter *pentagyna* P188 ▶
	Leaves lanate or with silky hairs and with poorly developed petioles; inflorescence compact; fruit orange or red often more than 1.1cm in diameter *orientalis* P190 ▶
5	Styles 2–3 **6**
	Styles 1 **7**

6 Leaves shallowly lobed with well-developed petioles; inflorescences lax; fruit rarely exceeding 1.1 cm in diameter *laevigata* P185 ▶

Leaves laciniate with short petioles; inflorescences compact; fruit exceeding 1.1 cm in diameter *azarolus* P191 ▶

7 Leaf-lobes with more or less entire margins or a few apical teeth; sepals more or less triangular or broadly lanceolate; fruit globose to ovate *monogyna* P186 ▶

Leaf-lobes with margins more or less serrate to base; sepals narrowly lanceolate; fruit narrowly ovate *calycina* P187 ▶

Prunus Cherries and Plums (p. 192)

1 Ovary and ripe fruit smooth 2

Ovary and ripe fruit hairy 20

2 Flower solitary, or in clusters, or in heads with all the stalks arising from the same point (umbels) 3

Flowers in branched heads, with the stalks arising from many different points (racemes or corymbs) 15

3 Fruit-stalk much longer than the ripe fruit; flower stalks rarely 1cm, usually 1.5–8cm long (if less than 1.5cm long, then petals exceeding 1.5cm) 4

Fruit-stalk shorter than, or about as long as ripe fruit; flower stalks 0.1–1.5cm, rarely up to 2cm (if more than 1.5cm then petals less than 1.5cm) 9

4 Flower-tube urn-shaped, more or less constricted at the mouth 5

Flower-tube narrowly or broadly bell-shaped, not constricted at the mouth 6

5 Leaves 1–3cm wide; petioles 6–7cm long *serrula* P202 ▶

Leaves 4–7cm wide; petioles 2–5cm long *avium* P198 ▶

6 Leaves 3–8cm long; flower-tube broadly bell-shaped *cerasus* P199 ▶

Leaves 8–20cm long, flower-tube narrowly bell-shaped 7

7 Young twigs downy; flowers in clusters of 5–6 *x yedoensis* P201 ▶

Young twigs smooth; flowers in clusters of 2–4 8

8 Teeth of leaves drawn out into hairlike points; flowers white or pink, the petioles 1.5–8cm long *serrulata* P201 ▶

Teeth of leaves sharp but not with hairlike points; flowers deep pink; petioles 1–2cm long *sargentii* P200 ▶

9 Flower-tube urn-shaped, constricted at the mouth *subhirtella* P202 ▶

Flower-tube broadly bell-shaped, not constricted at the mouth 10

10 Petals pink; the flowers without peduncles *persica* P192 ▶

Petals white or rarely pinkish; the peduncles 0.5–2cm long 11

11 Young twigs smooth and glossy 12

Young twigs dull and hairy 14

12 Leaves with large, pointed teeth *brigantina* P195 ▶

Leaves with rounded or very small forward-pointing teeth 13

13 Flowers usually solitary, the peduncles c. 1.5cm long *cerasifera* P194 ▶

Flowers in clusters of 2–4, the peduncles 2–4mm long *cocomilia* P197

14 Bark blackish; branches spine-tipped; fruit less than 2cm long, more or less erect *spinosa* P196 ▶

Bark brown; branches without spines, or rarely spine-tipped; fruit 2cm long or more, pendulous *domestica* P196 ▶

15 Flowers in short rounded heads (corymbs) of up to 10 flowers *mahaleb* P203 ▶

Flowers in elongated heads (racemes) of 12–100 flowers 16

16 Leaves deciduous, thin and soft 17

Leaves evergreen, thick and rather leathery 19

17	Petals 6–9mm; stone grooved *padus* P204 ▶
	Petals 3–5mm; stone smooth **18**
18	Bark bitter and aromatic; fruit purplish-black *serotina* P204 ▶
	Bark not aromatic; fruit deep red *virginiana* P205
19	Flower-heads 8–13cm long, shorter than the leaves *laurocerasus* P207 ▶
	Flower-heads 15–28cm long, longer than the leaves *lusitanica* P206 ▶
20	Leaves about as long as wide *armeniaca* P194 ▶
	Leaves more than twice as long as wide **21**
21	Petals deep pink; outer layer of ripe fruit succulent *persica* P192 ▶
	Petals white or pinkish; outer layer of ripe fruit leathery *dulcis* P193 ▶

Acacia Wattles or Mimosas (p. 212)

1	Adult leaves twice-pinnate **2**
	Adult leaves flattened phyllodes **5**
2	Stipules spiny; leaves deciduous with 2–8 pairs of pinnae **3**
	Stipules rudimentary; leaves ever-green with 7–20 pairs of pinnae **4**
3	Leaflets 3–5mm long, stipules up to 2.5cm long on old branches *farnesiana* P217 ▶
	Leaflets 0.6–1cm long; stipular spines up to 10cm long on old branches *karoo* P217 ▶
4	Twigs and young leaves whitish-tomentose; leaflets 3–4mm long; legume 1–1.2cm wide, not or scarcely constricted between the seeds *dealbata* P213 ▶
	Twigs and young leaves yellowish-villous; leaflets 2mm long; legumes 5–7mm wide, distinctly constricted between the seeds *mearnsii* P214 ▶
5	Flowers in axillary spikes; legume terete *longifolia* P214 ▶
	Flowers in heads in groups of 2–3 or racemes; legume flattened **6**

6	Phyllodes with 2–6 veins **7**
	Phyllodes with a single vein **8**
7	Flowers yellow *cyclops* P217 ▶
	Flowers creamy-white *melanoxylon* P215 ▶
8	Phyllodes falcate, oblong-lanceolate to obovate; 10–20 heads in each raceme *pycnantha* P216 ▶
	Phyllodes not or scarcely falcate, linear to lanceolate or oblanceolate; 2–9 heads in each raceme **9**
9	Capitula 1–1.5cm in diameter; legume distinctly constricted between the seeds; stalk encircling seed short, whitish *cyanophylla* P212 ▶
	Capitula 4–6mm in diameter; legume not or scarcely constricted between seeds; stalk encircling seed scarlet *retinodes* P217 ▶

Acer Maples and Sycamores (p. 230)

1	Leaves pinnate, with 3–7 leaflets **2**
	Leaves simple, undivided or palmately lobed **3**
2	Bark peeling in papery strips, leaves with 3 dark green leaflets *griseum* P231 ▶
	Bark smooth or shallowly fissured, never peeling; leaves with 3–7 light green leaflets *negundo* P234 ▶
3	Leaves undivided, or sometimes with 3–5 very shallow lobes **4**
	Leaves with 3–7 distinct lobes **5**
4	Wings of fruit subparallel, red; petiole grooved *tataricum* P241 ▶
	Wings of fruit almost horizontal, green; petiole not grooved *davidii* P231 ▶
5	Wings of fruit making an acute angle, or more or less parallel; leaves usually leathery, sometimes evergreen **11**
	Wings of fruit making an obtuse angle or more or less horizontal; leaves usually not leathery, deciduous **6**

6   Middle lobe of leaf separated nearly to the base; wings of fruit usually strongly curved *heldreichii* P231 ▶

Middle lobe of leaf not separated to more than one-third of the way to base; wings of fruit usually not strongly curved **7**

7   Fruits 5cm long or more, the wings horizontal **8**

Fruits 5cm long or less, the wings usually making an obtuse angle, or sometimes horizontal **9**

8   Fruit 5–6cm long, green or reddish; leaves with 3–5 lobes, ciliate *campestre* P230 ▶

Fruit 6–10cm long, yellow; leaves with 5–7 lobes, not ciliate *platanoides* P238 ▶

9   Flower clusters pendent; fruit 2cm long or more **10**

Flower clusters erect; fruit 2cm long or less *palmatum* P236 ▶

10   Leaves with 7–11 lobes; wings of fruit making an obtuse angle *japonicum* P237 ▶

Leaves with 5 lobes, wings of fruit making or nearly making a right-angle *pseudoplatanus* P239 ▶

11   Margins entire, leaves with 3 lobes **12**

Margins toothed, leaves usually with more than 3 lobes **13**

12   Leaves evergreen, green and glabrous below *sempervirens* P233 ▶

Leaves somewhat leathery but deciduous, slightly bluish and hairy below *monspessulanum* P233 ▶

13   Leaves silvery below **14**

Leaves green or whitish below, but not silvery **15**

14   Leaf sinuses cut less than halfway to the base, margins coarsely toothed; fruit 1cm long, red *rubrum* P241 ▶

Leaf sinuses cut more than halfway to the base, margins deeply toothed, fruit 5–6cm long, green *saccarhinum* P240 ▶

15   Leaf lobes triangular-ovate, cut less than halfway to the base **17**

Leaf lobes parallel-sided, cut halfway to the base **16**

16   Leaf up to 7cm long, densely hairy on lower surfaces *granatense* P232 ▶

Leaf up to 10cm long, more or less glabrous on the lower surface *hyrcanum* P232 ▶

17   Leaf lobes blunt, persistently hairy on the lower surface *obtusatum* P235 ▶

Leaf lobes acute, lower surface glabrescent *opalus* P235 ▶

Tilia Lime Trees (p. 254)

1   Leaves white beneath with a layer of stellate hairs; staminodes present **2**

Leaves smooth beneath or with simple hairs; staminodes absent **3**

2   Petioles up to 5cm long, usually less than half as long as the leaf blade *tomentosa* P254 ▶

Petioles up to 12cm long, usually more than half as long as the leaf blade *petiolaris* P255 ▶

3   Flowers in erect cymes; fruit shell membranous *cordata* P257 ▶

Flowers in pendent cymes; the fruit shell thick and woody **4**

4   Fruit strongly ribbed **5**

Fruit weakly ribbed or smooth **6**

5   Leaves with teeth ending in a hairlike tip *rubra* P257 ▶

Leaves with teeth pointed but not hairlike at the tip *platyphyllos* P256 ▶

6   Flowers yellowish-white; underside of leaves with whitish hair tufts in the vein axis *x vulgaris* P258 ▶

Flowers rich yellow; underside of leaves with reddish-brown hair tufts in the vein axils *x euchlora* P259 ▶

Tamarix Tamarisks (p. 264)

1 Perianth segments 4 in each whorl **2**

   Perianth segments 5 in each whorl **4**

2 Inflorescence 0.7–1cm wide; bracts exceeding the calyx *dalmatica* P268 ▶

   Inflorescence 3–7mm wide; bracts not exceeding the calyx **3**

3 Bark black; bracts herbaceous in proximal half; petals more than 2mm long *tetrandra* P267 ▶

   Bark brown to purple; bracts entirely scarious; petals less than 2mm long *parviflora* P267 ▶

4 Inflorescence 0.8–1.2cm wide *dalmatica* P268 ▶

   Inflorescence 3–8mm wide **5**

5 Petals 2–3mm long **6**

   Petals 1.25–2mm long **7**

6 Sepals 1.5mm long *africana* P264 ▶

   Sepals 2–2.5mm long *tetrandra* P267 ▶

7 Bracts equalling or exceeding the calyx; petals not more than 1.5mm long *canariensis* P265 ▶

   Bracts not extending beyond the calyx; petals 1.5–2mm long **8**

8 Petals elliptical to elliptic–obovate, more or less flat *gallica* P266 ▶

   Petals ovate-orbicular, strongly keeled *smyrnensis* P269 ▶

Eucalyptus Eucalyptus (p. 270)

1 Fruits more than 1cm long; flowers solitary *globulus* P276 ▶

   Fruits up to 1cm long; flowers in umbels **2**

2 Fruits distinctly pedicellate **3**

   Fruits sessile or subsessile **7**

3 Inflorescence with 3 (occasionally 5) flowers **4**

   Inflorescence with 5–10 flowers **5**

4 Mature leaves 10–25cm long *citriodora* P271 ▶

   Mature leaves 4–7cm long *gunnii* P279 ▶

5 Peduncles terete or nearly so *camaldulensis* P275 ▶

   Peduncles compressed, angular, or strap-shaped **6**

6 Fruit 1.2–1.5cm long, cylindrical to flask-shaped, valves enclosed or very slightly projecting *robusta* P272 ▶

   Fruit 5–8mm long, ovoid to hemispherical; valves strongly projecting *resinifera* P273 ▶

7 Inflorescence 3-flowered *viminalis* P278 ▶

   Inflorescence with 5–10 (rarely 3) flowers **8**

8 Bark smooth; leaves c. 20cm long; fruit glaucous *maidenii* P277 ▶

   Bark fibrous; leaves 10–17cm long; fruits not dull **9**

9 Peduncles 0.7–1cm long; fruit 7–9 x 7–9mm long, barrel-shaped or cylindrical *botryoides* P270 ▶

   Peduncles 2.5–3.5cm long; fruit 1.3–2 x 1.1–1.5cm long, bell-shaped *gomphocephalus* P274 ▶

Fraxinus Ashes (p. 286)

1 Corolla present; flowers appearing after the leaves *ornus* P286 ▶

   Corolla absent; flowers appearing before the leaves **2**

2 Calyx present; body of samara terete **3**

   Calyx absent; body of samara flattened **4**

3 Wing of samara decurrent on the body; base of blade usually decurrent on the petiolule *pennsylvanica* P287 ▶

   Wing of samara not decurrent on the body; base of blade not decurrent on the petiolule *americana* P287 ▶

4 Buds black; leaflets with more teeth than lateral veins *excelsior* P288 ▶

   Buds brown; leaflets with as many teeth as lateral veins **5**

5 Twigs, petiole and leaf-rachis desely hairy; samaras finely hairy *pallisiae* P289

   Twigs, petiole and leaf-rachis glabrous; samaras glabrous *angustifolia* P289 ▶

MAIDENHAIR TREE FAMILY GINKGOACEAE

Ginkgo biloba L.
Maidenhair tree

An irregularly or narrowly conical, deciduous, dioecious tree up to 30m high, with one to several trunks. The bark is rather corky, grey-brown with interconnecting ridges separated by wide fissures. The branches are spreading; the shoots are of 2 kinds: long shoots, greenish-brown with widely spaced leaves; and short shoots borne on the long shoots, brown, with closely spaced leaves or leaf-scars. The leaves are up to 12 x 10cm, fan-shaped with radiating veins, usually with one or several deep and several shallow divisions around the margin, yellowish to dark green, smooth; the petiole is 1–4.5cm long, somewhat grooved above. The male flowers occur in thick yellowish, upright, spreading catkins, in clusters of up to 6 on the short shoots; the female flowers occur singly or in pairs on a pedicel *c.* 5cm long.

Habit

Leaves

Catkins

Bark

The fruits are 2.5–3cm long, globose or sometimes ovoid, fleshy, smooth, turning yellow with a greyish bloom, becoming foul-smelling when ripe and containing a single seed in a stony layer. Male cones shed pollen in March–April. A species almost unknown in the wild (reputed wild in Chekiang Province, China) but cultivated for centuries in China for its edible fruits. It is widely planted in gardens and parks in much of Europe.

Fruit

YEW FAMILY TAXACEAE

Taxus baccata L.
Common Yew

A broadly conical dioecious evergreen tree or shrub up to 25m, the bole is often long and sinuous; the bark is reddish-brown, flaking and peeling to reveal reddish patches. The branches are rather stout, level or ascending, the twigs arising irregularly, somewhat pendulous. The leaves are 1–4cm x c. 3mm, linear, flattened, abruptly narrowing into a sharp point, entire, tapering at the base, glossy or dull, dark green above, with 2 pale yellowish-green bands below, sessile, arising spirally but flattened into a row on either side of the twig. The male flowers are solitary, consisting of a globose cluster of up to 14 anthers, yellowish; the female flowers are minute, solitary or in pairs, green. The fruit is 0.6–1cm long, ovoid to globose with a depression at the tip, the outer fleshy aril usually scarlet as it ripens in September. Male cones shed pollen in February–April. A native of much of Europe, some areas of N. Africa and parts of SW. Asia, usually on lime-rich soils. Many different cultivated varieties are planted widely for ornament, shelter and timber. All except Cr Ic.

Habit

Fruits

Male flowers

COW TAIL PINE FAMILY CEPHALOTAXACEAE

Cephalotaxus harringtonia (Forbes) C. Koch
Cow Tail Pine

A species similar to *Taxus baccata*, infrequently planted for ornament in parks and gardens.

Fruits

Habit

35

MONKEY PUZZLE FAMILY ARAUCARIACEAE

Araucaria araucana (Molina)
C. Koch
Monkey Puzzle

An evergreen, dioecious, broadly conical or domed tree up to 30m tall with a long cylindrical bole, sometimes suckering from the roots. The bark is dark grey, becoming wrinkled and ridged and marked with rings of old branch scars around the trunk. The branches are mostly horizontal to somewhat pendent, regularly arranged around the trunk; the shoots are densely covered with spirally arranged leaves. The leaves are 3–4cm long, ovate to triangular, gradually tapering into a sharp brown point, thick and leathery, dark glossy green. The male cones are *c.* 10–6cm long, occurring in clusters on the shoot tips, brown; the female cones are 10–17cm long, globose, erect, occurring on the upper side of a shoot, green until the second year and breaking up on the tree; each scale ends in a gradually tapering, outward-curving point. The seeds are *c.* 4cm long, brown, edible. Male cones shed pollen in June–July. A native of Chile and Argentina, commonly planted for ornament in parks and gardens of W. Europe.

Habit

Female cone

Bark

Shoot with male cone

CYPRESS FAMILY CUPRESSACEAE

Chamaecyparis lawsoniana (A. Murray) Parl.
Lawson Cypress
A narrowly conical, dioecious tree up to 45m high, the trunk often forking. The bark becomes cracked into long vertical grey-brown plates. The branches are numerous and small; the young shoots pendulous, forming flattened sprays. The leaves are opposite, the adjacent pairs at right-angles to each other, 0.5–2mm long, scale-like, closely pressed together, the smaller vertical pairs with translucent glands, whitish below, where they join. The male cones are *c.* 4mm long, pink or red, occurring at the tips of the twigs; the female cones are *c.* 8mm in diameter, globose, green with a bluish bloom, becoming yellowish–brown; the scales occur in 4 pairs, each depressed in the centre, with a transverse ridge. The seeds number 2–5 on each scale with broad wings and large resinferous tubercles. Male cones shed pollen in March. A native of the W. United States, widely planted for ornament (as cultivars), shelter and timber; sometimes naturalized. Au De Fr GB Ge Ir It No Po Ro Tu.

Shoot with male cones

Habit

Shoot with ripe female cone

Chamaecyparis obtusa (Siebod & Zucc.) Siebold & Zucc. in Endl.
Hinoki Cypress
Like *C. lawsoniana* but the bark reddish and shallowly fissured into long thin strips; the leaves are blunt with a minute gland and a conspicuous white marking underneath. A native of Japan, commonly planted for ornament.

Shoot with female cone

37

Chamaecyparis pisifera (Siebold & Zucc.)
Siebold & Zucc. in Endl.
Sawara Cypress
A species also like *C. lawsoniana* but the bark is reddish-brown with ridges and deep cracks, and the leaves have sharp, incurved tips with indistinct glands. Another Japanese native, commonly planted for ornament.

Chamaecyparis nootkatensis
(Lamb.) Spach
Nootka Cypress
Like *C. lawsoniana* but the female cones are *c.* 1cm in diameter, green with a bluish bloom, becoming dull brown; and each of the 4–6 scales has a long curved spine. A native of N. America planted infrequently for ornament.

Shoot with female cone

Female cone

x Cupressocyparis leylandii
(A.B. Jackson & Dallimore) Dallimore
Leyland Cypress
A narrowly conical to columnar monoecious tree up to 35m tall. The bark has dark reddish-brown shallow fissures. The branches are numerous, regular, ascending almost vertically, the foliage remaining alive at the base; the lateral shoots often arise on one side of the leading shoots. The leaves are opposite, the adjacent pairs at right-angles to each other, 0.5–2mm long, scale-like, closely pressed together, pointed, dark green. The male and female cones are rare; the male cones are *c.* 3mm in diameter, yellow, occurring at the tips of twigs; the female cones are 1–3cm in diameter, globose, each of the 4–8 scales with a large process in the centre, green becoming brown and shiny. Male cones shed pollen in March. The Leyland Cypress is a vigorous hybrid between the Nootka Cypress (*Chamaecyparis nootkatensis*) and the Monterey Cypress (*Cupressus macrocarpa*). There are two distinct sorts of cultivar: **'Haggerston Grey'**, with the Nookta Cypress as the

Male cones

Habit

female parent, has branches in several planes producing plumes of greyish foliage, and '**Leighton Green**', with the Monterey Cypress as the female parent, has branchlets more or less restricted to one plane, producing flattened sprays of greenish foliage.

Female cone

Cupressus macrocarpa
Hartweg
Monterey Cypress

An evergreen monoecious tree up to 35m tall, pyramidal while young, but becoming broadly domed at maturity. The bark is ridged and scaly, reddish-brown. The branches are numerous, rather stout, steeply ascending on young trees, much more spreading on old trees; the young shoots are stiffly forward-projecting, arranged irregularly around the leading shoot, the leaves are opposite, the adjacent pairs at right-angles, 1–2mm long, scale-like with a sharp point and a pale margin; the male cones are 3–5mm in diameter, yellow, carried on the lower parts of shoots, below the females, the female cones are 2–4cm in diameter, globose to ellipsoid, bright green becoming purplish–brown and shiny; the scales occur in 4–7 pairs, each with a shortly pointed central protuberance. The seeds number 8–20 on each scale, pale brown, with a papery wing. Male cones shed pollen in June. A native of S. California. Commonly planted in W. and S. Europe for ornament and shelter or occasionally for timber. Fr GB Ir It Pl Si Sp.

Habit

Female cone

Male cones

Cupressus lusitanica
Miller
Cedar of Goa, Mexican Cypress

Similar to *C. macrocarpa* but the bark is brown with peeling strips, the branches are spreading, more or less pendent at the tips, the leaves have spreading, sharp points; the female cones are 1–1.5cm in diameter, globose to ellipsoid, bluish-grey when young but becoming brown and shiny, and the scales number 6–8. A native of Mexico and Guatemala, planted for ornament and timber particularly in S. Europe. Fr It Pl Sp.

Female cone

39

Cupressus glabra
Sudworth
Smooth Arizona Cypress
Similar to *C. macrocarpa* but the bark flaking to reveal
yellow or red-brown patches the branches are widely
spreading and ascending at the tips; the young shoots
spread at right-angles to the leading shoot; the leaves
are greyish-green, occasionally with a central white
spot; the female cones are 1.5–2.5cm in diameter,
greenish-brown with a slight bloom; the scales each
with a small, rather blunt protuberance. A native of
C. Arizona occasionally planted for ornament or shelter
in parks and gardens.

Habit

*Shoot with
female cone*

Cupressus sempervirens L.
Italian Cypress
A narrow columnar or occasionally pyramidal, evergreen tree
up to 30m tall. The bark is shallowly, often spirally ridged,
grey-brown. The branches are upright occasionally diverging, the young shoots are somewhat 4-angled, arising
irregularly around the leading shoot, curved upwards at
the tips. The leaves are oppo-
site, the adjacent pairs at
right-angles to each other,
0.5–1mm in diameter, scale-
like, blunt dark green, all
similar, closely pressed
together. The male cones
are 4–8mm diameter, greenish–yellow; the female cones
are 2.5–4cm in diameter, ellipsoid oblong, green becoming
yellowish-grey in the second
year; the scales occur in 4–7
pairs and are blunt except for a
small point at the tip, the margins
somewhat wavy; there are 8–20
seeds on each scale, narrowly

*Shoot with
male cones*

Habit

winged. Male cones shed pollen in March. The wild form has rather spreading branches, forming a pyramidal tree, but the fastigiate form is much more widely planted and a conspicuous feature of Mediterranean landscapes. A native of SE. Europe and planted in other parts of S. Europe for ornament and timber. Al Bi Bu Cc Cr Fr FS FY Gr It Pl Sa Si Sp Sz Tu.

Female cone

Calocedrus decurrens (Torrey)
Florin
Incense Cedar

A monoecious, narrowly columnar evergreen tree up to 35m high and rounded at the top. The bark is cracked into large flakes, dark reddish-brown. The branches are numerous, short, ascending towards the tips; the shoots are covered with contiguous leaf-bases, green, becoming reddish-brown. The leaves occur in whorls of 4, are scale-like, narrow with short, incurving, acute tips, closely pressed together, all similar. The male cones are 3–6mm in diameter, ovoid, deep yellow occurring at the tips of lateral shoots; the female cones 2–3cm in diameter, oblong-ovoid, pointed; the two large fertile scales each with a short, outward-pointing, acute tip. Male cones shed pollen in January. A native of N. America, occasionally planted for ornament in large parks and gardens in Europe.

Shoot with male cones

Immature female cone

Mature female cone

Habit

41

Juniperus L.
Junipers

A genus of some 60 species of evergreen trees and shrubs.

Juniperus communis L.
Common Juniper

A dioecious shrub or small tree up to 15m high, initially conical, becoming much broader. The bark is reddish-brown, peeling in papery sheets. The twigs are slender, with ridges on the 3 angles, pale-brown, The leaves are all juvenile, 0.8–2 x 0.1–0.2cm, linear, spreading at right-angles, in whorls of 3, jointed at the base, sharply pointed at the tip, rigid, the upper surface with a single,

Fruit

Male flowers

broad, whitish stomatiferous band, rarely divided by a faint midrib near the base, lower surface faintly keeled, sessile. The male cones are solitary, yellow, produced in the leaf axils; the female cones are 6–9mm long, ovoid to globose, ripening in the 2nd or 3rd year, changing from green to glaucous-blue to black when fully ripe. There are usually 3 seeds. Male cones shed pollen in March. There are 2 further shrubby subspecies of the Common Juniper found mostly in mountainous regions of Europe. *J. communis* subsp. *nana* Syme in Sowerby has short, closely set leaves up to 1.5cm long, and often mat–like growth and grows on high

Female flowers

Leaf – upper side

Habit

mountains or occasionally near the coast in N. and NW. Europe. **J. communis** subsp. **hemisphaerica** (J. & C. Presl.) Nyman can be distinguished by its broad leaves, up to 2mm wide. It is a native of Europe, often found on lime-rich soils in the Mediterranean region, SW. Asia to the W. Himalayas and N. America. Found in all Europe.

Juniperus oxycedrus L.
Prickly Juniper

A dioecious shrub or small tree up to 14m high. The bark is reddish-grey. The twigs are stout, The leaves are all juvenile, 0.4–2.5 x 0.1 –0.2cm, linear, in whorls of 3, swollen and jointed at the base, sharply and stiffly pointed at the apex, the upper surface with 2 glaucous bands of stomata separated by a raised green midirib, the lower surface sharply keeled, sessile. The female cones are c. 1.5cm in diameter, more or less globose to pear-shaped, initially reddish and becoming yellow at maturity. The Prickly Juniper is native to S. Europe and is an extremely variable species. It can be divided into 3 subspecies: subsp. *oxycedrus*, with leaves c. 2mm wide and ripe cones 0.8–1cm in diameter occurs in dry hills and mountainous tracts (to 1900m) almost throughout the range of the species; subsp. *macrocarpa* (Sibth. & Sm.) Ball, with leaves up to 2.5mm in diameter and cones 1.2–1.5cm in diameter occurs in rocky places and maritime sands throughout much of the range; and the shrubby subsp. *transtagana* Franco, with leaves only 1–1.5mm wide and cones up to 1cm in diameter, is confined to maritime sands of SW. Portugal. Al Bl Co Fr FS FY Gr It Pl Sa Si Sp Tu.

Habit

Fruit

Leaf – upper side

43

Juniperus phoenicea L.
Phoenician Juniper

A small dioecious tree up to 8m high or a procumbent shrub. The twigs are c. 1mm in diameter, rounded in cross-section, scaly. The leaves are of 2 sorts: the juvenile leaves are 0.5–1.4cm x 0.5–1mm, linear, sharply pointed at the tip, the upper and lower surfaces with 2 whitish stomatiferous bands, carried usually in whorls of 3, spreading at right-angles; the adult leaves are 0.7–1mm long, scale-like, ovate to somewhat rhombic, obtuse to subacute, the margins whitish, the back of the leaf with a conspicuous furrowed gland, carried in opposite pairs or whorls of 3, closely appressed. The male cones are produced at the tips of branchlets; the female cones are 0.6–1.4cm long, globose to ovoid, ripening in the 2nd year, initially blackish, changing to green or yellowish and to dark red when fully ripe. The seeds number 3–9. Male cones shed pollen in March. A native of the Mediterranean region and the Atlantic coast of Portugal. Al Bl Co Cr Fr FY Gr It Pl Sa Si Sp.

Leaves

Habit

Female cone

Juniperus excelsa Bieb.
Grecian Juniper

A dioecious or monoecious tree, conical when young, later becoming a broad open pyramid up to 20m high at maturity. The twigs are 0.6–0.8mm wide, rounded in cross-section, scaly. The leaves are of 2 sorts: the juvenile leaves are very few, 56mm long, linear, sharply pointed at the tip, with 2 whitish stomatiferous bands on the lower surface, carried in decussate pairs, spreading at right-angles; the adult leaves are 1–1.5mm long, scale-like, ovate to

Female cone

Habit

rhombic, pointed, with an ovate or linear gland in the centre of the lower surface, carried in decussate pairs and mostly closely appressed. The male cones are produced at the tips of branchlets; the female cones are *c.* 8mm long, globose, ripening in the 2nd year, becoming dark purplish-brown with a slight bloom when ripe. The seeds number 4–6. Male cones shed pollen in March. A native of the Balkan Peninsula and the Crimea. Bu Cr FS FY Gr.

Juniperus foetidissima
Willd.
A dioecious or monoecious, columnar or narrowly conical tree up to 17m high. The twigs are *c.* 1mm wide, distinctly 4-angled, scaly, irregularly arranged, fetid when crushed. The leaves are of 2 sorts: the few juvenile leaves are 5–6mm long, linear, sharply pointed at the tip, with 2 whitish stomatiferous bands on the lower surface, carried in decussate pairs, spreading at right-angles; the adult leaves are *c.* 1.5mm long, ovate to rhombic, short or long-pointed, mostly without a whitish margin or gland, carried in decussate pairs, appressed but free at the apices. The male cones are produced at the tips of branchlets; the female cones are 0.7–1.2cm long, ripening in the 2nd year, becoming dark reddish-brown or blackish when ripe, The seeds number 1–3. Male cones shed pollen in April. A species very similar to *J. excelsa* with which it is often confused. A native of mountainous parts of the Balkan Peninsula and the Crimea. Bu Cr FS FY Gr.

Habit

Leaves

Female cone

Juniperus thurifera L.

A rather similar species to *J. foetidissima* but with the twigs regularly arranged in 2 ranks; the adult leaves are 1.5–2mm long, the margins sometimes slightly toothed, the back of the leaves with an oblong, furrowed gland; the female cones are 7–8mm long, becoming dark purple; the seeds number 2–4. A native of the French Alps and mountains of S., C. and E. Spain. Fr Sp.

Juniperus virginiana L.
Pencil Cedar

A pyramidal or columnar, usually dioecious tree up to 30m high. The twigs are 0.6–0.8mm in diameter, very slender, rounded in cross-section, scaly. The leaves are of 2 sorts: juvenile leaves 5–6mm long, linear, sharply pointed at the tip, the upper surface with a broad bluish stomatiferous band, the lower surface green, carried in decussate pairs, spreading often at the end of an adult shoot; the adult leaves are 0.5–1.5mm long, scale-like, ovate, with a sharp, often tapering tip, the back of the leaf with a small gland, carried in decussate pairs, appressed but usually free at the apices. The male cones are yellow, produced at the tips of branchlets, the female cones are 3–6mm long, ovoid, ripening in the first year, changing from bluish-green to brownish-violet when ripe. There are 1–2 seeds. Male cones shed pollen in March. A native to N. America, planted for timber in C. and S. Europe and several cultivated varieties, differing in habit and colour of the leaves are frequently planted in gardens and parks for ornament. Fr Hu It Ro.

Habit

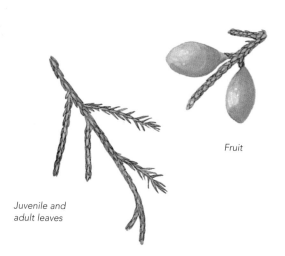

Fruit

Juvenile and adult leaves

Juniperus chinensis L.
Chinese Juniper

A dioecious tree or shrub up to 18m high, often narrowly conical but of variable habit. The twigs are 0.7–1mm in diameter, rounded in cross-section or slightly ridged on juvenile twigs. The leaves are of 2 sorts: the juvenile leaves are *c.* 8mm long, linear, sharply pointed at the tip, the upper surface with 2 broad bluish stomatiferous bands separated by the midrib, the lower surface green, usually carried in whorls of 3 or occasionally paired, spreading or at right-angles, often at the base of adult shoots; the adult leaves are *c.* 1.5mm long, scale-like, rhombic, blunt or slightly pointed, the back of the leaf with a small glandular depression, carried in decussate pairs and closely appressed. The male cones are yellow, produced at the tips of branchlets; the female cones are 6–7mm long, almost globose to top-shaped, ripening in the 2nd year, changing from bluish-white to purplish-brown when ripe. Male cones shed pollen in March and April. A native of Japan and China, commonly planted for ornament in gardens, parks and churchyards. Many cultivated varieties differing in habit and leaf colour are known.

Fruit

Habit

47

Tetraclinis articulata (Vahl)
Masters

A monoecious evergreen tree up to 15m high with a stout reddish-brown trunk. The twigs are erect, arranged in flattened sprays and regularly jointed. The leaves are in whorls of 4, the lateral pair larger than the central pair. The cones are solitary at the tips of branchlets; the female cones are 0.8–1.3cm in diameter. Male cones shed pollen in February and March. A drought-resisting species restricted to SE. Spain, Malta and N. Africa. Si Sp.

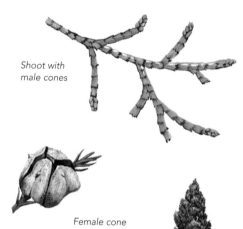

Shoot with male cones

Female cone

Thuja plicata
D. Don ex Lamb.
Western Red Cedar

A narrowly conical to pyramidal, evergreen monoecious tree up to 65m high in its native state, eventually with a broadly buttressed trunk. The bark is dark reddish-brown with wide ridges, soft, shedding irregular plates; the twigs are covered with leaf-bases, forming flattened sprays of foliage. The leaves are opposite and decussate, the lateral pair larger, 2–3mm long, scale-like, ovate with an acute or rather blunt apex, closely appressed, glossy and dark green above, paler and usually with whitish markings beneath, aromatic. The male cones are minute, initially pale yellow; the female cones are *c.* 1.2cm long, ovoid to conical, acute, brown

Shoot with male cones

Habit

when ripe; the scales number 10–12, each with a thickened protuberance on the inner side, projecting beyond the recurved spine-tipped apex. The seeds are 2–3 on each scale, elliptical, winged. Male cones shed pollen in March. A native to W. N. America, commonly planted for ornament and shelter and sometimes for timber. It is occasionally naturalized. Several other related species are occasionally planted, mainly for ornament. Au De GB Ge It No Pl.

Shoot with female cones

Thujopsis dolabrata L. fil
Siebold & Zucc.
Hiba
A monoecious, narrowly or broadly conical, evergreen tree up to 30m high, or sometimes a pyramidal shrub, the trunk often divided near ground level. The bark is dark reddish-brown, usually shredding into fine strings or papery strips. The twigs are rather pendulous, covered with scale-leaves, flattened, regularly arranged in flattened sprays. The leaves are opposite and decussate, the lateral pairs rather, larger, 4–7mm long, scale-like, broadly triangular, the apex pointed, incurved, appressed, glossy and dark green above, the underside with broad white markings, aromatic. The cones are solitary; the male cones are blackish-green, the female cones are 1.2–1.9cm long, irregularly globose, bluish-brown when ripe; the scales are 6–8, wedge-shaped, each with a triangular boss near the apex. There are 3–5 rounded winged seeds on each scale. Male cones shed pollen in April or May. A native of Japan, commonly planted for ornament.

Shoot with male cones

Female cone

Habit

DECIDUOUS CYPRESS FAMILY TAXODIACEAE

Sequoia sempervirens (Lamb.) Endl.
Coast Redwood

A large monoecious evergreen tree up to 100m high in its native state, conical when young, becoming broadly columnar with a stout, sometimes buttressed trunk, often sprouting and suckering from the base, occasionally forming a clump of trees. The bark is dark reddish-brown, the outer layers scaling away to reveal the thick, soft and fibrous, bright orange-red layers beneath. The branches are horizontal or somewhat pendulous. The twigs are irregularly whorled, green. The buds are surrounded by brown scales. The leaves are spirally arranged and of 2 sorts: those on leading shoots are 6–8mm long, linear, sharply pointed, loosely appressed; those on side-shoots are flattened into 2 rows, 0.6–2 x 0.2cm, linear to linear-oblong, pointed, flat, dark green above, the underside with a white band on either side of the midrib. The male cones are terminal, on young shoots, *c.* 2mm long, yellow; the female cones are on stouter shoots, 1.8–2.5cm long, globose to ovoid, woody, ripening reddish-brown in the 2nd year; the 14–20 scales are spirally arranged, rhomboidal, wrinkled. The seeds are *c.* 1.5mm long, winged, 3–7 on each scale, light brown. Male cones shed pollen in February. A native of the W. United States, planted for ornament in parks and large gardens, or occasionally for timber. Fr GB Ir It.

Female cone

Male cones

Bark and suckers

Habit

Sequoiadendron giganteum (Lindley)
Buchholz
Californian Big Tree, Giant Redwood or Wellingtonia

A large monoecious evergreen tree up to 90m high in its native state, the crown narrowly conical, becoming rounded, The trunk of old trees is up to 7m in diameter, buttressed at the base, tapering and bare of branches in the lower half. The bark is dark, reddish-brown or blackish, thick, fibrous, shredding from the ridges to reveal brighter reddish-brown layers beneath, deeply furrowed. The branches are ascending, becoming more pendulous below but upturned at the tips. The twigs are stout, turned upwards, covered with scale-leaves, green, becoming brown. The buds are without protective scales. The leaves are spirally arranged, crowded, 0.4–1 cm long, all scale-like, ovate to lanceolate, acute, flat above, convex beneath, initially bluish at the base, becoming shiny dark green, appressed or spreading towards the tips. The male cones are solitary on the tips of young shoots, 6–8mm long, pale yellow; the female cones are solitary or in pairs on stouter shoots, 5–8 x 2.5–5cm, ovoid, woody, ripening dark reddish-brown in the 2nd year; the 25–40 scales are spirally arranged, rhomboidal, each with a slender spine in the central depression, wrinkled. The seeds are 3–6mm long, oblong, winged, 3–7 on each scale, light brown. Male cones shed pollen from March to April. A native of the western slopes of the Sierra Nevada in the W. United States, often planted for ornament in parks and the largest gardens; or occasionally for timber. Au Fr GB.

Bark

Shoot with male cones

Female cone

Habit

51

Female cone

Male cones

Cryptomeria japonica (L. fil.) D. Don
Japanese Red Cedar

A narrowly conical or pyramidal, monoecious evergreen tree up to 50m high in its native state, with a dense crown and eventually a rounded apex, the trunk becoming buttressed at the base. The bark is orange-brown, becoming dark brown, thick, fibrous, shredding away in strips. The branches are irregularly whorled, level or the lowermost ones drooping. The twigs are sparsely branched, often pendulous, green. The buds are protected by small immature leaves. The leaves are spirally arranged, 0.6–1.5cm long, linear, acute, curved inwards at the tips, rhombic in cross-section, bright green. The male cones are towards the tips of young twigs, in clusters of *c.* 20 in the leaf axils, 6–8mm long, bright yellow or orange; the female cones are terminal on stouter branchlets, 1.2–3cm long, almost globose, woody, ripening in the first year; each of the 20–30 scales usually with 5 recurved spines at the tip. The seeds are *c.* 6mm long, very narrowly winged, dark brown, 2–5 on each scale. Male cones shed pollen in March. A native of China and Japan with many

Habit

different cultivars commonly planted for ornament in parts of W. and S. Europe. De GB It.

Taxodium distichum (L.) L. C. M. Richard
Swamp Cypress

A monoecious deciduous tree up to 50m high in its native state, narrowly conical, becoming broad and domed at maturity; plants near water produce some 'breathing roots' near the base of a fluted trunk. The bark is pale, reddish–brown, fibrous, scaling or peeling in strips, fissured. The branches are upright or spreading. The shoots are of 2 sorts: long shoots with spirally arranged leaves; and alternate side-shoots, *c.* 10cm long with flattened leaves arranged into 2 ranks. The buds are scaly. The leaves are alternate, 0.8–2cm long, linear, flat, pale green, the underside with a greyish band on either side of the midrib. The male cones are in slen- der branched heads,

Base of trunk with breathing roots

Habit

Female cone

5–15cm long, produced at the end of previous
year's shoots, dull yellow or purplish; the
are solitary or in small clusters
wigs, 1.2–3cm long, globose
woody, ripening pur-
in the first year, the
omboidal, each with
curved spine; the
c. 3mm long. The
3mm long, 3–angled,
nged, 2 to each scale.
shed pollen in April.
wamps in SE. and S. United
uently planted for ornament
nd gardens, especially on
und and sometimes for timber
e. Bu Fr Ge It Ro.

DAWN REDWOOD (Metasequoia glyptostroboides). Famous fast growing deciduous conifer with striking red/brown autumn colour. Outdoors all year. Feed and water frequently in growing season.

Metasequoia glyptostroboides
Hu & Cheng
Dawn Redwood

Similar to *Taxodium distichum*, but the side-
shoots and leaves arranged in opposite pairs; the
leaves 1.2–4cm (occasionally 6cm) long, linear,
soft, flat, pale green, greyish-green beneath; the
male cones clustered at the base of leaves
towards the ends of shoots; the female cones
with 20–30 scales in opposite and decussate
pairs, each scale grooved, with 2–9 ovules;
the pedicel *c.* 5cm long. A native of
E. Szechuan and NE. Hupeh in SW. China,
frequently planted for ornament in parks and
gardens in Europe.

Habit

*Male
cones*

PINE FAMILY PINACEAE

Abies
Miller
Silver Firs

About 50 species of evergreen resiniferous trees from the temperate northern hemisphere, many of which are cultivated for timber or ornament.

Abies alba
Miller
Common Silver Fir

A pyramidal tree up to 50m high with a stout trunk. The bark is smooth, becoming fissured to form scales, greyish-brown. The young twigs are densely pubescent, greyish. The buds are not resiniferous. The leaves are 1.5–3cm x 1.5–2mm, shallowly notched at the tip, thick but flexible, the underside with 2 white bands, spreading horizontally from the sides of the twigs, more or less erect above but spreading to leave a distinct gap above the centre of the twig. The female cones are 10–20 x 3–4cm, cylindrical, ripening pale brown, with a projecting spine beneath each scale, becoming bent backwards. Male cones shed pollen in April. A distinctive native forming natural forests in the mountainous parts of C. Europe, from N. Spain to Macedonia, and from S. Italy and Corsica to E. Poland. It is widely planted for timber elsewhere and also for ornament. Al Au Be Bu Co De FC Fr FY GB Ge Gr Hu It No Pl Po Ro Sp Sw Sz.

Female cone

Habit

Male cones

Shoot

Abies delavayi
Franchet
Delavay's Silver Fir
Similar to *A. alba* but the young twigs almost smooth or sometimes downy, reddish-brown; the winter buds resiniferous; the leaves 2–4cm long, usually notched or sometimes pointed, glossy dark green, the margin revolute, partly hiding the broad white bands beneath. The female cones are 6–10 x 2.5–4.5cm, cylindrical or oblong-elliptical, dark purplish or bluish–green, with a long projecting spine, usually becoming bent backwards, beneath each scale. A native of China, from W. and SW. Szechuan to the Yunnan. *A. delavayi* var. *forrestii* (C.C. Rogers) A.B. Jackson is the most commonly planted variety, recognizable by its deeply notched leaves and the rather shorter, narrower spines on the cones. It is grown for ornament in parks and large gardens.

Female cone

Shoot

Abies cephalonica
Loudon
Grecian Fir
A pyramidal tree up to 30m high with a fairly stout trunk. The bark is greyish-brown, smooth, eventually becoming fissured into oblong plates. The young twigs are hairless, light brown. The buds are very resiniferous. The leaves are densely arranged on the stems, projecting evenly at right-angles from the upper surface and sides of the twig but usually leaving a gap beneath, 1.5–3.5cm x 2–2.5mm, sharply pointed, thick, rigid, glossy green above, with two white bands beneath. The female cones are 12–16 x 4–5cm, cylindrical, ripening yellowish-brown; each scale with a projecting triangular backward-pointing spine. A native to the mountains of Greece up to 1700m altitude, planted for timber in Italy and for ornament elsewhere. Gr It.

Female cone

Bark

Habit

Shoot

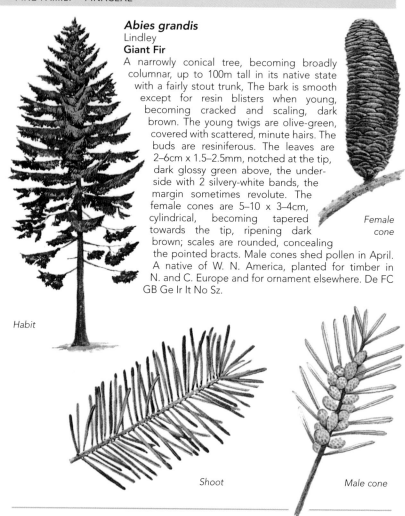

Abies grandis
Lindley
Giant Fir

A narrowly conical tree, becoming broadly columnar, up to 100m tall in its native state with a fairly stout trunk, The bark is smooth except for resin blisters when young, becoming cracked and scaling, dark brown. The young twigs are olive-green, covered with scattered, minute hairs. The buds are resiniferous. The leaves are 2–6cm x 1.5–2.5mm, notched at the tip, dark glossy green above, the underside with 2 silvery-white bands, the margin sometimes revolute. The female cones are 5–10 x 3–4cm, cylindrical, becoming tapered towards the tip, ripening dark brown; scales are rounded, concealing the pointed bracts. Male cones shed pollen in April. A native of W. N. America, planted for timber in N. and C. Europe and for ornament elsewhere. De FC GB Ge Ir It No Sz.

Female cone

Habit

Shoot

Male cone

Abies concolor (Gordon)
Hildebrand
Colorado White Fir

Similar to *A. grandis* but up to 55m high, the bark blackish-grey, becoming deeply fissured; the young twigs sometimes smooth, yellowish-green; the buds very resiniferous; the leaves in 2 ranks, curving upwards to almost vertical, 4–5.5cm x *c.* 2mm, shortly pointed at the tip, bluish-grey, the underside with 2 faint bluish bands; the female cones 12–15 x 3–7cm, cylindrical to barrel-shaped. A variable native of W. N. America, frequently planted for ornament in parks and gardens.

Abies lasiocarpa (Hooker)
Nutt.
Alpine Fir

Similar to *A. grandis* but up to 48m high in its native state, with a slender pyramidal crown and a slender trunk; the bark silvery-grey, slightly fissured, the branches drooping; the young twigs with scattered reddish hairs, sometimes almost smooth, grey; the leaves arranged irregularly in 2 ranks or curving upwards, those on the upper surface pointing forwards to obscure the upper surface of the twig; the female cones 5–10 x 3.5cm, dark purplish, becoming brown. A native of W. N. America, occasionally planted for timber in N. Europe and sometimes cultivated for ornament. Ic Sw.

Cone

Shoot

Abies nordmanniana (Steven)
Spach
Caucasian Fir

A conical to narrowly columnar tree up to 70m high with a stout trunk. The bark is smooth but gradually becoming fissured to form scales or plates, greyish-brown. The young twigs have scattered short hairs, brown or greyish-brown. The buds are not resiniferous. The leaves are 1.5–3.5cm x 1.5–2mm, notched at the tip, thick but flexible, glossy green above, the underside with 2 conspicuous white bands. The female cones are 12–18 x 4–5cm, cylindrical, ripening dark brown; with a projecting, strongly deflexed spine beneath each scale. Male cones shed pollen in April. A native to NE. Turkey and the W. Caucasus, widely planted for timber in C. Europe, especially in C. Europe, and frequently cultivated for ornament. Au De FC It Pl Ro Sw Tu.

Female cone

Shoot

Habit

Abies pinsapo
Boiss.
Spanish Fir

A pyramidal tree up to 30m high with a fairly stout trunk. The bark is smooth, gradually becoming irregularly fissured into plates, dark grey or blackish. The young twigs are greenish-brown, without hairs. The buds are resiniferous. The leaves are densely but evenly arranged at right-angles to the twig, on all sides, 1–1.8 x 0.2–0.3cm, thick, stiff, sometimes curved, the tip sharply pointed, bluish-grey above, with 2 grey bands beneath. The female cones are 10–16 x 3–4cm, cylindrical, gradually tapering towards the tip, ripening brown, each scale rounded, concealing the short spine-tipped bract. Male cones shed pollen in May. A native of the mountains of SW. Spain, near Ronda, where it grows on limestone slopes up to 2000m. It is occasionally planted for ornament in large gardens, parks and churchyards or sometimes for timber. Au Pl Sp.

Male cones

Habit

Female cone

Bark

Shoot

Abies x insignis
Carrière ex Bailly

A hybrid between *A. pinsapo* and *A. nordmanniana* with leaves 1–3.3cm x 1.5–2.5mm, arranged all round the twig or with a gap on the underside; the female cones are 11–20 x 3.5–5cm with some of the pointed bracts slightly projecting from the scales. It is frequently planted for ornament in parks and large gardens.

Abies sibirica
Ledeb.
Siberian Fir

Similar to *A. pinsapo* but with a slender trunk; the bark with resin blisters; the young twigs grey with scattered hairs; the buds very resiniferous; the leaves spreading horizontally from the sides of the twigs, leaving a gap below, those on the upper surface pointing forwards and upwards, obscuring the surface of the twig 1.5–3cm x 1–1.3mm, thin, flexible, blunt or slightly notched, bright green above, the underside with 2 greyish bands; the female cones 6–8 x 3cm, cylindrical, bluish while young, becoming brown. A species forming large natural forests in N. and E. Russia, planted for timber in some parts of Europe, De Fi FS Ic.

Female cone

Shoot

Abies procera
Rehder
Noble Fir

A narrowly conical tree, eventually becoming broadly columnar with a rounded top, up to 80m high usually with a stout trunk. The bark is smooth except for resin blisters, gradually becoming deeply fissured, grey and eventually brown on old trees. The young twigs are reddish-brown, densely covered with reddish hairs. The buds are resiniferous at the tip. The leaves are 1–3.5cm x 1–1.5mm, blunt at the tip, slender, flexible, greyish-green above, the underside with 2 greyish bands, spreading horizontally from the sides of the twig, curving upwards, leaving a gap below, those from the upper surface spreading forwards and curving upwards. The female cones are 12–20 x 5–8cm, cylindrical, tapered towards the tip, ripening purplish-brown; with a protruding, backward-pointing, green spine beneath each scale. Male cones shed pollen in May. A native of W. N. America, planted for timber in N. and W. Europe and widely planted for ornament in parks and gardens, especially those forms with bluish-white foliage. De GB Ge Ir No.

Shoot

Female cone

Habit

Cedrus
Trew
Cedars

A small genus of 4 evergreen tree species. They are very similar to one another and sometimes regarded as geographical races of the same species.

Cedrus deodara (D. Don)
G. Don in Loudon
Deodar, Himalayan Cedar
or **Indian Cedar**

A conical tree initially with a slender pointed apex, eventually broader, up to 65m high in its native state. The bark is greyish-brown, irregularly fissured into oblong plates. The branches are pendulous or more or less level on old trees. The young shoots are pendulous, densely pubescent; the short shoots with 15–20 leaves in a cluster. The leaves are 2–5cm long, dark green with faint grey lines. The male cones are 5–12cm long, dark purple before shedding pollen; the female cones are 8–12 x 5–8cm, rounded at the apex. A species frequently planted for ornament in parks and large gardens and cultivated for timber in S. Europe. A native to Afghanistan and the NW. Himalayas. Fr Gr It Pl.

Female cone

Shoot with male cones

Habit

Cedrus atlantica (Endl.) Carrière
Atlas Cedar or **Atlantic Cedar**

A pyramidal tree becoming broadly domed, up to 40m high. The bark is dark grey, becoming cracked into large plates, then deeply fissured. The branches are ascending, or level on the oldest trees. The young shoots are ascending, rather stiff, downy; the short shoots with 10–45 leaves in a cluster. The leaves are 1–3cm long, shiny deep green or bluish-green. The male cones are 3–5cm long, pinkish-yellow; the female cones are 5–8 x 3–5cm, squarish or often sunken

Young shoot

with a central boss at the tip. A native of the mountains of Algeria and Morocco, planted for ornament or for timber in S. Europe. The most common cultivar is the **Blue Atlas Cedar**, cv. *'Glauca'*, with bright bluish-grey or whitish leaves. It is a pollution-tolerant species and is widely planted in town parks and gardens, occasionally as fastigiate or pendulous cultivars.

Female cone

Cedrus libani A. Richard in Bory
Cedar of Lebanon

A medium-sized tree, conical when young, becoming broadly domed or flat topped, up to 40m high at maturity, often with a very stout trunk. The bark is dark grey with short ridges, scaling, becoming deeply fissured and dark brown. The branches are ascending in young trees, becoming level, forming a massive flat surface of foliage, the lowermost branches descending to the ground, The young shoots are spreading, hairless, the short shoots with 10–15 leaves in a cluster. The leaves are 2–3cm long, dark green. The male cones are 5–7.5cm long, greyish-green; the female cones are 7–12 x 5–7cm, blunt at the tip. A native to SE. Turkey, Syria and the Lebanon. Very commonly planted for ornament in gardens, parks and churchyards. It is particularly tolerant of air pollution.

Habit
(Cedrus atlantica)

Male cone

Habit

Bark

Female cone

Larix
Miller
Larches

A small genus of some 10 species from the colder parts of the northern hemisphere. Unlike other conifers all larches are deciduous with long shoots and spirally-set leaves, short shoots on old wood, spur-like, bearing leaves in the whorls.

Bark

Larix decidua
Miller
Common Larch
A narrowly conical tree up to 35m (sometimes up to 50m) high. The bark is greyish, becoming brown, fissured and scaling away, very thick at the base of old trees. The branches are rather short, level except for lowest descending branches on old trees, The long shoots are rough with old leaf-bases, pendulous, hairless, yellowish or greyish. The terminal buds are globose, shortly pointed, yellowish-brown. The leaves are in clusters of 30–40, 1.2–3cm long, soft, blunt or slightly pointed, light green above, with 2 greenish stomatiferous bands below. The female cones are with conspicuous red or white bracts while young, 2–3.8 x 1.5–2.5cm, conicalovoid, ripening brown; the scales are 40–50, rounded, entire, loosely appressed, with fine linear markings, covered with soft brown hairs, the pointed tips of the bracts sometimes protruding. Male cones shed pollen in March and April. A native of the Alps and W. Carpathian mountains, widely planted for timber, shelter, along roadsides or for ornament in parks. Trees from the Carpathians with smaller cones and

Summer shoot with mature female cones

Spring shoot

Habit

more concave scales than the typical form are sometimes treated as a separate subspecies, **L. decidua** subsp. *polonica* (Racib.) Domin, the **Polish Larch**. Au Be FC Fi Fr FS FY GB Ge It No Po Sw Sz.

Larix kaempferi (Lamb.)
Carrière
Japanese Larch
A broadly conical tree up to 40m high, The bark is reddish-brown, scaling, The branches are long, widely spreading. The long shoots are stiff, usually reddish-brown with a greyish waxy bloom, smooth or with soft brownish hairs. The terminal buds are conical, pointed, reddish-brown, resiniferous. The leaves are in clusters of *c.* 40, 1.5–3cm long, pointed or blunt, greyish-green above, the underside with conspicuous white stomatiferous bands. The female cones are with pointed, reflexed, greenish bracts when young, 1.5–3.5 x 1.2–3cm, ovoid, ripening brown; the scales are *c.* 40, the tips rounded and curved outwards, slightly downy, more or less concealing the bracts. Male cones shed pollen in March. A native of Japan, commonly planted for timber in NW. Europe and occasionally for ornament. Au Be De Fi Fr FS GB Ge Ir Ne Sw.

Habit

Summer shoot with cones

Spring shoot

63

Habit

Larix x eurolepis
A. Henry
Dunkeld Larch

A vigorous conical tree up to 35m high. The bark is greyish to reddish-brown, becoming fissured and scaling, The long shoots are yellowish-brown, with a slight grey waxy bloom, hairless or slightly downy. The terminal buds are pale reddish-brown, not resiniferous. The leaves are in clusters of *c.* 40, up to 5cm long, pointed or blunt, greyish-green above, the underside with 2 greyish stomatiferous bands. The female cones are with pinkish reflexed bracts while young, 3–4 x 2–2.5cm, conical, ripening to pale brown; the scales are rounded, loosely appressed, the margins slightly exposed. Male cones shed pollen in March. A rather variable hybrid between the Common Larch *Larix decidua* and the Japanese Larch, *L. kaempferi*. Most of the characteristics are rather intermediate between the two parent species, although the hybrid is usually more vigorous than either parent. It is much planted for timber or shelter belts in NW. Europe, although a precise distribution cannot be given, since it intergrades with *L. decidua*.

Spring shoot

Summer shoot with cones

Summer shoot with cone

Larix gmelinii (Rupr.)
Kuzen.
Dahurian Larch

A conical or rather slender tree up to 30m high. The bark is reddish-brown with irregular scales. The branches are more or less level, sometimes forming a large flat surface. The long shoots are yellowish or reddish-brown, often with a covering of soft hairs. The terminal buds are yellowish–brown, not resiniferous. The leaves occur in clusters of *c.* 25, 1.2–4cm x 0.5mm, blunt, bright green above, the underside with 2 pale greenish stomatiferous bands. The female cones are with pinkish or yellowish-green bracts while young, 2–2.5 x 1.8cm, ovoid, blunt, ripening pale brown; the scales are c. 20, rounded, hairless, squarish at the tip with the margins slightly curved outwards, the points of the bracts often projecting. Male cones shed pollen in March. A native of E. Asia, sometimes planted for timber or rarely for ornament in N. Europe. De Fi No.

Spring shoot

Habit

Pseudolarix amabilis (A. Nelson) Rehder
Golden Larch

A deciduous conical tree up to 40m high, The bark is light reddish-brown, becoming fissured. The branches are irregularly whorled, level, producing flattened plates of foliage. The long shoots are reddish-brown, hairless, with scattered, spirally arranged leaves; the short shoots are with clusters of 15–30 leaves. The leaves are up to 6.5 x 0.3cm, pointed, bright yellowish–green above, the underside with 2 greyish bands. Male and female cones occur on the same tree from short shoots; the male cones densely clustered, c. 2.5cm long, cylindrical; the female cones are 5–7 x 4–5cm, ovoid, woody, ripening light brown in the first year; the scales are triangular, blunt or notched, eventually falling away. The seeds are winged, 2 to each scale, Male cones shed pollen in May and June. A native of E. China, occasionally cultivated for ornament, especially in S. Europe.

Habit

Summer shoot with cones

65

Picea
A. Dietr.
Spruces

About 50 species from the temperate northern hemisphere, many of which are planted for timber or ornament.

Picea abies (L.)
Karsten
Norway Spruce

A conical tree up to 65m high The bark is reddish-brown, scaling. The branches are short, the lowermost on old trees descending. The young twigs are reddish-brown, usually hairless or with scattered hairs. The buds are *c.* 6mm long, pointed, reddish-brown. The leaves are 1–2.5cm long, 4-angled in cross-section, stiff, pointed, dark green with greyish lines, spreading from the sides of the twig, exposing the under surface; those above point forwards and upwards, concealing the twig. The female cone is usually 10–18cm long, cylindrical, ripening brown; the scales are irregularly rhombic and usually squarish or notched at the tip. Male cones shed pollen in May. Two subspecies are currently recognized: *P. abies* subsp. *obovata* (Ledeb.) Hultén, the **Siberian Spruce**, is a smaller tree than typical *P. abies*, only up to 30m high ; the twigs are densely pubescent; the leaves are 1–1.8cm long; the female cones are 6–8cm long, with scales more rounded; restricted to NE. Europe and N. Asia. Typical *P. abies* subsp. *abies* is found from N. Europe to the S. Alps and the Balkan Peninsula. It is commonly planted for timber, ornament or in plantations for Christmas trees. Al Au Be Bu De FC Fi Fr FS FY GB Ge Hu Ir It Ne No Po Ro Sp Sw Sz.

Habit

Female cone

Bark

Shoot with male cones

Picea pungens
Engelm.
Colorado Spruce
Similar to *P. abies*, but up to 50m high, with brownish-grey bark. The twigs are hairless, yellowish-brown. The buds are 0.6–1.6cm long. The leaves are 2–3cm long, bluish-green, sharply pointed, spreading almost around the shoot. The female cones are 6–10cm long, cylindrical, initially purplish, ripening to greyish-brown; the scales tapering to a squarish, irregularly toothed apex. A native of N. America, commonly planted for ornament and for timber in C. and NW. Europe. Au Fr GB Ge Ir It Ne No.

Shoot

Female cone

Habit

Picea breweriana
S. Watson
Brewer's Weeping Spruce
Similar to *P. abies* but up to 40m high, with grey flaking bark. The branches are short, curving upwards except for the lowermost ones; the side-shoots are long and slender, pendent with greyish hairs. The buds are *c.* 3mm long, blunt. The leaves are 2.5–3cm long, flattened, dark green with 2 whitish bands beneath. The female cones are 6–13 x 2–2.5cm, cylindrical, purplish becoming reddish-brown; the scales have rounded margins. A native of the W. United States, frequently planted for ornament in parks and gardens.

Habit

Cone

Picea glauca (Moench) Voss
White Spruce

A narrowly conical tree, gradually becoming more rounded at maturity, up to 30m high. The bark is greyish-brown, becoming cracked into rounded plates. The branches are somewhat deflexed, turning upwards at the tips. The twigs are hairless, greyish, becoming yellowish-brown. The buds are *c.* 6mm long, ovoid, blunt, The leaves are 1.2–1.3cm long, stiff, 4-angled in cross-section, pointed or somewhat blunt, pale green or bluish, emitting a fetid smell when crushed, mostly spreading from the sides and the upper surface of the twig. The female cones are 2.5–6 × 1.2–2cm, more or less cylindrical, ripening orange-brown, the scales have rounded margins. Male cones shed pollen in April. A native of Canada and N. United States, frequently planted for timber and occasionally for ornament in N. Europe. Au Be De Fi Ic No.

Habit

Female cone

Shoot

Picea orientalis (L.) Link
Oriental Spruce

A tree up to 40m (occasionally 60m) high with a dense conical crown. The bark is pale brown, cracking into small scales which gradually flake away. The branches are rather slender, ascending or level; the twigs are densely hairy, whitish, becoming pale brown. The buds are *c.* 3mm long, conical, pointed, reddish-brown. The leaves are dense, spreading more or less horizontally from the sides of the stems, exposing the lower surface, those from the upper surface pointing forwards and upwards, concealing the twig, 0.6–1cm

Female cone

Habit

long, 4-angled in cross-section, usually blunt, glossy dark green. The female cones are 6–9cm long, elongated-ellipsoid, slightly purplish, ripening to shiny brown; the scales are rounded. Male cones shed pollen in April. A native to E. Turkey, the Caucasus and parts of SW. Asia. Frequently planted for ornament in parks and gardens, and occasionally for timber. Au Be It Tu.

Shoot

Picea engelmannii
Parry ex Engelm.
Engelmann Spruce

A slender conical or pyramidal tree up to 50m high. The bark is reddish or greyish-brown, becoming scaly. The branches are ascending or curved upwards at the tips. The young shoots are slender, pendulous, covered with minute glandular hairs, pale yellowish-brown. The buds are *c.* 1.5cm long, conical, blunt. The leaves are 1.5–2.5cm long, flexible, 4-angled in cross-section, pointed, bluish-green, emitting a somewhat fetid smell when crushed, spreading more or less horizontally from the side of the twig, exposing the lower surface; those from the upper surface point forwards and upwards, concealing the twig. The female cones are 3.5–7.5cm long, oblong-elliptic but tapered towards the tip, initially crimson-tinged, becoming shiny brown when ripe; the scales are elongated-rhombic, squarish at the tip with small irregular teeth. Male cones shed pollen in May. A native of W. N. America, planted for timber in N. Europe and occasionally for ornament in parks and gardens. Au Be De Fi Ic No.

Female cone

Shoot

Habit

Picea sitchensis (Bong.)
Carrière
Sitka Spruce

A conical tree with a slender tapering apex, up to 60m high, the trunk stout and sometimes buttressed. The bark is greyish-brown, becoming darker, purplish-grey with thin lifting scales. The branches are ascending. The side-shoots are slightly pendent, stiff, hairless, greyish becoming light brown. The buds are *c.* 6mm long, ovoid, rather blunt, pale brown. The leaves are 15–30cm long, sharply pointed, thick and rigid, flattened, bright green above, the underside with 2 broad white bands, spreading all round the shoot but becoming parted below to spread more horizontally, those on the upper side of the twig pointed forwards, obscuring the twig. The female cone is 6–10 x 2.5–3cm, cylindrical, rather blunt at the top, initially pale, olive-green ripening to light brown; the scales are elongated, rhombic, tapering to a squarish, irregularly toothed apex. Male cones shed pollen in May. A native of W. N. America, commonly planted as a timber tree or for ornament in NW. Europe and parts of C. Europe. Au Fr GB Ge Ic Ir Ne No.

Mature female cone

Young female cones

Bark

Habit

Shoot

Picea omorika (Pančić)
Purkyně
Serbian Spruce

A narrowly columnar or somewhat conical tree up to 30m high with a very slender trunk. The bark is reddish or orange-brown, with thin scales or roughly rectangular plates on older trees. The branches are short, ascending or level, the lowest descending then curving upwards. The side-shoots are often somewhat pendent, covered with rather stiff persistent hairs, light brown. The buds are *c.* 6mm long, conical, reddish-brown. The leaves are 0.8–2cm long, the apex sharp or blunt on old trees, rather flexible, flattened, dark bluish-green above, the underside with 2 broad white bands, spreading more or less horizontally from the sides of the twigs, curving downwards, those from the upper surface pointing forwards, overlapping and obscuring the surface of the twig. The female cone is 3–6 x 1.5–3cm, oblong-ovoid to somewhat conical, bluish-black or bluish-green, ripening to dark brown; the scales are almost orbicular, the tips with very small irregular teeth, Male cones shed pollen in May. The Serbian Spruce has a natural distribution restricted to the Drina basin of C. Yugoslavia, growing on limestone rocks up to 1800m. It is planted for timber in other parts of Europe, especially in Scandinavian countries, and since it is tolerant of air pollution it is frequently planted in town gardens and parks. De FY Sw.

Habit

Shoot

Female cone

Bark

Tsuga heterophylla (Rafin.) Sarg.
Western Hemlock

Female cone

An evergreen tree with a dense, narrowly conical or somewhat columnar crown up to 70m high in its native state. The bark is reddish-brown, becoming fissured with scaling ridges. The young shoots are slender, pendulous at the tips, greyish-brown covered with long pale brown hairs. The buds are globose, greyish-brown. The leaves are 0.6–2cm long, oblong, flattened, blunt, the margins minutely toothed, dark green above, the underside with 2 whitish stomatiferous bands; one resin canal is present. The male cones are in the leaf axils of the previous year's shoots, globose; the female cones are solitary, terminal on the previous year's wide shoots, 2–2.5cm long, ovoid, blunt, pendent, ripening reddish–brown in the first year; the scales are roundish, entire, exceeding the bracts, persistent. The seeds are winged, 2 to each scale. Male cones shed pollen in April. A native of W. N. America, occasionally planted for ornament or as a timber tree in NW. Europe. De Fr Ge Ir No.

Habit

Bark

Male cones

Tsuga canadensis (L.) Carrière
Eastern Hemlock

Like *T. heterophylla* but broader, up to 30m high, often with a forked trunk; the buds ovoid; the leaves spreading on the side of the twig but some obscuring the upper surface, 0.8–1.8cm long, rather narrowed towards the tip, the underside with 2 narrow white stomatiferous bands; the female cones 1.5–2cm long, dark brown. A native of N. America with many cultivars differing mostly in habit, frequently planted for ornament and occasionally as a timber tree. Ge.

Female cone

Habit

Pseudotsuga menziesii (Mirbel) Franco
Douglas Fir

An evergreen resiniferous tree with a conical crown up to 100m high in its native state. The bark is greyish-green, smooth but with resin blisters, becoming dark, reddish-brown and ridged on old trees. The shoots are yellowish to grayish-green with slightly projecting elliptical leaf-scars, downy. The buds are ovoid, slender sharply pointed, brown. The leaves are 2–3.5cm, linear, blunt or pointed at the tip, dark green and grooved above, the underside with 2 distinct white stomatiferou bands; 2 resin canals are present. The male cones are in the leaf axils of the previous year's shoots, conical, yellow; the female cones are usually terminal on the previous year's shoots, 5–10 x 2–5cm long, oblong-ovoid, pendent, ripening lig brown in the first year, the scales rounded, entire, minutely pubescent, persistent, the bracts 3-pointed, projecting beyond the scales. The seeds are winged, 2 to each scale. Male cones shed pollen in May. A native of the Pacific coast of N. America, widely planted for timber in much of Europe and for shelter or occasionally ornament in large gardens. Au Be Bu De FC Fi Fr FY GB Ge Gr Ir It Pl Po Ro Sw Sz.

Bark

Female cone

Habit

73

Pinus L.
Pines

Evergreen trees or shrubs with a conical habit and horizontal branches disposed in regular whorls; the mature crowns may become flat, round or spreading. Isolated trees are usually large at the base, tapering rapidly as they advance in height. Plantation trees have long clean columnar trunks, losing their lower branches early. The bark is usually thick, rough and deeply furrowed or thin and scaly. The leaves are of 3 kinds: (i) the primordial leaves of seedlings are solitary, spirally arranged, linear-lanceolate and toothed; (ii) the scale-leaves are triangular-lanceolate, falling early, bearing short shoots in the axils; (iii) the adult leaves are needle-like, persistent for, two or more years, borne in clusters of 2, 3 or 5, although some species are inconstant in number. The flowers are borne separately on strobili; the male strobili are catkin-like, clustered at the base of young twigs, shedding pollen in May–June; the female strobili are borne at the tips of new shoots, or in whorls some way below the tip. Cones develop from the enlarging female strobili and are at least 2 years old when ripe; the scales are woody; the exposed part of the scale has a prominent protuberance usually ending in a spine or prickle.

Pinus contorta
Douglas ex Loudon

A small to large tree 3–30m tall with short contorted branches; young trees have a broad bushy base and a vigorous central shoot; old trees usually tall and narrow, densely bushy-domed or spired. The shoots are glabrous, green in the 1st year, orange-brown and striped white in the 2nd year, The leaves are 3–7cm x *c.* 1mm, sharply pointed, very densely set over young shoots, spreading on older shoots, appearing in pairs, and twisted. The male strobili occur in dense whorls; the female strobili occur in clusters of 2–4, at or just below the tip of the shoot. The cone is 2–6 x 2–3cm, ovoid-conical, symmetrical, pale brown-yellow, shining; each scale has a slender, fragile, sharp tip. The seeds are 4–5mm long with a wing up to 8mm long. A very variable species of Pacific United States origin, widely planted for timber on peatlands and moors throughout much of C. or NW. Europe. Be De FC Fi GB Ge Ic Ir It No Ro Sw.

Habit
(var. contorta)

Mature cone

Habit
(var. latifolia)

Pinus contorta var. *latifolia* S. Watson, **Lodgepole Pine** is similar to the type but has a less dense crown; the bark has shallow fissures, forming scales; the leaves are broader and those of each pair spread apart more widely. Planted for timber in similar regions to the type.

Leaf bundles

Shoot with winter bud

Pinus pinaster
Aiton
Maritime Pine

A large tree 30–40m tall; young trees with broad whorls of widely spaced branches; the trunks of old trees bare for a greater part of their length, with wide flat crowns. The bark is thick, deeply fissured, dark red-brown. The shoots are glabrous, dark red or pale green when young, becoming pink-brown above, pale olive below. The leaves are 10–25cm x c. 0.2mm, spiny, stout, rigid, occurring in pairs, pale grey-green. The male strobili are scattered along the basal third of new shoots; the pink, female strobili are in groups of 3–5 around the terminal bud. The cones are 8–22 x 5–8cm, conical, ovoid, symmetrical or almost so, light brown and shining; the exposed part of the scale is rhomboidal, keeled with a prominent prickly protuberance. The seeds are 7–8mm long with a wing up to 3cm long. A native of the Mediterranean region growing on light soils and sea sand, now cultivated as far eastward as Greece and reaching the Atlantic shores of France and Portugal. Al Co Cr Fr GB Gr It Pl Sa Si Sp.

Habit

Leaf bundle

Cone

Shoot with female summer buds

75

Pinus radiata
D. Don
Monterey Pine

A long pointed conical tree when young, but dense and high domed when mature, 30–40m high. The bark is rugged, deeply fissured into thick, more or less vertical parallel ridges, dull grey on older trees. The main branches are heavy, wide and spreading and some-times touching the ground. The young shoots are glabrous, pale grey or white-green. The winter buds are ovoid, short-pointed, with close-fitting, resiniferous, brown scales. The leaves are 10–15cm long, in clusters of 3, persisting for 3–4 years, with finely toothed margins, a sharp apex and central resin canal. The male strobili are crowded at the base of new shoots, bright yellow at flowering time; the female strobili occur in clusters of 3–5 around the shoot tip. The Mature cones are 7–15 x 6–9cm; the scales are broad, thick and woody, rounded on the outer, exposed sides. The seed is up to 6mm long, black with a well-developed wing. A species of rather restrict-ed distribution in Monterey County, Guadalupe Island and Baja California, now widely planted as a shelter tree in W. Europe, particularly near sea coasts and on light soils. Fr GB Ir It Pl Sp.

Cone

Habit

Leaf clusters

Pinus rigida
Miller
Northern Pitch Pine

A conical tree up to 25m, with rigid horny leaves occurring in clusters of 3, and small cylindrical or barrel-shaped cones with thin scales. A N. American, Atlantic species planted for timber on a small scale in Europe.

Cone

Habit

Pinus banksiana
Lamb.
Jack Pine
A variable tree in habit, 8–25m (rarely 30m) high, the branches forming a thin and irregular, somewhat oval crown on young trees but tough and wide-spreading on mature trees. The bark is reddish-brown, vertically striped, with a grey finish. The young shoots are smooth, glabrous, initially pale yellow-green, becoming reddish-brown in the 2nd year. The winter buds are cylindrical, 3–6mm long, resiniferous, with closely appressed scales. The leaves are 1.5–3.5cm long, in pairs, lasting 2 or3 years, olive-green, stiff, with minutely toothed margins, a sharp pointed apex, and marginal resin canals. The male strobili are numerous on the smaller shoots, yellow; the female strobili are globose, pale red. The cones are 3–6 x 1–2cm, curving forwards, lumpy, pointed, persisting unopened for years on mature trees; the scales are 1.5 x 0.5cm, spineless. The seeds are up to 4mm long, triangular, blackish-brown, mottled. An E. Canadian species originating from the McKenzie river in the Arctic Circle, and common in the Canadian forest belt. Because of its hardiness it is widely planted for timber on well-drained soils of cold, exposed places. Au De FC GB Ge Ro.

Branch with winter bud and leaf clusters

Cone

Habit

Pinus ponderosa
Douglas
Western Yellow Pine
A tall tree up to 50m high (70m in the wild) with a straight clean trunk and a long spire-like crown. The bark is yellowish or dark reddish-brown, breaking up into irregularly shaped scaly plates which become very large and thick in old trees. The shoots are glabrous, orange-brown or green at first, becoming black at maturity. The leaves occur in threes, persisting for 3 years and are 15–30 x *c.* 0.3cm, spreading, densely crowded on the shoots, curved, rigid, with minutely toothed margins and a sharp horny apex. The cones are subterminal, either solitary or occurring in clusters ovoid, 7–15 x 3.5–5cm, sessile or on short peduncles, light reddish-brown often leaving a few of the basal scales attached to the branchlets when falling off; the scales are oblong, *c.* 3 x 1.5cm, the exposed part of the scale swollen, rhomboidal, transversely ridged; the central boss is armed with a minute prickle. The seeds are *c.* 5cm long, oval, mottled, with a wing up to 2cm long. A wide-ranging tree of W. N. America planted in Europe on a small scale for timber, but mostly for ornament. Au Ge Gr It Ro. Related species planted on a lesser scale include: *P. jeffreyi* Balf., **Jeffrey Pine**, with a darker bark, larger cones with recurved prickles and heavier seeds; and *P. sabiniana* Douglas, the **Digger Pine**, a very slender tree with blue-white foliage.

Habit

Shoot with winter buds

Leaf bundle

Mature cone

Pinus nigra
Arnold
Austrian Pine or **Corsican Pine**

Mature cone

A large tree 40–50m high, pyramidal when young, becoming flat-topped when mature. The bark is greyish-brown or dark brown and very rough when mature. The branches are densely crowded. The shoots are glabrous, yellowish-brown and ridged; the branchlets become roughened by persistent leaf-bases as they lose their leaves. The leaves occur in pairs, persisting very densely on the branchlets for about 4 years; they are 10–15cm long, stiff, stout, straight or curved, with minutely toothed margins and a thickened apex; the resin canals are central and the basal sheaths initially *c.* 1.5cm long but gradually getting shorter with age. The cones are solitary or in clusters, 5–8cm long, up to 3cm wide, subsessile; the scales are 2–2.5cm long, transversely keeled near the apex and terminating with a persistent prickle. The seeds are *c.* 3mm long, greyish-brownish with a long wing. A very variable and wide-ranging species with several distinct varieties described. It can be broadly divided into 2 main types; the **Austrian Pine**, subsp. *nigra*, with broad, rigid, persistent leaves; and the **Corsican Pine**, subsp. *laricio* (Poiret) Maire, with soft narrow leaves. It succeeds on poor chalky or neutral soils in C. European and S. coastal areas and is widely planted for timber, as a windbreak and as a sand dune stabilizer. Al Au Be Bu Co Cr De FC FS FY GB Ge Gr Ir It Ne Ro Si Sp Sw Sz Tu.

Habit
(subsp. nigra)

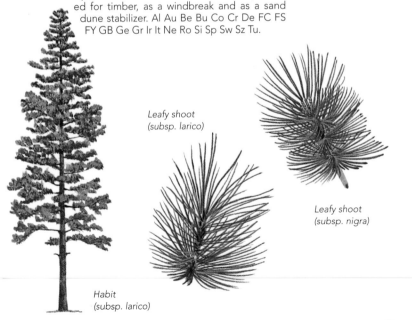

Leafy shoot
(subsp. larico)

Leafy shoot
(subsp. nigra)

Habit
(subsp. larico)

Leaf bundle

Pinus sylvestris (L.)
Scots Pine

A moderate-sized tree 25–35m (occasionally up to 50m) tall with a straight cylindrical bole up to 3.5m in diameter. The bark on the main portion of the bole is fissured into irregular longitudinal plates, reddish-brown or greyish-brown, but light red to orange and in papery scales towards the top. The branch-es are usually regularly whorled in young trees, but in old trees branch-ing only at the top, giving rise to a flat crown. The shoots are initially green, smooth and shining, becoming grey-ish-brown in the 2nd year, somewhat marked by the bases of the scale-leaves. The winter buds are c. 1cm long, oblong-ovate with lanceolate fringed scales, the upper ones free at the apex. The leaves are 2.5–8cm long, in pairs, grey-green, glaucous,

Habit

short-pointed with finely toothed margins and well-defined lines of stomata on the flat inner surface, but with interrupt-ed lines on the outer surface; the resin canals are marginal; the basal sheaths are initially white, later becoming grey, about 1cm long. The cones are solitary or in groups of 2–3 on short peduncles. usually ovoid-conical, 2–8cm long, grey or dull brown; the scales are narrowly oblong, the exposed part flat or protruding, the central boss terminat-

Mature cone

Shoot with
winter buds

ing in a small prickle. The seeds are 2–4mm long, black or dark grey, with a wing up to 1.5cm long. The Scots Pine has the widest distribution of all the pines, occurring as a native on light montane soils throughout Europe and W. and N. Asia. In the British Isles it survives as a native only in Scotland. More than 150 variants have been described, some regarded as subspecies, but the variation is somewhat continuous and often difficult to determine. However, it may be distinguished from other 2-leaved pines by its glaucous twisted foliage, the reddish upper trunk and its characteristic spire-like mature crown. All except Co Cr Ic. *P. resinosa* Aiton, the **Red Pine** from E. N. America, resembling *P. ponderosa* with the bark of *P. sylvestris*, is grown on small scale for timber in Europe.

Pinus mugo

Turra

Mountain Pine (incl. *P. uncinata* Miller)

A shrub or small tree with many crooked, irregularly spreading branches. The bark is grey-black and scaly. The buds are ovoid-cylindrical and very resiniferous. The leaves are 3–8cm x 1.5–2mm, in pairs, bright green, curved, rigid, persisting 5 years or more. The cones are subterminal, solitary or in groups of 2–3, ovate to ovate-conical, up to 5cm long x 1.5–2.5cm wide; the exposed part of the scale is flat, or convex above and concave below; the boss is central or below the middle with a small prickle. The seeds are small. A common species to the mountains of C. Europe and the Balkan Peninsula. It is frequently planted for sand binding and shelter in N. Europe. Al Au Bu FC Fr Ge Gr It Po FS Ro Sw FY.

Habit

Leafy shoot

Mature cone

Habit

Pinus leucodermis
Antoine
Bosnian Pine

A stout pyramidal tree up to *c.* 30m, the trunk with a girth of up to 2m. The bark is ash-grey, dividing into irregular plates. The young twigs are glabrous but glaucous for about the first 3 years. The winter buds are dark brown but not resiniferous. The leaves are 7–9cm x *c.* 1–2mm, occurring in pairs, densely covering the shoots, dark green, rigid, erect, pungent, with minutely toothed margins, sharply pointed apices stomatic lines on both surfaces, and 4–6 central resin canals. The cones are ovoid-conical, 7–8 x *c.* 2.5cm, shortly stalked, dull brown and somewhat shining; the exposed part of the scale is pyramidal with a recurved prickle. The seeds are about 7mm long with a wing up to 2–5cm long. The Bosnian Pine is closely allied to *P. nigra* and considered by some authors to be a montane form of it, although it is readily recognized by the compact branching system and denser foliage. A SW. Italian and Balkan species, occurring on dry limestone; it is frequently cultivated in other parts of Europe. Bu FY Gr It.

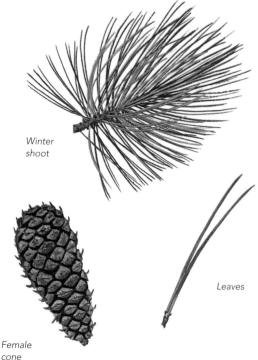

Winter shoot

Leaves

Female cone

Pinus heldreichii
Christ

A tree or shrub up to 20m tall with a rounded pyramidal crown. The bark is ashy-grey, flaking to leave yellowish patches. The twigs are glabrous but glaucous in their first year. The buds are green, not resiniferous. The leaves are 6–9cm x *c.* 1.5mm, occurring in pairs, rigid, more or less spine tipped; there are 2–11 central resin canals. The cones are 7–8 x 2–5cm, brown and slightly shining; the exposed part of the scale is flat with a very short straight prickle. The seed is *c.* 7mm long with a wing *c.* 2.5cm long. Many authorities consider *P. leucodermis* and *P. heldreichii* as the same species but the latter can be distinguished by the brown 2nd year twigs, the exposed part of the scale being flat and the short, acute prickles. A resistant montane species occurring on limestone in the Balkan Peninsula. Al FY Gr.

Winter shoot

Leaves

Habit

Pinus halepensis
Miller
Aleppo Pine

A stout tree (at maturity) rarely exceeding 20m high, with twisting branches and fine twigs and a bole with a girth up to 5m. The bark is smooth, silvery grey and shining at first, becoming reddish-brown, fissured and scaly on old boles. The shoots are grey-glaucous and glabrous, remaining grey for many years but eventually becoming green. The winter buds are conical, *c.* 8mm long, with fringed scales and often reflexed at the tips. The leaves are 6–15cm x 0.7mm, occurring in pairs, persisting for *c.* 2 years, slender, clear green, curved, twisted above, with minutely toothed margins and a short horny apex; there are 3–8 submarginal or central resin canals. The cones are 5–12 x 4cm, ovate-conical, solitary or in groups of 2–3, spreading or deflexed, reddish, occurring on thick scaly peduncles up to 2cm long; the scales are shiny, about 2.5cm long; the exposed part is convex. The seeds are *c.* 7mm long with a wing up to 2cm long. A species common to the countries surrounding the Mediterranean; being particularly drought-resistant it is commonly planted in hot dry places to check soil erosion and as a windbreak. Bl Co Cr Fr FY Gr It Pl Sa Si Sp.

Female cone

Habit

Leaves

Shoot with winter bud

Pinus brutia
Ten
Calabrian Pine

Closely related to *P. halepensis* but the leaves are longer (8–12cm x *c.* 1–1.5mm) darker green and more rigid; the cones are more spreading, never deflexed. It occurs in similar localities in Calabria, Crete and Turkey. Cr It Tu.

Female cone

Pinus canariensis
Sweet & Sprengel
Canary Island Pine

Superficially similar to *P. halepensis* but the leaves are 20–30cm long, occurring in threes; the shoots are yellow in colour; the bud scales are fringed, and the cones are very large. It is planted in Italy and on a smaller scale in other Mediterranean countries as a timber tree.

Female cone

Pinus pinea L.
Stone Pine or Umbrella Pine

A stout, parasol-shaped tree up to 30m tall. The bark on old trees is reddish-grey with deep longitudinal fissures, flaking to leave reddish-orange patches, The twigs are glabrous, greyish-green, becoming brown at maturity. The winter buds are 0–5–1.2cm long, with reflexed scales. The leaves are 10–20cm x 1.5–2mm, occurring in pairs, persisting for 2–3 years, slightly twisted, acute, with 12 stomatic lines on the outer surface and 6 on the inner surface; the resin canals are marginal. The cones are 8–14 x 10cm, ripening shining brown after 3 years, the exposed part of the scale weakly pyramidal. The seeds are 1.5–2 x 0.7–1.1cm with a wing less than 1mm long. A native of light sandy soils in Mediterranean Europe. Al Bl Co Cr Fr FY Gr It Pl Sa Si Sp Tu.

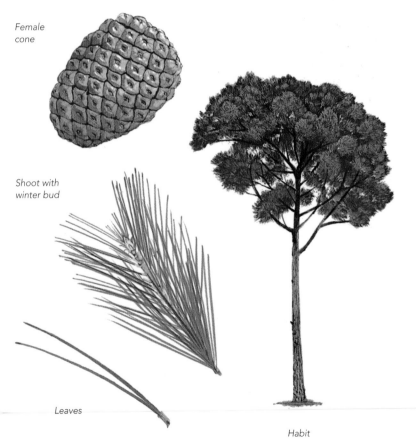

Female cone

Shoot with winter bud

Leaves

Habit

Pinus cembra L.
Arolla Pine

A pyramidal tree 20–40m high with stout spreading branches. The bark is reddish-grey, separating into thin scaly patches on older trees and sometimes covered with blisters of resin. The twigs are strongly pubescent with an orange-brown tomentum. The winter buds are about 5mm long, dotted with long, pointed, dull resiniferous scales. The leaves are in groups of 5, persisting for 3–5 years, 5–8cm x 1mm, rather rigid, erect and crowded on the shoot, with toothed margins, the stomata confined to the inner surfaces in 2 faint lines; there are 2 central resin canals. The cones are 5–8 x 3.5–5cm, less than one and a half times as long as wide, on short peduncles, violet-tinged at first, later purplish-brown when ripe; the scales are rounded in outline, c. 2–5 x 2cm, with a thickened apex, minutely downy on the outer surface. The seeds are virtually or completely wingless. A tree readily distinguished from other 5-leaved species by its distinct habit and the shaggy, orange-brown pubescence of the young shoots. It is native to the Alps and Carpathians, seldom found below 1700m and often occurring up to the tree line. It is often planted in other parts of N. Europe for its light wood. Au FC Fi Fr FS FY Ge Ic It No Po Ro Sw Sz.

Habit

Leaves

Mature cone

Young shoot with winter bud

Pinus wallichiana
A.B. Jackson
Bhutan Pine

A slender, elegant tree up to 50m high, with horizontal spreading branches below and ascending branches above. The bark is thin, smooth, resiniferous and grey-brown on young trees, becoming shallowly fissured when older. The young shoots are glabrous, yellowish-green at first, becoming brownish-yellow. The winter buds are cylindrical or conical, up to 6mm long, with dull lance-like scales often matted with resin. The leaves are in fives, persisting for 3–4 years, those on the young shoots more or less erect, the older ones spreading or drooping, 8–20cm x 0.7mm, flexible, greyish-green, minutely toothed on the margins, the apex pointed; the resin canals are marginal. The cones are 15–25 x 3cm, cylindrical, straight, becoming pendent, light brown when mature, very resiniferous; the scales are c. 3.5 x 2.5cm, wedge-shaped, longitudinally grooved with a thickened apex, the basal ones sometimes reflexed. The seeds are oval-shaped, with a wing up to 2cm long, shed readily, leaving empty cones on the tree. A native of the temperate Himalayas at 2000–4200m, the Bhutan pine is planted on a small scale in Italy for timber and in other parts of N. Europe as an ornamental.

Spray of leaves

Young shoot with winter bud

Mature cone

Habit

Pinus peuce
Griseb.
Macedonian Pine

A narrowly conical tree up to 30m tall with a thin trunk, and with a narrow dense pyramidal crown. The bark is greyish-green and smooth on young trees, becoming brown and fissured on old trees. The young shoots are smooth, glabrescent or remaining hairy at the leaf-traces, becoming greyish-brown in the 2nd year. The winter buds are ovoid, sharply and abruptly pointed, about 1cm long and somewhat resiniferous. The leaves are 7–12cm x *c.* 0–7mm, in clusters of 5, persisting for about 3 years, slender, flexible, suberect on the branches, with finely toothed margins, a sharp apex and with marginal resin canals. The male strobili are in clusters at the base of the shoot, conical, pointed, purplish-yellow; the female strobili are terminal, slender ovoid, initially pale-green but rapidly becoming purple The cones are 8–20 x 3–4cm, subterminal, pendent, subcylindrical and often curved near the apex; the scales are broadly wedge-shaped, grey-tipped and convex with incurving tips; the seed is 5–8mm long with a wing up to 2.5cm long. A restricted native of Europe found in small montane localities of the Balkan Peninsula between 600–2000m. Its robust habit and resistance to extreme environments has led to high altitude planting in Germany. Al Bu FY Ge Gr.

Cone

Habit

Shoot

Pinus strobus L.
White Pine or **Weymouth Pine**

A moderately large tree up to 50m with a tapering trunk. The branches of old trees form a round-topped or conical crown with the leaves in horizontal masses. The bark is thin, smooth and greyish-green on young trees, becoming rugged, fissured and brown on old trees. The young twigs are slender with tufts of short hairs below the insertion of the leaf-bundles but glabrescent elsewhere. The winter buds are conical with a sharp point, c. 3mm long, resiniferous, with some of the scales free at the tips. The leaves are 5–14cm long, slender, sharply pointed, bluish-green, flexible, with finely toothed margins, and marginal resin canals. The cones are 8–20 x 3–14cm, subterminal, pendulous, cylindrical, often curved near the apex; the scales are thin, smooth, light brown. The seeds are 5–8mm long with a rounded wing 1.8–2.5cm long. A species easily recognized by its horizontal masses of bluish-green foliage and tufts of hairs below the point of insertion of leaves, the Weymouth Pine is one of the most distinctive N. American species now planted on a wide scale particularly in C. Europe as a timber tree. Au Be Bu De FC Fr FS Ge It Po Ro Sw Sz Tu.

Shoot

Habit

Cone

Habit

Pinus aristata
Engelm.
Bristle-cone Pine

A small slow-growing tree only attaining 10m in European conditions. The leaves are 2–4cm long, in groups of 5, deep green, often flecked with white resin, and persisting for 14 years or more. The cones are 5–6cm long when mature, with a spreading spine up to 6mm long on each scale. A relatively rare species originating from the Rocky Mountains of the SW. United States. It is usually found in private collections and cultivated on a small scale for its timber.

WILLOW AND POPLAR TREE FAMILY SALICACEAE

Salix L.
Willows

Dioecious trees or shrubs. The leaves are alternate and stipules are present. The flowers are arranged in catkins, each growing in the axil of an entire bract with 1–2 small nectaries but no perianth; male flowers usually have 2, 3 or 5 stamens; the female flowers have numerous ovules. Many species hybridize with one or more different species, creating confusion as to their correct identity.

Salix fragilis L.
Crack Willow

A tree up to 25m high with a broad tapering crown, the branches curving upwards. The bark is blackish-grey, scaly, becoming thickly ridged. The 1-year-old twigs are very easily snapped off at the base. The buds are pointed, conical, yellow, pale green or brown. The leaves are 6–15 x 1.5–4cm, lanceolate, usually 4–9 times as long as wide, with a slender, tapering, somewhat twisted apex, rather coarsely serrate, glabrous, shiny green above, bluish-green or greyish-green beneath; the petiole is 1–2cm long with 2 glands at the top; the stipules usually fall early. The catkins appear with the leaves, drooping, densely cylindrical; the males are 2–5cm long, yellow, the females are *c.* 10cm long, green, with 2 nectaries. Flowering period: May. An abundant species around lowland rivers and streams in much of Europe except the Arctic. The hybrid *S. x rubens* Schrank (*S. fragilis x alba*) is perhaps the most common *Salix* hybrid. Its resemblance and similar habi-tat to *S. fragilis* means that the two are often confused. It differs in having silky leaves.

Habit

Leafy shoot

Female catkin

Male catkins

Male flower

Salix pentandra L.
Bay Willow

A shrub or small tree up to 7m high, forming a densely branched, broad, rounded crown. The bark is greyish-brown with fine pale fissures. The twigs are glabrous, shining. The buds are 5mm long, more or less conical, pale brown. The leaves are 5–12cm long, elliptic to somewhat oblong, 2–4 times as long as wide, acuminate, rounded or broadly wedge-shaped at the base, finely and evenly serrulate, dark shiny green above, whitish beneath, with yellow glands, somewhat leathery when mature, sticky and fragrant when young; the petiole is up to 8mm long with 1–3 pairs of glands near the top; the stipules are small, falling early. The catkins are 2–5 x 1cm, cylindrical, bright yellow, appearing after the leaves on leafy pubescent peduncles; the males have 4–12 but usually 5 stamens; the females are smaller with 2 nectaries. Flowering period: May–June. A species widespread along river banks and wet meadows in much of Europe except the extreme N. and S. and most of the islands. Al Au Be Bl Bu De FC Fi Fr FS FY Ge Hu Ir It Ne No Po Ro Sp Sw.

Male catkin

Leafy shoot

Salix alba L.
White Willow

A stout tree up to 25m high (although often pollarded); the crown is a rather irregularly shaped dome. The branches are ascending, silvery-grey. The dark grey bark does not flake, but has thick interconnecting ridges. The shoots are slender silky pubescent when young, soon becoming glabrous, grey to greenish-brown. The buds are 2mm long, with a curved tapering tip, reddish-tinged and covered with a grey down. The leaves are 5–10cm long, usually *c.* 5–8 times as long as wide, acuminate, sometimes slightly asymmetrical at the apex, wedge-shaped at the base, finely serrate, covered with long white hairs which are pressed closely to the surface of the leaf; the petiole is *c.* 5mm long, and without glands. The stipules usually fall early. The catkins appear with the leaves; the male catkins are most abundant, 7–8cm long, slender, curved upwards, yellow with 2 stamens; occasionally female flowers with 1 nectary occur with the males; female catkins are 4–6cm long, green, soon becoming white with seed. Flowering period: May–June. A very common species of waterways and wet woods in Europe, N. Africa and Asia. Al Au Be Bu Co Cr De FC Fi Fr FS FY GB Ge Gr Hu Ir It Ne No Pl Po Ro Sa Si Sp Sw Tu.

Mature female catkin

Leafy shoot

Male catkins

Habit

92

There are many described variants and it frequently hybridizes with other species. Subsp, *coerulea* (Sm.) Rech. f. is frequently cultivated, particularly in the British Isles, for the manufacture of cricket bats. The hybrid *Salix x chrysocoma* Dode (= *S. alba subsp. vitellina* L. Arcangeli x *babylonica*) the **Weeping Willow**, is a favourite cultivar in many parts of Europe since it combines the silky indumentum of *S. alba* with the weeping habit of *S. babylonica*.

Salix babylonica L.
Chinese Weeping Willow

A graceful tree up to 20m high. The branches and twigs are long, pendent, drooping almost entirely to the ground. The leaves are 8–16 x 0.8–1.5cm long, narrowly lanceolate or linear-lanceolate, acuminate at the apex, finely toothed, usually glabrous at maturity; the petiole is 3–5mm long. The catkins are up to 2cm long x 0.3–0.4cm wide; the bracts are all the same colour, becoming smooth; the female flowers have 1 nectary; the ovary is glabrous, sessile. Flowering period: May. A species of Chinese origin widely cultivated in many parts of Europe and frequently naturalized. It has browner twigs and poorer growth characteristics than the Weeping Willow which is usually cultivated in preference.

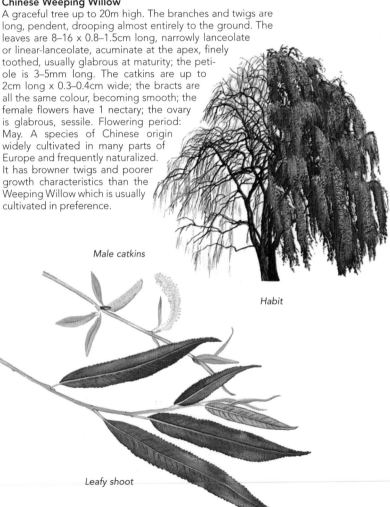

Male catkins

Habit

Leafy shoot

93

Salix triandra L.
Almond Willow

A shrub or more rarely a small tree 4–10m high. The bark is smooth, flaking off in patches. The shoots are glabrous, except initially, rather fragile, olive or reddish-brown. The buds are ovoid, brown, glabrous. The leaves are 5–10cm long, usually *c.* 3–8 times as long as wide, oblong-ovate or oblong-lanceolate, acuminate or acute symmetrical, rounded at the base, serrate, glabrous, dark, somewhat glossy green above, glaucous or less often pale beneath; the petiole is 0.6–1.5cm long, glabrous, with 2–3 glands near the top; the stipules are ovate, dentate, 0.5–1cm long, usual persistent. The catkins are cylindrical and erect, appearing with

Male flower

the leaves on short leafy shoots; the males are 3–5cm long, slender, greenish-yellow, persistent, with obovate scales of a single colour and 3 stamens having yellow anthers and filaments hairy at the base; the females are denser and shorter, each with 1 nectary and sometimes a short style diverging at a wide angle and shallowly notched at the tip and a pedicel ultimately 3–4 times as long as the nectary. Flowering period: March–May (and sometimes July–August). A widespread

Female catkin

and rather common species of pond and river banks in much of Europe, except the Arctic, and rather local in the Mediterranean region. The shrubby forms are frequently confused with such hybrids as **S. x mollissima** Hoffm. ex Elwert (*S. triandra x viminalis*), **S. x speciosa** Host (*S. fragilis x triandra*) and **S. x leiophylla** E. G, & A. Camus (*S. purpurea L. x triandra*) which occur in similar habitats and are frequently planted as Osiers. Al Au Be Bu FC Fi Fr FS GB Gr Hu Ir Ne No Pl Po Ro Sa Sp Sw Sz.

Habit

Male catkin   *Leafy shoot*

Salix borealis

Fries

A shrub or small tree with irregularly thick erect branches. The young shoots have a dense white indumentum. The leaves are 2–7cm (occasionally to 10cm) long, *c.* 1–4 times as long as broad, orbicular-ovate to more or less elliptical, acute or shortly acuminate, often deeply serrate with large glands, leathery, somewhat glaucous beneath with long whitish hairs and a prominent network of veins. The catkins appear with the leaves on thick woolly peduncles; the males are 1.5–2.5cm long, subsessile, ovoid or oblong with free stamens and yellow anthers. The female are 1.5–3cm long in flower, lengthening to 5–8cm long in fruit, rather lax, with long slender styles and stigmas; the pedicel is 3–4 times as long as the nectary. A species of wetlands in N. Scandinavia and Russia. Fi FS. It is frequently confused with the more widespread shrubby **S. nigricans** Sm., the **Dark-leaved Willow**, which has more slender, glabrescent twigs and branches, more glaucous leaves (which turn black on drying), longer, more slender styles and stigmas; and which occurs on lakesides and streamsides in much of N. and C. Europe.

Leafy shoot

Male catkin

Female catkin

Habit

95

Salix pedicellata
Desf.

A tall shrub or tree up to 10m high with numerous prominent ridges on the peeled wood. The bark is grey. The young shoots are grey-tomentose, gradually becoming glabrescent as the trees get older. The leaves are oblong or obovate-lanceolate, crenate to almost entire, glabrescent above and thinly pubescent beneath; the lateral veins occur in 10–12 pairs, connected by a fine network of veins, impressed above but prominent beneath; the stipules are large, deciduous, dentate, semicordate. The bracts have short hairs. The catkins are 3–6 x 1–1.5cm, the females have short or moderately long styles; the pedicels are 3–4mm long and the ovary is glabrous. An indistinct species found in wet places in the Mediterranean region. Co Gr It Sa Si Sp Tu.

Habit

Female catkin

Male catkin

Young leafy shoot

Salix appendiculata
Vill.

A tall shrub or small tree up to 3m high with short branches spreading at a wide angle, the peeled wood displaying somewhat indistinct ridges. The young shoots are pubescent with short hairs, eventually becoming glabrescent. The leaves are extremely variable in size and shape, up to 14cm long x 1.5–3cm (occasionally to 5cm) wide, usually widest above the middle, more or less dark green and glabrous above but paler, light green and pubescent beneath, the margins roughly and irregularly toothed to entire, somewhat asymmetrical at the apex and the veins distinct beneath; the petiole is *c.* 1cm long; the stipules are prominent, semicordate and coarsely serrate. The catkins are *c.* 3 x 1cm, very lax; the filaments in the male flowers have a few long hairs near the base; the pedicel is as long as or longer than the grey pubescent ovary. An alpine or montane species invariably above 500m in the Alps of C. Europe, the Appennines and the NW. Balkan Peninsula. It readily hybridizes with other montane species, particularly *S. caprea* L. (*S. x macrophylla* Kerner). The hybrids invariably inherit its distinctive rough leaf character and the prominent veins. Au Fr FY Ge It Sw.

Male catkin

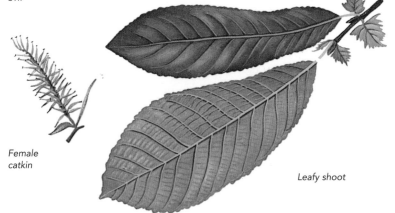

Female catkin

Leafy shoot

Salix cinerea L.
Grey Willow or Common Sallow

A shrub or very rarely a tree up to 6m high, readily recognized by its rather stout, persistently grey-tomentose twigs, and the fine raised linear markings on the 2-year-old wood when the bark is stripped off; the leaves are 2–4 times as long as broad, the short styles and the pedicel 2–5 times as long as the nectary. Flowering period: March–April. It is extremely common in much of Europe, although rare in the west and the Mediterranean region. Al Au Be Bu Co De FC Fi Fr FS FY GB Ge Gr Hu It Ne No Po Ro Sw Tu.

Bark

Salix atrocinerea
Brot.
Common Sallow

Male catkins

Female catkin

A tall shrub or small tree up to 10m high. The young shoots are initially brown-pubescent, becoming reddish in winter and remaining thinly pubescent or becoming glabrous. The buds are thinly pubescent or glabrous. The leaves are usually reddish-green or fawn, pubescent above when young, thinly and shortly pubescent on the veins beneath, glaucous at maturity and with some or all of the bristly hairs rust-coloured, more or less prominently veined; the stipules are usually small. The catkins are the same as those of *S. cinerea.* A prominent species of woods, heaths, ponds and stream sides, and in marshes and fens throughout W. Europe from Britain to Portugal. The pure form is often difficult to find since it freely hybridizes with **S. aurita** L., the **Eared Sallow**, *S. caprea* L., and *S. cinerea* whenever they meet. Be Fr GB Ir Pl Sp.

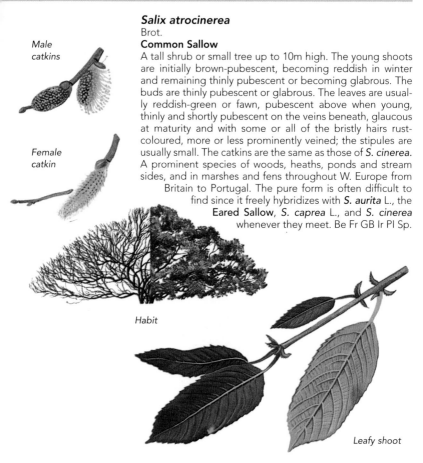

Habit

Leafy shoot

Salix caprea L.
Pussy Willow, Great Sallow or Goat Willow

A dioecious shrub or small tree 3–10m high, often with a short, twisting bole. The bark is light greyish-brown and shallowly fissured. The shoots are rather stout, covered with long grey hairs, becoming smooth, shiny and reddish-brown. The leaves are rather variable, 6–11 x 3–6cm, usually broadly ovate to ovate-oblong the base rounded, sinuate-dentate or almost serrate, dark green and eventually almost glabrous above, persistently softly and densely grey-tomentose beneath; the margins are somewhat undulate, shallowly toothed or entire; there are 6–9 pairs of lateral veins, forming almost a right-angle with the midrib and very distinctive on the lower surface; the petiole is *c.* 1cm long, dark red; the stipules are semicordate and very large. The catkins are dense, subsessile and appear before the leaves; the male catkins are 2–3.5 x 1.5–2cm, oblong–ovoid, initially with projecting silvery hairs, later with yellow stamens; the female catkins are eventually 3–7cm long, looser than the males, initially pale green with projecting styles, later covered with long wavy hairs which turn from brown to white at maturity; the bracts are blackish at the apex; both male and female flowers have 1 nectary. A species of woods, scrub and hedgerows from lowland to montane stations in much of Europe. Au Be Bu Co De FC Fi Fr FS FY GB Ge Gr Hu Ir It Ne No Po Ro Si Sp Sw Sz Tu. The European Sallows or Pussy Willows are a difficult group to identify as there are many different subspecies and hybrids. The Sallows range from shrubs to trees, Scandinavian and Scottish plants with the 2nd year twigs hairy, and cuneate leaves hairy above, are generally given a different name – *S. coaetanea* (Hartman) B. Flod.

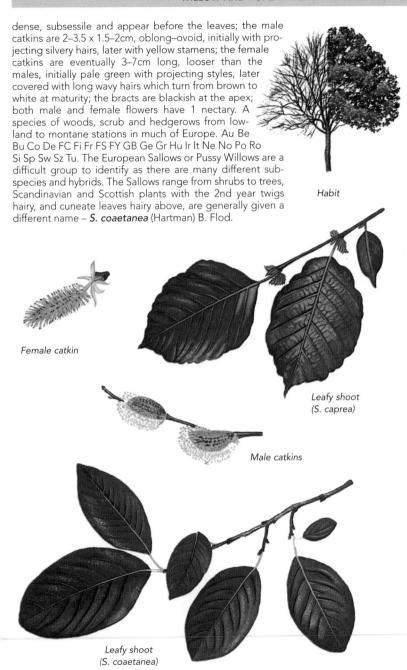

Habit

Female catkin

*Leafy shoot
(S. caprea)*

Male catkins

*Leafy shoot
(S. coaetanea)*

Salix xerophila B. Flod.

A shrub and more rarely a tree up to 6m high with erect branches, The shoots are dull and more or less woolly. The buds are conical, somewhat right-angled and reddish-brown. The leaves are oblanceolate, woolly-grey, with appressed, some-what curved hairs, entire margins and 7–8 pairs of lateral veins; stipules are usually absent. The catkins are 1.5–3 x 0.5–1cm long, lax on peduncles up to 2.5cm long; the bracts are obovate, brown; the nectaries are slender, ovate, one-quarter to one-third as long as the bracts; the filaments are hairy; the stigmas are divergent, cylindrical, usually deeply cleft. A waterside species of N. Finland, Norway and Russia. Fi FS No.

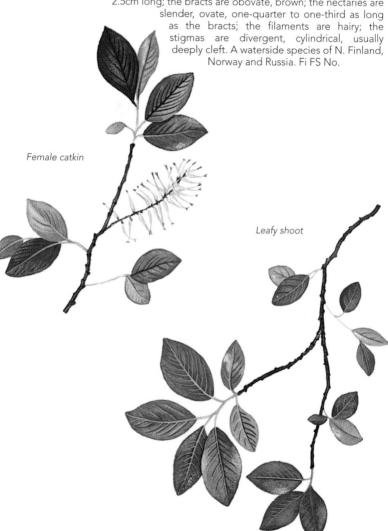

Female catkin

Leafy shoot

Salix viminalis L.
Common Osier

A shrub or small tree 3–5m (rarely up to 10m) high with long, straight, leafy, flexible branches. The young shoots are densely pubescent, becoming glabrous later without linear markings beneath the bark. The buds are ovoid–oblong, acute to acuminate, pubescent. The leaves are 10–25cm long, *c.* 1.5cm wide when mature 4–18 times as long as broad, narrowly linear, with a very narrow cuneate base, dark green and glabrous above, silvery silky-tomentose beneath; the margins are wavy, revolute when young, entire or nearly so, with 20–35 pairs of lateral veins; the petiole is up to 1–2cm long; the stipules are small, linear-lanceolate, usually falling early. The catkins are subsessile; the bracts are black at the tip, the nectaries are long, linear; the males appear before the leaves, 2.5–4cm long, ovoid–oblong, with free stamens and bright yellow anthers; the females appear with the leaves cylindrical and up to 6cm long in fruit; the capsule is ovoid-conical, silky-tomentose, sessile or subsessile; the style is very long – more than half as long as the ovary in fruit and as long as the flowers; the stigmas are entire, slender and bifid. Flowering period: April–May. A native species of streams and pond sides and in marshes and fens, mostly in C. Europe, extending westwards to Ireland and eastwards to the Ukrainian Carpathians and Bulgaria. Au Be FC Fr FS FY GB Ge Gr Hu Ir Ne Po Ro Sz. It is frequently planted as an Osier in De Fi It No Pl Sp Sw. In Russia *S. viminalis* is largely replaced by *S. rossica* Nasarov, which differs in its more obtuse buds, the leaves rounded at the base and its shorter styles. *S. viminalis* is difficult to determine anywhere in its pure form because it is so similar to *S. caprea*, *S. cinerea* and **S. aurita** and readily produces shrubby hybrids with them, many of which are cultivated and frequently escape into the wild.

Habit

Male catkins

Female catkins

Leaves

Salix elaeagnos
Scop.
Hoary Willow

A shrub up to 6m high or more rarely a tree up to 16m high. The shoots are slender, thinly covered with whitish hairs when young, yellowish to reddish-brown. The leaves are 5–12cm long, up to 1 cm wide, 6–14 times as long as wide, erect, linear-lanceolate to narrowly linear, tapering at both ends, densely lanate on both surfaces when young but becoming more or less glabrescent above, remaining lanate beneath, dull, margin deflexed or revolute and finely glandular-serrate, particularly in the apical part; the veins are more or less impressed above and slightly prominent beneath although often not visible because of the dense indumentum; the petiole is up to 5mm long; stipules are usually absent. The catkins are up to 6 x 0.8cm on peduncles up to 1cm long, bearing small lanceolate leaves; the bracts are about half as long as the ovary; the filaments are united at the base or up to the middle and hairy at or near the base; the ovary is glabrous and the pedicel is about one-quarter as long as the ovary. A species of lowland or montane valley waterways, usually occurring in large stands with other trees. It is common in C. Europe extending to France, Spain, Italy and the Ukrainian Carpathians. Al Au Bu Co FC Fr FS FY Ge Gr Hu It Ne Po Ro Sp Sw. It is an extremely variable species and hybrids are common along riversides in the Alps. It readily hybridizes with *S. cinerea*, *S. viminalis* and **S. nigricans** as well as several other shrubby species. The most prominent inherited characters from *S. elaeagnos* are the long, narrow, curved catkins, and leaves with more or less parallel margins and lanate undersides.

Habit

Female catkin

Male catkin

Leafy shoot

Salix daphnoides
Vill.
Violet Willow
A tall shrub or a tree 7–10m tall with slender branches. The shoots are dark shining purple and covered with a waxy bloom. The buds are narrowly conical, blackish-purple. The leaves are 5–10cm long, *c.* 2–4 times as long as wide, oblong-lanceolate or oblong-ovate, acute or acuminate, glandular-serrulate, soon glabrous dark green and shining above, glaucous, pale yellow beneath, with 8–12 pairs of lateral veins and a broad white midrib; the petiole is 2–4mm long, crimson above; the stipules are large, cordate. The catkins are 3–5cm long, appearing before the leaves, sub-sessile, cylindrical, dense; the bracts are ovate, hairy and black at the apex; the male catkins are bright yellow; the females are more slender and green. Flowering period: March. A native of Europe to N. Scandinavia, also the Himalayas and C. Asia, widely planted in C. and S. Europe for its colourful violet-tinged year-old shoot, which are especially attractive in winter.
Au Fr Ge No Sw.

Leafy shoot

Habit

Female catkins

Male catkin

Female flower

Populus L.
Poplars

Deciduous dioecious fast-growing, often large trees. The flowers are borne in pendulous catkins and appear before the leaves.

Populus alba L.
White Poplar

A medium-sized tree up to 30m high with a broad and often one-sided crown and a sturdy bole with numerous suckers around the base. The bark of immature trees and young branches is smooth and white or greyish-green, becoming rougher and much darker with age. The branches are horizontal or slightly pendent, and twisted. The buds are small, ovoid, orange-brown and covered with white down. The leaves of the long shoots are 6–12cm long, ovate with 3–5 lobes, the lobes coarsely toothed or with 1–2 lobules on each side, dark greyish-green above, downy-white beneath; the leaves of short shoots are smaller and narrower, with wavy dentate margins and a greyish down beneath; the petiole is 3–4cm long, flattened and covered with a white down. The catkins are 4–8cm long in flower, 8–10cm long in fruit; the males are grey, each flower with 6–10 crimson stamens; the females are green. Flowering time: March–April. A species of wet and well-watered places, and also of sandy coasts where it is resistant to salt and winds. It is frequently planted in gardens, streets and parks for ornament and for shelter along coasts. Al Au Be Bu De FC Fr FS FY GB Ge Gr Hu It Ne Pl Po Ro Sa Sp Sz Tu.

*Twig with
male catkin*

Leaf

*Male
flower*

*Female
catkin*

Bark

Habit

Populus canescens (Aiton)
Sm.
Grey Poplar

Similar to but larger than *P. alba*, up to 30m high; the crown conical when young but broad and many-domed in older specimens. The bark of young trees has diamond-shaped pits, becoming coarse and rugged and changing from dark grey to brown or black in mature trees. The branches are relatively few, massive and ascending, the twigs dense and rather pendulous, covered with white or greyish hair. The buds are red-brown, hairy towards the base, glabrous towards the tip. The leaves of the long shoots are triangular-ovate, slightly heart-shaped at the base, toothed or lobed, dark glossy green above, downy grey beneath. The leaves of the short shoots are ovate to more or less orbicular, becoming glabrous. The catkins are 3–4cm long in flower, the male flowers with 8–15 reddish-purple stamens. Flowering period: early February. It is usually found in river valleys. It is intermediate and thought to be a hybrid between *P. alba* and *P. tremula*. Au Be Bu De Fr FS GB Ge Gr Hu Ir It Ne Pl Po Ro Sp Sw Sz. *Populus x hybrida* Bieb. (*P. canescans x P. tremula*), the **Hybrid Poplar**, may be found in areas where the parents grow together and is sometimes planted.

Leaf

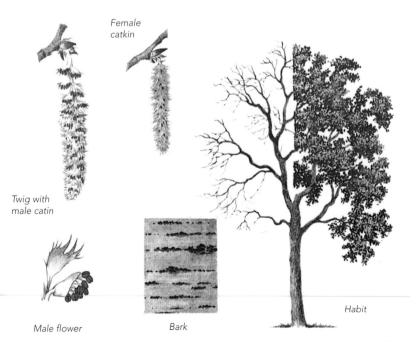

Female catkin

Twig with male catin

Male flower

Bark

Habit

Populus tremula L.
Aspen

A short-lived tree up to 20m high, the crown open, narrow or conical when young, becoming broader and irregular, the bole often leaning and suckering freely at the base at maturity. The bark is smooth with diamond-shaped depressions, greyish-green. The buds are ovoid, pointed, glabrous and slightly viscid; the leaf buds are yellow and brown and appressed against the twig; the flower buds are broader, *c.* 1 cm long, brown, shiny, and borne towards the tip of the twig. The leaves are 3–8cm long (up to 15cm on young plants and suckers), suborbicular with a sinuate margin and short blunt teeth, thin, green or greyish-green above, paler below; the petiole is 4–6cm long, laterally flattened and rather pale; the catkins are about 4cm long, the flowers having numerous white hairs. The male flowers are thicker than the female, with 5–12 stamens; the female catkins are up to 12cm long in fruit. Flowering period: March. A typical species of damp and muddy areas of hillsides, valleys, hedgerows and copses. In S. Europe it is restricted to montane areas. The flattened petiole allows easy movement of the leaf, giving rise to the name Trembling Aspen. Al Au Be Bu Co De FC Fi Fr FS FY GB Ge Gr Hu Ic Ir It Ne No Po Ro Sa Sp Sw Sz Tu. Several exotic species are planted in Europe, eg. the hybrid *P. tremula x tremuloides*, common in Scandinavia and Austria, *P. gileadensis*, planted for timber and occasionally naturalized in N. Europe, and *P. simonii*, grown for timber and for ornament in C. Europe.

Leaf from mature tree

Habit

Bark

Male catkins

Leaf from sucker

106

Populus trichocarpa
Torrey & A. Gray ex Hooker
Western Balsam Poplar
A medium-sized fragrant resiniferous tree up to 35m high with a narrow conical crown. A fast-growing native of western N. America, sometimes planted in Europe. It is very similar to *P. balsam-ifera* and hybrids between the two are often planted in damp soils.

Leaf

Habit

Populus balsamifera L.
Balsam Poplar
A tree up to 30m high though often much smaller, with a domed crown, the bole producing numerous suckers at the base. The bark is rather thin and shallowly fissured. The branches are erect or ascending, the young shoots terete, smooth and thickly covered with resin giving a varnished appearance. The buds may be up to 2.5cm long, pointed, and also thickly covered in resin. The leaves are 5–10cm long, those on vigorous suckers often much larger, more or less ovate, long-pointed, the margins with small blunt teeth, dark shiny green above, paler or whitish and somewhat downy beneath. The petiole is 1.5–5cm. The male catkins are 7.5cm long; the female catkins are 10–12.5cm long. Flowering period: May. A common species of wet woods, along rivers and shorelines in northern N . America. Cultivated in Europe for timber and sometimes for the fragrant balsam resin. Only male plants appear to be in cultivation.

Habit

Leaf

107

Populus candicans
Aiton
Balm of Gilead
An open-crowned, freely suckering tree with downy shoots and resin-covered buds. The leaves are heart-shaped, fragrant when young, ciliate and downy below; the petiole is downy. It is commonly cultivated in Europe and frequently confused with the closely related Balsam Poplar *P. balsamifera*.

Fruiting catkin

Populus nigra L.
Black Poplar
A medium-sized tree up to 30m high with an uneven, broadly domed crown and a short bole which usually bears large bosses and burrs but rarely suckers. The buds are ovoid and slightly pointed; the lateral leaf buds are appressed, pale brown; the flower buds are larger, less appressed, green. The leaves on the long shoots are 5–10cm long, ovate-rhombic, pointed, with minute forward-pointing teeth, pale green below; those on the short shoots are smaller and broader; the petiole is flattened. The male catkins are 5cm long, grey at first, becoming crimson, each flower with 20–30 stamens; the female catkins are greenish, 6–7cm long in flower, 10–15cm long in fruit, Flowering period: March. A species of roadsides and fields. A native of S., C. and E. Europe, frequently planted elsewhere and naturalized in places. Al Au Be Bu Co Cr De FC FS GB Ge Gr Hu Ir It Ne Pl Po Ro Sa Si Sp Sz Tu. *Populus nigra* cv. 'Italica', the **Lombardy Poplar**, has a narrow columnar habit and is more common in cultivation than *P. nigra*.

Leaf

Habit

Bark

Male flower

Populus x canadensis
Moench
Hybrid Black Poplar
This name covers a number of hybrids between *P. del-toides* and *P. nigra*. All are similar to *P. nigra* in general features but lack bosses on the bole, and have leaves.

Leaf

Populus x berolinensis
C. Koch
Berlin Poplar
A columnar, densely branched tree with angular yellowish twigs and ovate or somewhat rhombic leaves. It is frequently planted for shelter in C. and S. Europe and believed to be a hybrid between *P. laurifolia* Ledeb. and *P. nigra* cv. *'Italica'*.

Populus deltoides
Marshall
Cottonwood
A fast-growing tree up to 30m high with a broad crown. The branches are slightly ascending, the twigs markedly angled, greenish when young, becoming greyish or brownish. The terminal bud is viscid and glabrous. The leaves are 10–18cm long, somewhat variable in shape but longer than wide, typically broadly triangular truncate or heart-shaped at the base, densely covered with ciliate hairs, shortly pointed at the tip, with sharp-toothed margins, the teeth callus-tipped and with glands at each base. The male flowers have 30–60 stamens. The female catkins are 15–20cm long in fruit. A species of low woods and moist prairies throughout E. N. America. In Europe it is planted as a timber tree and along roadsides, and has become naturalized in a number of areas. Au Be Bu FY GB Ge Gr Hu It Ne Pl Sp.

Habit

Bark

Male catkin

Leaf

109

BOG MYRTLE FAMILY MYRICACEAE

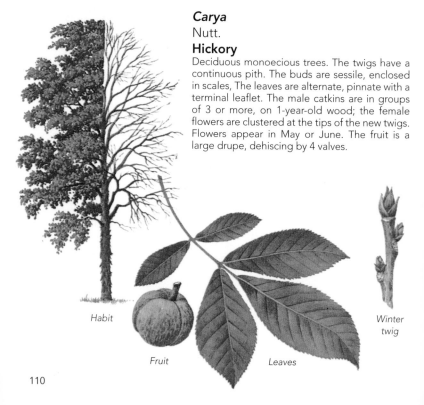

Myrica faya
Aiton

A small evergreen dioecious tree or shrub up to 8m high. The twigs are covered with small reddish-brown, peltate hairs. The leaves are alternate, 4–11 cm long, widest above the middle, entire, the margins rolled downwards, glabrous. The flowers are solitary in the axils of bracts, grouped in branched catkins on new wood; the male flowers lack bracteoles; the female flowers have 2 or more bracteoles. The fruit is a somewhat fleshy drupe. Flowering period: April–May. A species of the drier parts of broad-leaved evergreen forest in the Atlantic Islands. A doubtful native but certainly naturalized in C. and S. Portugal. Pl.

Flowering twig

Fruit

WALNUT FAMILY JUGLANDACEAE

Carya
Nutt.

Hickory

Deciduous monoecious trees. The twigs have a continuous pith. The buds are sessile, enclosed in scales, The leaves are alternate, pinnate with a terminal leaflet. The male catkins are in groups of 3 or more, on 1-year-old wood; the female flowers are clustered at the tips of the new twigs. Flowers appear in May or June. The fruit is a large drupe, dehiscing by 4 valves.

Habit

Fruit

Leaves

Winter twig

Carya alba L.
Nutt.
Shagbark Hickory
Up to 40m high with a broad crown. The grey bark splits into long scales. The branches are few and widely arched; the twigs are reddish-brown, The buds have 10–12 overlapping scales, the outer dark, the inner yellowish or purplish. The leaflets are 10–20cm long in groups of 5 (rarely 3 or 7), the upper 3 largest, the terminal one with a stout petiole, all elliptic, oblong-lanceolate, acuminate, the margin sharply toothed except at the base, with tufts of white hairs between the teeth, hairy beneath, becoming glabrous later. The male catkins are 10–15cm long. The fruit is 3.5–6cm long, more or less globose or broadly ovoid, not winged, the pericarp splitting to the base. The seed is white and somewhat angled. A native of E. N. America, planted for timber in central Europe. FC Ge Ro.

Male catkins

Flowers

Carya cordiformis (Wangenh.)
C. Koch
Bitternut
Up to 30m high with a conical crown. The bark is greyish and smooth, becoming wrinkled and scaly, showing orange where the scales have lifted. The branches are numerous, straight, ascending. The buds have 4–6 scales, the scales touching one another but not overlapping, all bright yellow. The leaflets are 8–15cm long, 9 (rarely 5–8), the terminal one sessile, ovate-lanceolate to lanceolate, acuminate, the margins sharply toothed, hairy beneath when young. The male catkins are 5–7cm long. The fruit is 2–3.5cm long, more or less globose or pear-shaped, 4-winged above the middle, the pericarp splitting to below the middle. The seed is grey, more or less smooth. A native of E. N. America, used as a timber tree in Germany. Ge.

Fruit

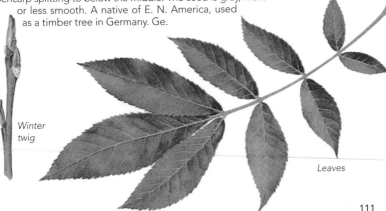

Winter twig

Leaves

111

Pterocarya fraxinifolia (Poiret) Spach.
Caucasian Wing-nut

A tree up to 30m high, with a rounded crown and a short solitary bole or with many long, twisted boles, suckering freely around the base. The bark is deeply fissured, grey. The pith of the twigs has transverse walls. The buds are without scales, stalked, dark brown. The leaflets are up to 18cm long, in 11–20 pairs, ovate-lanceolate, acuminate, the margins sharply toothed, the midrib with long brown or white stellate hairs below. The male catkins are solitary; the female catkins are pendent with numerous flowers. The fruit is a broad-winged nut. Flowering period: April. A SW. Asian native, frequently planted on a small scale in Europe.

Twig with leaf and female catkin

Habit

Juglans L.
Walnuts

Deciduous monoecious trees, the pith having transverse walls. The buds are sessile, enclosed in scales. The leaves are alternate, pinnate with a terminal leaflet, aromatic. The male catkins are solitary, occurring on the previous year's wood; the female flowers are few, in terminal racemes on the current year's wood. The fruit is a large indehiscent drupe.

Juglans regia L.
Common Walnut

A moderate tree up to 30m high with a wide spreading crown. The bark is smooth, becoming deeply fissured and grey at maturity. The lower branches are large and sinuous, the smaller shoots crowded and twisted. The buds are dark purplish-brown. The leaflets are 6–15cm long, 7–9, elliptical or widest above the middle, thick, leathery, acute or acuminate, becoming glabrous, the margins almost entire. The male catkins are 5–15cm long, yellow; the female flowers are in clusters of 2–5, with greenish hairs. The fruit is 4–5cm long, more or less globose, smooth dotted with glands, green, glabrous.

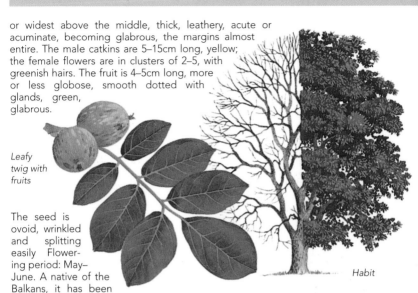

Leafy twig with fruits

The seed is ovoid, wrinkled and splitting easily Flowering period: May–June. A native of the Balkans, it has been planted and become naturalized in much of Europe. Al Au Bu Co Cr Fr FS FY GB Gr Hu It Pl Sa Si Sp Sz.

Habit

Juglans nigra L.
Black Walnut

Up to 50m high, the crown tall and domed. The bark has a diamond pattern of deep fissures, black or dark brown. The main branches are slightly sinuous. The buds are pale brown. The leaflets are 6–12cm long, 15–23, ovate, acuminate, the margins irregularly toothed, becoming glabrous above, hairy and glandular below. The male catkins are 5–15cm long, green at first, becoming yellow; the female flowers 5, with greyish-green hairs. The fruit is 3.5–5cm long, globose or slightly pear-shaped, smooth, green, hairy, not splitting. The seed is ovoid, ridged. Flowering period: May–June. A N. American species widely planted as a timber tree in parts of C. E. Europe. Au De FC Ge It Ro.

Juglans cinerea L.
Butter-nut

Up to 30m high with a conical crown. The grey bark is fissured. The buds are pink or white. The leaf-scars have a hairy band on the upper edge; the 11–19 leaflets are finely hairy above, hairy and glandular below. The male catkins are 5–8cm long. The fruit is 4–6.5cm long, ovoid-oblong, hairy. The seed is ridged, not splitting. A N. American species sometimes planted for timber. De Ro.

Leafy twig with fruits

113

BIRCH AND ALDER FAMILY BETULACEAE

Betula L.
Birches

Monoecious trees or shrubs. The flowers are in catkins; the pendent male flowers have a minute perianth and 2 stamens; the female flowers are in groups of 3 and lack a perianth. The fruiting catkins are cylindrical or narrowly ovoid.

Betula pendula
Roth
Silver Birch

A medium-sized tree up to 30m high with a narrow, pointed crown when young, becoming broader with age. The bark is fissured at the base, forming rectangular plates, smooth above and silvery-white, sometimes with scaly patches showing darker grey. The branches are erect on young trees, becoming pendulous with age; the young twigs are slender, pendulous, glabrous and brown, with numerous white resin glands. The leaves are 2–7cm long, ovate-triangular, pointed at the apex, the margins with protruding primary teeth separated by several smaller secondary teeth, thin and more or less glabrous when mature; the petiole is glabrous. The male catkins are 3–6cm long, in groups of 2–4 at the tips of small twigs, brownish in winter, becoming yellowish and maturing with the young leaves; the female catkins are borne in the axils of leaves, greenish at first, becoming brown. The fruiting catkins are 1.5–3.5cm long, the scales have 2 broad, curved lateral lobes and a somewhat triangular central lobe, The wing of the fruit is 2–3 times as wide as the nutlet, Flowering period: April–May. A pioneer species, forming woods on light soils. It is short-lived, does not grow in shade and is eventually replaced by other, larger species. In S. Europe it is local and confined to mountains. It is sometimes grown in gardens as an ornamental and is often used as a street tree. All except Bl Cr Fi Gr Ic Sa Tu.

Habit

Bark

Nutlet

Flowering twig with male and female catkins

Scale

Leaf

Betula pubescens
Ehrh.
Downy Birch
A small tree up to 25m high, or sometimes a shrub, with an irregular crown. The brown or greyish bark is never fissured into rectangular plates at the base, being entirely smooth or with faint patterning. The branches are dense and twisted, spreading but not pendulous; the twigs lack resin glands but have a covering of soft white hairs. The leaves are similar to those of Silver Birch but usually more rounded, the teeth coarse and equal, with white hairs in the axils of the veins beneath; the petiole is hairy. The catkins are similar to Silver Birch but the scales have slightly broader lateral lobes and an oblong central lobe. The wing of the fruit is 1–1.5 times as wide as the nutlet. Flowering period: April–May. A very variable species forming extensive woods and scrub on poor, especially peaty, soils in N. Europe and the mountains of S. Europe. Au Be De FC Fi Fr FS FY GB Ge Hu Ir It No Pl Po Ro Sp Sw Sz.

Habit

*Leafy twig
with fruiting
catkins*

Nutlet

Scale

Bark

Betula papyrifera
Marshall
Paper-bark Birch
A N. American species with peeling bark, ovate, more or less glabrous leaves up to 10cm long, male catkins up to 10cm long and scales with suberect lateral lobes. It is sometimes planted in gardens and parks.

Bark

Alnus
Miller
Alders

Monoecious trees or shrubs, with flowers similar to the birches but the males having 4 stamens, with anthers separated by a forked connective, and 2 female flowers in the axil of each bract. The fruiting catkin is ovoid and cone-like with persistent, woody, 5-lobed scales.

Alnus viridis (Chaix)
DC.
Green Alder

A small tree up to 5m high, or sometimes a shrub. The buds are 1.2–1.5cm long, pointed, sessile, shiny and reddish. The twigs are glabrous or minutely hairy, greenish or reddish. The leaves are 6cm long, elliptic to suborbicular, sharply double-toothed, hairy on the midrib and in the axils of the veins beneath, sticky when young. The catkins appear with the leaves, the male catkins are 5–12cm long, yellow; the females are 1cm long, green when young, becoming reddish, in slender, stalked clusters of 3–5. The fruiting catkins are up to 1.5cm long, green at first, blackish when mature, persisting until the spring. The nutlet has a broad, membranous wing. Flowering period: April. A montane species with variable leaves and indumentum. Au Bu Co FC Fr FS FY Ge Hu It Po Ro Sz.

Habit

Immature fruiting catkins

Scale

Flowering twig with male catkins

Leafy twig with fame catkins

Nutlet

Alnus glutinosa L.
Gaertner
Common Alder

A small tree up to 20m high or sometimes a shrub, with a broad conical crown. The bark is fissured into square or oblong, grey or brown plates. The branches are ascending, spreading later; the twigs are glabrous, sticky when young, with raised orange lenticels. The buds are 7mm long, narrow, with a stalk about 3mm long. The leaves are 4–10cm long, widest above the middle, or more or less orbicular sometimes notched at the apex, doubly toothed or wavy at the margins, with 5–8 pairs of veins and long yellowish hairs in the axils of the veins beneath. The catkins appear before the leaves; the male catkins are 2–3cm long, in clusters of 2–3, purplish in winter; the female catkins are 0.8–1.5cm long, pendunculate, purplish-red when young, becoming green, in inflorescences of 3–8. The fruiting catkins are 1–3cm long, dark brown, persisting until the following spring. The nutlet has a narrow wing. Flowering period: February–March. Common Alder is frequently found growing by water throughout Europe. All except Bl Cr Fi Ic. Three other related species occur in Europe: **A. *incana***, the **Grey Alder**, is similar to *A. glutinosa* but has sessile female catkins and is native to mountain regions of Europe; **A. *cordata***, **Italian Alder** is distinguished by having female catkins in clusters of 1–3, grey pubescent twigs and pale grey bark, is native to Corsica and S. Italy and sometimes planted in parks and by roadsides. **A. *rugosa***, **Smooth Alder** has leaves with red hairs in the axils of the vein and is a N. American species frequently planted in C. Europe.

Habit

Scale

Nutlet

Flowering twig with male and female catkins

Twig with fruiting catkins

117

HORNBEAM AND HAZEL FAMILY CORYLACEAE

Carpinus
Hornbeams

Deciduous monoecious trees or shrubs. The buds are tapered at each end, acute at the tip. The leaves are alternate, simple, with 9 or more pairs of veins. The male catkins have solitary flowers in the axil of each bract, but lack bracteoles and a perianth. The female flowers are in pairs in the axil of each bract with obvious bracteoles and perianth. The fruit is a nut, borne in the axil of a lobed or toothed involucre, occurring in groups of drooping spikes.

Carpinus betulus L.
Hornbeam

A distinctive tree up to 30m high, the bole often twisted and gnarled. The bark is silvery-grey, often with darker bands and deep fissures. The branches are ascending, sinuous; the twigs are sparsely hairy, greyish-brown. The leaves are 4–10cm long, ovate to oblong-ovate, shortly pointed, rounded at the base, sharply double-toothed, with about 15 pairs of veins, and hairy on the veins below; the petiole is about 1cm long. The male catkins are up to 5cm long, greenish-yellow, with reddish outer scales. The fruiting spike is 5–14cm long with about 8 pairs of nuts; the involucre is 3-lobed. Flowering period: April–May, It is common as hedgerow tree and in deciduous woods, sometimes forming pure stands. It is sometimes pollarded and the cv. *'Fastigiata'* is frequently planted as a boulevard and park tree. Native to much of Europe. Al Au Be Bu De FC Fr FS FY GB Ge Gr Hu It Ne Po Ro Sw Sz Tu.

Male catkins

Leaf

Single fruit

Fruiting spike

Habit

Carpinus orientalis
Miller
Eastern Hornbeam

A small tree or shrub up to 11m high. The bark is purplish with pale brown marks. The leaves are 2–6cm long, ovate or elliptical, shortly pointed, tapering or rounded at the base, the margins doubly toothed, with 11–15 pairs of veins, and sparsely hairy on the veins below. The fruiting spike is 3–5cm long; the involucre is toothed but not lobed. A native of SE. Europe, reaching Italy and Sicily. Al Bu FS FY Gr Hu It Ro Si Tu.

Leaf with single fruit

Ostrya carpinifolia
Scop.
Hop Hornbeam

A deciduous monoecious tree with a conical crown, and sometimes several spreading boles. The bark is brown, smooth at first, later fissured and sometimes peeling. The twigs are hairy, brown with raised orange lenticels. The buds are tapered at each end, acute at the tip. The leaves are 5–8cm long, alternate, simple, ovate with a pointed tip, sharply double-toothed, with 12–15 pairs of veins, hairy when young, becoming glabrous. The male catkins are up to 10cm long, pendulous, with solitary flowers in the axil of each bract; bracteoles and perianth absent; the female flowers are in pairs in the axils of each bract. The fruiting head is 3–5cm long, compact and semi-cylindrical; the involucre is 1.5–2cm long, elliptical, with a short, hairy point, bladder-like, white or greenish with long hairs, enclosing a single nut. Flowering period: April. A native of S. and SE. Europe. Al Au Bu Co Fr FY Gr Hu It Sa Si Sz.

Habit

Leafy twig with fruiting spike

Male catkins

Single fruit

Corylus L.
Hazels

Deciduous monoecious trees or shrubs. The buds are ovoid, obtuse. The leaves are alternate, simple, with less than 8 pairs of veins. The male catkins have solitary flowers in the axils of the bracts; bracteoles 2, perianth absent. The female flowers are in short bud-like inflorescences; the prominent stigmas are red. The fruit is a large nut, solitary or in clusters of 2–4, surrounded by a tubular involucre which is toothed or irregularly divided above.

Corylus avellana L.
Common Hazel

A small tree or shrub up to 12m high with a broad and bushy crown and a rather short bole. The brown bark is smooth, shiny, peeling in strips. The twigs are covered with stiff glandular hairs. The buds are ovoid and smooth. The leaves are up to 10cm long, more or less orbicular, heart-shaped at the base, sharply double-toothed, sometimes lobed, stiffly hairy, the hairs white on the veins beneath; the petiole is densely glandular-hairy. The male catkins are up to 8cm long, pendulous, pale yellow when open. The fruiting head has 1–4 nuts; the involucre is about as long as the nut, divided to about half its length into irregular teeth or lobes. The nut is 1.5–2cm long, brown when ripe with a woody shell. Flowering period: January–April. Common as coppice in hedgerows and as undershrub in woods throughout Europe, and frequently planted in gardens. All except BI Cr Ic.

Cluster of nuts

Twig with male and female flowers

Leaf

Habit

120

Corylus colurna L.
Turkish Hazel

A small tree up to 22m high with a conical crown and a stout bole. The bark is rough. The branches are horizontal and often twisted; the twigs are covered in glandular hairs. The leaves are up to 12.5cm long, ovate or widest above the middle, heart-shaped at the base, abruptly pointed at the tip, double-toothed and sometimes almost lobed. The male catkins are up to 12cm long, pendulous. The involucre is much longer than the nut and deeply divided into toothed lobes which are often recurved. The nut is slightly larger than that of *Corylus avellana*. Flowering period: February. A native of SE. Europe and Asia Minor but introduced in other parts of Europe. Al Bu FY Gr Ro Tu.

Twig with male
and female
flowers

Leaf

Cluster
of nuts

Corylus maxima
Miller
Filbert

A small tree or shrub up to 6m high. It is very similar to *C. avellana* except for the nuts. They are solitary or in clusters of 2–3, and completely enclosed by a tubular involucre, constricted above the nut and toothed or lobed at the apex. A native of the Balkan Peninsula, it is often planted for its nuts in other countries and has become naturalized in parts. A purple-leaved form, var. **atropurpureus**, is frequently grown as a garden ornamental. FY Gr It Tu.

Cluster of nuts

121

BEECH FAMILY FAGACEAE

A large family of deciduous and evergreen trees, or sometimes shrubs.

Fagus sylvatica L.
Common Beech

Mature leaf

A large broadly-domed deciduous tree up to 40m. The bark is smooth and grey, or sometimes slightly rough. The main branches are numerous, usually ascending but sometimes arching; twigs dull purplish-brown, smooth. The buds are *c.* 2cm long, slender, with a long tapering point, reddish-brown, smooth. The leaves are 4–10cm long, ovate to elliptical, pointed, the margin wavy and fringed with hairs when young, sometimes with short teeth, dark green, covered with silky hairs when young, becoming more or less smooth, with 5–8 pairs of almost parallel veins; petiole 1–1.5cm. The flowers are unisexual; the male flowers are numerous, carried in terminal clusters, long-stalked, with a perianth divided almost to the base. The female flowers are surrounded by a 4-lobed involucre, and usually occur in pairs on a short stalk. The nuts are 1.2–1.8cm long, 3-angled, brown, usually occurring in pairs in the cupule. Flowering period: May; fruits ripening September–October. In woods on well-drained soils, especially on chalk. Widespread in W. and C. Europe, cultivated for timber, shelter and ornament. Al Au Be Bu Co De FC Fr FS FY GB Ge Gr Hu It Ne No Po Ro Si Sp Sw Sz.

Habit

Bark

Spring shoot with flowers

Nuts

Fagus orientalis
Lipsky
Oriental Beech
Similar to *F. sylvatica* but the bark may
be furrowed; the leaves are 9–14cm long,
with 7–12 pairs of veins, male flowers with
perianth divided up to one-third of its
length, and a cupule with narrowly oblong
scales above and paddle-shaped scales below.
Usually in more sheltered localities than *F. sylvatica*.
SE. Europe and Asia Minor. Bu FS Gr Ro Tu.

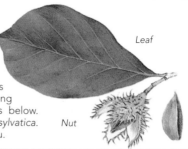

Leaf

Nut

Nothofagus procera
(Poeppig & Endl.) Örsted
Rauli
A large, broadly conical tree up to 30m. The greenish-
grey bark has wide, vertical dark cracks. The main
branches are level below, ascending above, twigs
stout, green, becoming dark brown. The buds are *c.*
1cm, narrowly conical, reddish-brown. The leaves
are 4–8cm, ovate to oblong-ovate, acute or somewhat blunt, the margin wavy, finely toothed, the
underside with silky hairs on the veins; there are
14–20 pairs of lateral veins; petiole is 0.5–1cm.
The male flowers are solitary in leaf axils
towards the tip of the shoot. The nuts are *c.* 1cm
long, usually occurring in threes, in a 4-lobed,
deeply fringed cupule. Flowering period: May;
fruiting in September. A native of Chile and Argentina, now planted in small forestry plantations in
Britain and for ornament.

Nuts

Spring shoot
with flowers

Habit

Nothofagus obliqua (Mirbel)
Blume
Roble Beech
Like *N. procera* but the bark becoming
cracked into small square flakes; the twigs
slender, branching in a regular alternating pattern; the buds *c.* 5mm, light brown; the
leaves with an irregularly toothed margin, with 7–11
pairs of veins; nuts *c.* 5mm long, enclosed in a
cupule with short projecting scales. A native of
Chile and W. Argentina. Planted in Britain for
timber and ornament.

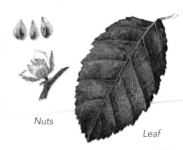

Nuts

Leaf

123

Castanea Miller
Chestnuts

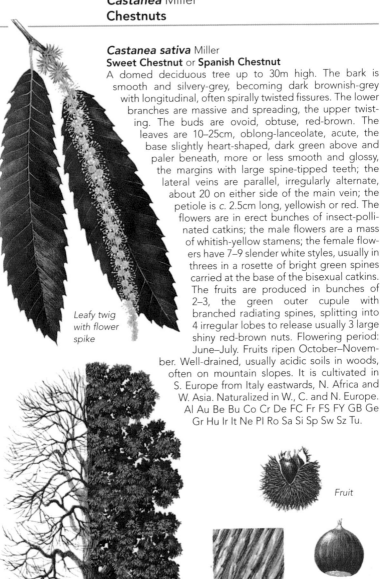

Castanea sativa Miller
Sweet Chestnut or Spanish Chestnut

A domed deciduous tree up to 30m high. The bark is smooth and silvery-grey, becoming dark brownish-grey with longitudinal, often spirally twisted fissures. The lower branches are massive and spreading, the upper twisting. The buds are ovoid, obtuse, red-brown. The leaves are 10–25cm, oblong-lanceolate, acute, the base slightly heart-shaped, dark green above and paler beneath, more or less smooth and glossy, the margins with large spine-tipped teeth; the lateral veins are parallel, irregularly alternate, about 20 on either side of the main vein; the petiole is *c.* 2.5cm long, yellowish or red. The flowers are in erect bunches of insect-pollinated catkins; the male flowers are a mass of whitish-yellow stamens; the female flowers have 7–9 slender white styles, usually in threes in a rosette of bright green spines carried at the base of the bisexual catkins. The fruits are produced in bunches of 2–3, the green outer cupule with branched radiating spines, splitting into 4 irregular lobes to release usually 3 large shiny red-brown nuts. Flowering period: June–July. Fruits ripen October–November. Well-drained, usually acidic soils in woods, often on mountain slopes. It is cultivated in S. Europe from Italy eastwards, N. Africa and W. Asia. Naturalized in W., C. and N. Europe. Al Au Be Bu Co Cr De FC Fr FS FY GB Ge Gr Hu Ir It Ne Pl Ro Sa Si Sp Sw Sz Tu.

Leafy twig with flower spike

Fruit

Habit

Bark

Quercus L.
Oaks

Large deciduous trees or sometimes shrubs. The leaves are usually toothed or lobed, though sometimes entire. The flowers are of 2 sexes, in wind-pollinated catkins; the male flowers with 6–12 stamens in slender, pendent, many–flowered catkins; the female flowers with 3–6 styles, in separate few-flowered catkins, each flower in a small cuplike involucre. The fruit is a single-seeded, oblong or ellipsoidal nut (acorn) carried in the enlarged, cuplike involucre or cupule. Hybrids are common in areas where related species grow together (eg. *Q. x hispanica* Lam = *Q. cerris* x *Q. suber*) tending to make identification difficult.

Quercus rubra L.
Red Oak

A large, broadly-domed deciduous tree up to 35m high. The bark is smooth and silvery-grey, the old trees sometimes having shallow fissures. The main branches are straight and radiating; the twigs are stout, reddish-brown. The leaves are 12–22 x 10–15cm, ovate to obovate with several lobes on either side, dividing the leaf about halfway to the midrib, each with 1–3 large whisker-tipped teeth, matt, green above, matt greyish and smooth below except for slight downiness in the axils of veins; the petiole is 2–5cm long, yellowish with a swollen reddish base. The acorn ripens in the 2nd year, the shallow cup 1.8–2.5cm wide with thin oval scales closely pressed together, finely downy, carried on a 1cm stout stalk. Flowering period: May. Fruits ripen in October of the following year.

Bark

An E. N. American species, commonly planted for ornament, timber and shelter, especially in C. Europe. Au Be De FC Fr FS GB Ge Gr Hu It Pl Po Ro Sp Sw Sz.

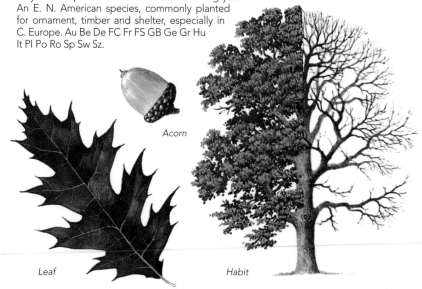

Acorn

Leaf

Habit

125

Quercus palustris
Muenchh.
Pin Oak
Similar to *Q. rubra* but with more slender, often pendulous twigs; buds *c.* 3mm, pale brown; the leaves with deeper cuts, more ragged lobes, the underside with conspic-uous tufts of brown hairs in the axils of the veins. The acorn cup is 1–1.5cm wide. Another species from E. N. America, but planted less commonly than *Q. rubra* for ornament and timber, especially in E. C. Europe Au De GB Ge Hu Ro.

Acorn

Leaf

Quercus coccinea
Muenchh.
Scarlet Oak
Similar to *Q. rubra* but with leaves 7.5–15 x 5–12cm, more deeply cut, the middle lobe longest, shiny on both sides; fewer hair tufts. The acorn cup is 1–2cm wide. A species of E. and C. North America. Planted less com-monly than *Q. rubra* for orna-ment. GB.

Acorn

Leaf

Quercus coccifera L.
An evergreen shrub or rarely a small tree up to 5m tall. The bark is dull grey, finely scaled in old trees. The main branches are numerous, ascending and repeatedly divided; the twigs are yellowish-brown, covered with stellate hairs, soon becoming smooth and grey. The leaves are 1.5–4cm, ovate to oblong with a heart-shaped or rounded base, the margin wavy with spiny teeth, the

Habit

Leaf

Acorn

blade with a rigid texture, the veins slightly raised on the dark green upper surface. The acorns ripen in the 2nd year, the cup *c.* 1.8cm wide, the scales rigid, almost spiny. Flowering period: April–May; fruits ripen in October–November of the following year. A native of the Mediterranean region, except for much of Italy. The host plant for coccid insects from which important red dyes were extracted in antiquity. Al Bl Bu Co Cr Fr FY Gr It Po Sa Si Sp Tu.

Quercus ilex L.
Holm Oak

A broadly domed evergreen tree up to 25m high. The bark is brownish-black, cracked into shallow square plates. The main branches are ascending, almost straight, often emerging from near the bottom of the trunk; the twigs are slender grey-brown and tomentose. The buds are 1–2mm long, light brown, grey-tomentose. The leaves are 4–10 x 3–8cm, oblong-ovate to lanceolate with a pointed tip, rounder or shortly tapering at the base, the margin wavy, entire or with spiny teeth on young trees, the blade with a thick but not rigid texture, dark green becoming smooth above, grey-tomentose with raised veins below, 7–11 pairs of veins from a straight midrib; the petiole is 0.6–2cm long and densely hairy; the stipules are very narrow, hairy. The acorns ripen in the first year, the cup *c.* 1.2cm wide, enclosing the bottom third to half of the nut, the scales flat and pressed together, felted. Flowering period: late June; fruits ripen in October. A native of Mediterranean region, widely planted for ornament; rarely naturalized in W. and S. Europe. Al Bl Co Cr Fr FS FY GB Gr It Po Sa Si Sp Sz Tu.

Habit

Acorn

Bark

Leaf

127

Quercus suber L.
Cork Oak

Acorn

An evergreen tree up to 20m. The bark is thick and corky, forming sinuous interconnecting ridges; pale greyish-brown when present but revealing a smooth and red-brown bole when stripped. The main branches are low, massive and twisting; the twigs are grey-green, tomentose. Buds *c.* 2mm long, ovoid, dark purple. The leaves are 3–7 x 2–3cm, ovate-oblong, pointed, the margin wavy, with spine-tipped teeth, dark green and smooth above, grey-pubescent beneath; 5–8 pairs of lateral veins emerge from a somewhat sinuous midrib; the petiole is 0.8–1.5cm long, densely pubescent. The acorns ripen in the 2nd year on spring-flowering trees and on some autumn-flowering trees in the following season; the cup is 1.2–1.8cm wide, enclosing about half of the nut, the scales long and projecting at right-angles, the lower ones shorter and pressed together. Flowering period: May–June; fruiting in October. A common species of the W. Mediterranean region, widely planted elsewhere for its bark (the cork of commerce) or for ornament. Co Fr FY It Pl Sa Si Sp.

Habit

Bark

Leaf

Quercus cerris L.
Turkey Oak

Leaf

Acorn

A broadly domed deciduous tree up to 35m. The bark is greyish and deeply fissured, eventually cracking to form square convex plates. The main branches are long and ascending, swollen at the base; twigs rough, brownish or green-grey, shortly pubescent. The buds are ovoid, pale brown, hairy, surrounded by long thin twisted stipules. The leaves are 9–12 x 3–5cm, oblong or wider above the middle, rounded or slightly tapering at the base, the margin with 4–10 pairs of lobes or teeth, blunt or rarely with a small point, slightly rough with stiff hairs above, pubescent or almost smooth below; petiole 0.8–1.5cm long. Acorns ripen in the 2nd year, half to two-thirds enclosed in a cup 1.5–2.2cm wide, the scales long, pointed, curving outwards, downy, Flowering period: May–June; fruits ripening in October. C.S. and SE. Europe, planted elsewhere for ornament. Al Au Be Bu Cr FC Fr FY GB Ge Gr Hu It Ro Si Sz Tu.

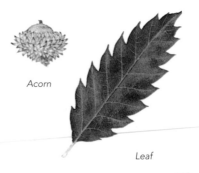

*Habit
(Quercus cerris)*

Quercus macrolepis
Kotschy

Like *Q. cerris*, but semi-evergreen and rarely more than 15m tall. The leaves are 6–10cm long, the margin with 3–7 pairs of triangular, bristle-tipped lobes; the petiole 1.5–4cm long. The acorn cup is up to 5cm wide, the scales wide, thick, flat, usually projecting at right-angles. At one time an important cultivated crop for the high tannin content of the acorn-cups. SE. Italy, the Aegean and the Balkan Peninsula. Al Cr FY Gr It Tu.

Acorn

Leaf

Quercus trojana
Webb in Loudon
Macedonian Oak

Like *Q. cerris* but semi-evergreen, up to 15m tall. The leaves are 3–7cm long, the margin with 8–14 pairs of slightly spiny teeth, smooth and shiny on both sides; the petiole 2–5mm long. The acorn cup is 1.5–2.2cm wide, enclosing about two-thirds of the acorn, the lowest scales pressed together, the upper spreading or incurved. SE. Italy and the Balkan Peninsula. Al Bu FY Gr It Tu.

Acorn

Leaf

129

Quercus petraea
(Mattuschka) Liebl.
Sessile Oak or **Durmast Oak**

A domed deciduous tree up to 40m high. The bark is finely fissured, mostly forming vertical ridges, grey. The main branches radiate from a straight bole; the young twigs dark, purplish-grey, glabrous, becoming greyish-bloomed. The buds are 4–8mm long, ovoid, the apex slightly pointed, orange-brown, with long white hairs. The leaves are 7–12 x 4–5cm, obovate, acute, the base cuneate or slightly heart-shaped, the margin with 5–9 pairs of rounded regular lobes, dark green above, paler beneath with very fine appressed hairs and tufts of brownish hairs in the axils of the veins; the lateral veins often with several smaller veins leading to the sinuses; petiole 1.8–2.5cm. The acorns ripen in the first year, the cup 1.2–1.8cm wide; the scales are ovate-lanceolate, thin, not tuberculate, downy, up to 6 nuts grouped together, sessile or on a peduncle up to 1cm long. Flowering period: May; the fruits ripen in October. A widespread and often dominant tree in woods, especially on lighter, more sandy soils. It is found throughout Europe except for the extreme N. and NE. and parts of the Mediterranean region. Al Au Be Bu Co De FC Fr FS FY GB Ge Hu Ir It Ne No Po Ro Si Sp Sw Sz Tu.

Habit

Acorn

Leaf

Quercus dalechampii
Ten.

Like *Q. petraea* but the leaves have 4–7 pairs of narrow, subacute, irregular lobes with a petiole 1.5–2cm long. The acorn cup has diamond-shaped blunt scales, is strongly tuberculate and very shortly downy or almost smooth, greyish. SE. Europe Au Bu FY Gr Hu It Ro Si.

Acorn

Leaf

Quercus robur L.
English Oak

A large irregularly domed deciduous tree up to 45m. The bark is fissured, forming narrow, vertical, pale grey plates. The few main branches are massive, twisting, usually carried low on the trunk; young twigs brownish-green, pubescent, becoming greyish-bloomed and glabrous. The buds are 3–6mm long, ovoid-conical, blunt or slightly pointed, light brown, smooth. Leaves 10–12 x 7–8cm, obovate, blunt, the base usually with a pair of auricles, the margin with 5–7 pairs of wavy-edged lobes, dark green above, paler beneath and sometimes pubescent when young; the lateral veins make various angles with the midrib, some leading to the sinuses; petiole 0.4–1cm long.

Bark   *Habit*

Acorn

The acorns ripen in the first year, the cup 1.1–1.8cm (or up t 2.3cm) wide; the scales flat, slightly downy, joined together except at the tips; up to 3 nuts are carried on a peduncle 4–8cm long. Flowering period: May–June; fruits ripen in October. A widespread and often dominant species especially on heavy basic soils. Distributed throughout Europe except for the extreme N. and parts of the Mediterranean region. Al Au Be Bu De FC Fi Fr FS FY GB Ge Hu Ir It Ne No Pl Po Ro Sa Si Sp Sw Sz.

Leaf

Quercus pedunculiflora
C. Koch

Like *Q. robur* but with leaves somewhat glaucous above, the lateral veins making an acute angle with the midrib then curving out to the margin, the underside with a persistent yellow-grey tomentum. Acorn cup up to 2cm wide, the scales warty, more closely joined together, with yellowish down. SE. Europe. Bu FS Gr Ro Tu

Acorn

Leaf

131

Quercus frainetto
Ten.
Hungarian Oak

A domed deciduous tree up to 30m. The bark is closely and deeply fissured, forming short small ridges, pale grey or brownish. The main branches are long and straight, radiating from a stout bole; twigs are grey-green or brownish, softly downy. The buds are *c.* 1cm long, ovoid, grey-brown, surrounded by persistent stipules. The leaves are clustered towards the end of the branches, 10–25 x 8–14cm, obovate, the base tapered often with a pair of auricles, the margin deeply pinnatifid with 7–10 pairs of broad, oblong, often wavy-edged lobes, dark green above, the underside paler with grey or brownish down; the main lateral veins are parallel with a few smaller veins leading to the sinuses; petiole 2–6mm. The acorns ripen in the first year, the cups 0.6–1.2 x 1.2–1.5cm, the scales oblong, blunt, downy, loosely overlapping. Flowering period: May; acorns fall in October. The Balkan Peninsula, Hungary, Romania and S. Italy. Al Bu FY Gr Hu It Ro Tu.

Habit

Acorn

Leaf

Quercus pubescens
Willd.
Downy Oak

Acorn

A deciduous tree up to 25m, or sometimes a shrub. The bark is finely and deeply fissured, forming small rough plates, dark grey. The main branches are swollen where they join the bole; twigs brown, densely grey-pubescent. The buds are 4–7mm long, orange-brown, grey-pubescent. The leaves are 4–13 x *c.* 6cm, obovate, broadly cuneate at the base, the margin sinuate to pinnatifid with 4–8 pairs of broad, rounded, forward-directed lobes, becoming grey-green and glabrous above, densely tomentose

Leaf

Habit

beneath when young, becoming almost smooth; petiole 0.5–1.2cm, densely pubescent. The acorns ripen in the first year, the cup up to 1 .5 x 1.4cm, the scales lanceolate, acute or obtuse, pubescent, pressed closely together. Flowering period: end of May; fruit falls in October. S., C. and W Europe and Western Asia. Al Au Be Bu Co FC Fr FS FY Ge Gr Hu It Po Ro Sa Si Sp Sz Tu.

Quercus pyrenaica
Willd.
Pyrenean Oak
Like *Q. pubescens* but often suckering and with pendent twigs; leaves up to 20cm long with narrow, rather pointed lobes, completely downy at first, becoming more or less smooth above with dense white down below; petiole up to 2.2cm. Acorn cup with blunt, loosely overlapping scales. SW, Europe and N. Italy, Fr It Po Sp.

Acorn

Leaf

Acorn

Leaf

Quercus virgiliana
(Ten.) Ten.
Like *Q. pubescens* but leaves up to 16cm, the lobes often wavy-edged; petiole 1.5–2.5cm; acorn cup with the scales loosely pressed together, the tips erect. S. Europe. Bu Co Cr FY Hu It Ro Sa Si Tu.

Quercus canariensis
Willd.
Mirbeck's Oak or **Algerian Oak**
Like *Q. pubescens* but semi-evergreen, young shoots densely woolly, becoming almost smooth. Leaves up to 18cm, the margin with 9–14 pairs of almost acute teeth, woolly when young, becoming almost smooth, glaucous beneath; petiole 0.8–3cm. Acorn cup with the lower scales tuberculate, the upper ones pressed closely together. Hybridizes extensively with *Q. pubescens* in Spain. SW. Europe, N. Africa. Pl Sp.

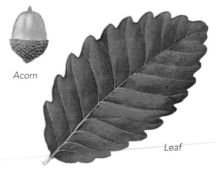

Acorn

Leaf

133

ELM FAMILY ULMACEAE

Ulmus L.
Elms

Large deciduous trees, often forming suckers, The bark is fissured and cracked. The leaves are simple, alternate, with an asymmetrical base, a double-toothed margin and paired lateral veins. The flowers are hermaphrodite, appearing in clusters before the leaves on the previous year's twigs. The fruit is dry and flattened, forming a broad papery wing encircling the seed.

Ulmus glabra
Hudson
Wych Elm

A broad, multiple-domed tree up to 40m very rarely producing suckers. The bark is smooth and grey when young, becoming cracked and ridged, turning grey-brown. The few main branches spread outwards and often become almost level; young twigs are stout, dark red-brown, with short stiff hairs, becoming smooth and grey. Winter buds are ovoid, blunt, reddish-brown with reddish hairs. Leaves 10–18cm, almost round or obovate to elliptical; the tip tapers into a long point; the base is very unequal with the long side overlapping the petiole; the veins are in 10–18 pairs; the upper side of the leaf has short stiff hairs while the underside has fewer, soft hairs; the petiole is 2–5mm, thick and hairy. The dense flower clusters have purplish-red anthers. Fruits are 1.5–2cm, obovate, borne on a very short pedicel. Woods and hedges, especially by water. Flowering late February–March. Fruit shed from May to July. Al Au Be Bu De FC Fi Fr FS FY GB Ge Gr Hu Ir It Ne No Po Ro Sp Sw Sz.

Flowering twig

Fruit

Habit

Leafy twig

Ulmus x hollandica
Miller
Dutch Elm

A hybrid between *U. glabra* and species of the *U. minor* group. Cv. *'Hollandica'* and cv. *'Vegeta'* are the common clones in Britain, but many others are planted elsewhere in Europe. Dutch Elms usually have large broad leaves, up to 15 x 8cm, like *U. glabra*, but with more or less shiny upper surfaces, a very unequal base and a petiole 1–2cm long. *'Hollandica'* has numerous suckers with corky flanges up to 2cm wide on the stems. The hybrids are commonly planted. Au Be Fr GB Ge Ir Ne Sz.

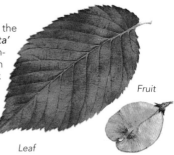

Fruit

Leaf

Ulmus procera
Salisb.
English Elm

A domed tree up to *c.* 35m commonly producing numerous suckers. The bark is dark brown and deeply fissured, forming square plates. The few main branches are large and ascending; the twigs are rather stout, reddish-brown, and remain densely hairy. Winter buds are 2–3mm, ovoid, pointed, dark brown and slightly hairy. The leaves are up to 10cm, oval to rounded with a short tapering tip, the base unequal but not overlapping the petiole, the veins in 10–12 pairs; the upper side of the leaf is rough while the lower side has white down on both sides of the main vein; the petiole is 1–5mm long, finely downy. The flowers have dark red anthers. The fruit is 1–1.7cm, rounded, borne on a very short pedicel, often sterile. Flowering in late February–March. Fruits when present are shed from May to July. Hedgerows. Bu Fr FY GB Gr Hu Ro Sp (planted in Ir).

Bark

Fruit

Leafy
shoot

Habit

Ulmus minor
Miller

An open, narrowly crowned tree up to 30m, commonly producing suckers. The bark is greyish-brown with long deep furrows and ridges. The main branches are narrowly ascending to almost upright; young twigs are slender, commonly pendulous, pale brown and becoming smooth. Winter buds are ovoid, shiny dark red and somewhat downy. Leaves 6–8cm (sometimes up to 12cm), obovate or ovate to oblanceolate, tapering to a slender point; the veins are in 7–12 pairs; the upper side of the leaf is shiny and dark green, the underside has downy tufts in the axils of the veins; petiole *c.* 5mm, downy. The flowers are red with white stigmas. Fruits 0.7–1.8cm, elliptical, with the seed above the centre, close to the notch in the wing. The name *U. minor* has been applied to include the 4 species described below. The species are not easily distinguished and hybrids have been reported between each of them, and with *U. glabra*. By roads and in hedges, commonly in deep, moist soils. Flowering in March. Fruit shed in July. Widely planted as an amenity tree around towns and along roads. Native in much of Europe, N. Africa and SW. Asia. Al Au Be Bu Co Cr De FC Fr FS FY GB Ge Gr Hu It Ne Pl Po Ro Si Sp Sz Tu.

*1–year
twig with
flowers*

Ulmus carpinifolia
G. Suckow
Smooth Elm

The crown is domed, young twigs are long and pendulous. Leaves are usually widest above the middle with the midrib almost straight, the base is rather unequal, the margin of the longer side is straight in the lower one-third to one half, turning at right-angles into the petiole. Throughout the range of *U. minor.*

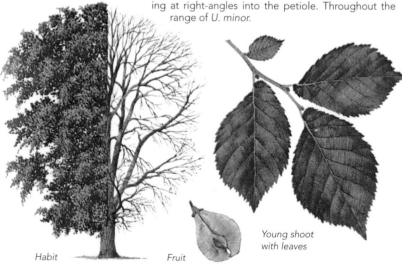

Habit

Fruit

*Young shoot
with leaves*

136

Ulmus coritana
Melville
Coritanian Elm

Leaf

The crown is rather spreading, young twigs are stout. Leaves are usually widest at or below the middle with the midrib curving towards the short side; the base is very unequal with the longer side often forming a rounded lobe. SE. Britain. GB.

Habit

Ulmus angustifolia (Weston)
Weston
Cornish Elm

The crown is narrow and somewhat conical, especially when young; twigs are short and rather stiff. Leaves are usually broadest above the middle, often concave, with the midrib more or less straight; the base is more or less equal. SW. Britain; may also be native in France. Fr GB.

Leaf

Habit

Ulmus plotii
Druce
Plot's Elm

The crown is narrow and upright with an arching, one-sided leading shoot; young twigs are long and pendulous. Leaves are rather narrow, widest near the middle with the midrib almost straight and the base more or less equal; some short shoots proliferate and produce smaller, rounder leaves. GB.

Leaf

Habit

Ulmus canescens
Melville

This species closely resembles *U. minor* but the young twigs have a dense soft white down. Leaves are ovate-elliptic with rounded teeth and have a dense grey down; lateral veins are in 12–16 (sometimes 18) pairs. Native in C. and E. Mediterranean region. Al Cr FY Gr It Ro Si.

Leaf

Ulmus laevis
Pallas
European White Elm
A wide-spreading tree up to 35m with a rather open crown. The bark is brownish-grey, smooth when young, becoming deeply furrowed with broad ridges. Young twigs dark red-brown with a soft grey down, becoming smooth. Winter buds small, pointed and dark orange-brown. Leaves are 6–13cm, almost round to oval with a short tapering point, the base very unequal; the veins are in 12–19 pairs, the longer side with 2–3 extra veins; the upper surface is smooth or occasionally with stiff hairs, the lower surface is usually clothed with a soft grey down; the petiole is 3–5mm long. The flowers are borne in clusters on long pedicels 3–6 times as long as the flowers. The pendulous fruit is 1–1.2cm, obovate, the two halves of the wing fringed with white hairs and curving together above the notch. Flowering period: March. Sometimes planted as a shelter tree. Al Au Be Bu FC Fr FS FY Ge Gr Hu Po Ro Sw Sz (planted in It).

1 –year twig with flowers

Fruit

Leaf

Zelkova
Spach
Large deciduous trees or shrubs. The simple leaves are alternately arranged with a slightly asymmetrical or level base and a toothed margin. Flowers appear in the axils of leaves on young stems; male flowers are at the base of new growth, sometimes at the tip; the lobes of the perianth are leaf-like and joined together, enclosing an erect cluster of stamens. Fruits are dry and form single-seeded nutlets. This smal genus from Caucasus, Crete and E. Asia is closely related to the elms, but differs mainly in having separate male and female flowers, and fruits without an encircling wing.

Zelkova carpinifolia (Pallas)
C. Koch
Caucasian Elm
An unusual, often many-stemmed tree up to 30m with a domed crown, sometimes producing suckers. The short fluted bole is usually 1–3m, with a smooth greyish- or greenish-brown bark, flaking away as rounded scales, revealing orange underneath. The main branches are very numerous and almost upright; the twigs are slender, greyish- or greenish-

Late summer twig with fruit

brown, covered with a white down. Winter buds are ovoid, blunt, dark reddish–brown with a white down. The leaves are 5–10cm, oval or elliptic, pointed, with large rounded teeth, the side veins are in 6–12 pairs; the upper surface of the leaf is dark green, often with scattered stiff hairs, the underside has stiff white hairs either side of the veins, the petiole is 1–2mm. The male flowers have clusters of yellow stamens and are borne on the lower, leafless portion of young twigs, female flowers being carried in the axils of terminal leaves. Fruits 5mm, globose with 4 distinct ridges or small wings. Flowering in April. A native of the Caucasus mountains infrequently planted for ornament in C. and W. Europe.

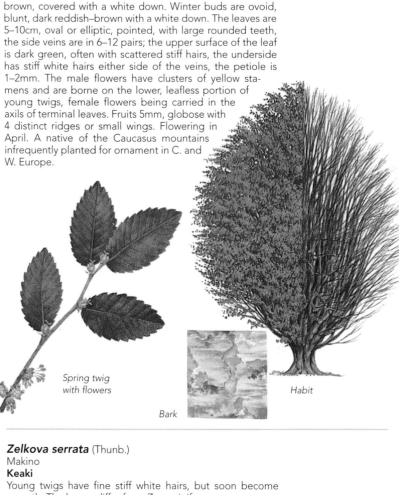

Spring twig with flowers

Bark

Habit

Zelkova serrata (Thunb.)
Makino
Keaki

Young twigs have fine stiff white hairs, but soon become smooth. The leaves differ from Z. carpinifolia in having more pointed teeth and a smooth underside. The fruit is smooth and rounded. Infrequently planted for ornament in parks or gardens. Japan.

Late summer twig with fruit

Celtis L.
Nettle-trees

Deciduous trees or shrubs. The bark is smooth or sometimes wrinkled, but does not form scales. The alternately arranged simple leaves are level at the base; the middle section of the margin has usually uneven teeth but these are often absent from the base and the tapering tip; three prominent veins diverge from the base; the stipules soon fall off. Flowers appear in the axils of leaves on young stems; male flowers are at the base of new growth with hermaphrodite flowers towards the tip; the lobes of the perianth are brownish and separate, enclosing a cluster of upright stamens with yellow anthers. The fruit is small and fleshy, enclosing a single seed with a stony layer. A genus of about 70 species from the northern hemisphere and the tropics.

Celtis australis L.
Southern Nettle-tree

A round-domed tree up to 25m. The bark is grey and pale brown. Young twigs are reddish-brown. Leaves are 4–15cm, lance-shaped to narrowly oval, with a long tapering tip which is often twisted; the base is rounded or heart-shaped; the margin is often wavy and has sharp pointed teeth; the upper side of the leaf has short, stiff hairs while the underside has white down, especially on the veins and petiole. The fleshy fruit is 0.9–1.2cm in diameter, globose, smooth and brownish-red, becoming blackish when ripe; the outer layer of the stone has irregular projections. Flowers open in May. Fruits ripen in September. Native to S. Europe and SW. Asia. Planted in France and Italy as a street tree, occasionally for ornament elsewhere. The fruits are edible though rather small. Al Bu Co Cr Fr FY It Po Ro Sp Sz.

Habit

Bark

Young twig with flowers

Twig with young fruit

Celtis tournefortii
Lam.

A shrub or small tree up to 6m. Young twigs are reddish-brown with whitish down. Leaves are 5–8cm, broadly oval with a short tapering apex; the base is rounded; the margin has rounded teeth, each with a small point; the dark green upper surface of the leaf has short stiff hairs or is almost smooth, while the underside is paler and slightly downy. The fleshy fruit is 0.7–1.1 cm, ovoid, brownish-yellow when ripe; the outer layer of the stone has 4 ridges. Bu FS FY Gr Si.

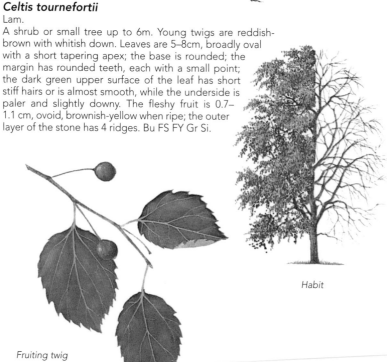

Habit

Fruiting twig

MULBERRY AND FIG FAMILY MORACEAE

Morus L.
Mulberries

Large monoecious or dioecious trees with flowers on catkins. The compound 'fruit' is composed of closely packed drupes, each enclosed by persistent fleshy sepals.

Morus alba L.
White Mulberry

A deciduous tree up to c. 15m with a narrow to rounded crown of brittle branches and a broad bole up to 2m in girth. The sinuously ridged bark is generally grey but may have a pinkish appearance. The shoots are slender, initially bearing fine hairs. The buds are minute, narrowly conical, dark brown. The leaves are 6–18cm long, broadly ovate with a heart-shaped base, thin, flat, coarsely toothed, usually smooth, glossy green above, glabrous or pubescent on the veins and midrib beneath; the petiole is up to 2.5cm long, finely hairy and with a groove on the upper side. The female flowers occur on stalked cylindrical spikes up to 1.5cm long; the male spikes are longer. The fruits are 1–2.5cm long, white, pinkish or purplish, edible although insipid long before being ripe. Flowering period: May. A native of China and other parts of Asia, and cultivated for centuries in many S. European and oriental countries as food for silkworms and as a roadside tree. It has frequently become naturalized in SE. Europe and occasionally elsewhere. Al Au Bu Cr FS Gr Ro Tu.

Habit

Fruit

Leafy twig with male and female flowers

Morus nigra L.
Common Mulberry or Black Mulberry

A deciduous tree up to *c.* 12m high with a rugged aspect, forming a dense spreading crown of twisted branches usually wider than the tree is high, the short rough bole with many bosses and burrs. The bark is dark orange-brown, fraying or shredding along the sides of wide cracks. The young shoots are pubescent, exuding a milky juice when cut, initially pale green and later becoming purple-grey. The buds are squat and pointed, the scales dark, glossy and purple-brown. The leaves are 6–20cm long, broadly ovate, with a deep heart-shaped base, curled, acute, irregularly dentate or lobed, shiny green above, paler and pubescent below; the petiole is stout, 1.5–2.5cm long, hairy. The flower spikes are cylindrical, occurring on downy peduncles. The male flower spikes are *c.* 2.5cm long, pallid; the females are about half as long. The fruits are 2–2.5cm long, dark red to deep purple, very acid unitil ripe, when they have an agreeable flavour. Flowering period: May. Fruiting: July–September. Although undoubtedly an oriental native, the Common Mulberry has been in cultivation for so long that its native boundaries have been obliterated. It is mostly cultivated for its fruit and has become naturalized in S. Europe. Al Bu Cr Gr It Ro Sp.

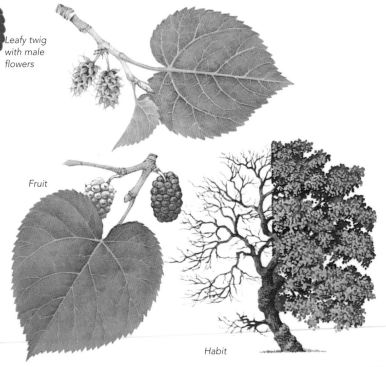

Leafy twig with male flowers

Fruit

Habit

Maclura pomifera (Rafin)
C. K. Schneider
Osage Orange

A deciduous dioecious tree up to 14m tall or higher, with spiny branches forming an irregular domed crown. The bark is cracked and ridged, with an orange coloration. The young shoots are initially downy, soon becoming glabrous. The leaves are 5–12cm long, oval or ovate to oblong-lanceolate, acuminate, mostly rounded at the base, dark glossy green above, downy beneath and paler, especially on the veins and midrib. The male flowers are in dense clusters or more rarely racemes, green, inconspicuous on short peduncles; the female flowers are in dense globose or subglobose inconspicuous clusters, and develop into compound fruits which are orange-shaped, pitted, covered with a white inedible pulp and a tough bright yellowish-green rind. Flowering period: June, fruits ripening October–November. A native of the S. and C. United States, cultivated in Europe as a hedge plant and for ornament. It has become locally naturalized in some parts of S. Europe. FS It Ro.

Habit

Bark

Fruit

Shoot with male flowers

Ficus carica L.
Fig

A deciduous dioecious tree or shrub with a low spreading crown and robust branches. The smooth, pale-grey bark has a tracery of darker markings. The leaves are alternate, 10–20cm long and wide, usually 3–5 palmately lobed, the lobes rounded, heart-shaped at the base, and usually with a scalloped toothed margin, sparsely hispid and rough to the touch, especially below, dark green, thick, leathery, with prominent veins below; the petiole is 5–10cm long. The flowers are produced on the inner surface of a pear-shaped receptacle almost enclosed at the top, which develops later into the sweet, succulent fig. A species perhaps native to SW. Asia, the Iberian Peninsula and the Balkan Peninsula, now extensively cultivated for its fruit and widely naturalized in S. Europe but also found in gardens throughout N. and W. Europe. Many different cultivars exist and the fruits are eaten both fresh and dried. Al Au Bl Co Cr FC Fr FS Gr Hu It Pl Sa Si Sp Sz Tu. Its evergreen relative **F. elastica** Roxb. with entire, glossy dark green leaves is the commonly cultivated 'Rubber' plant, forming large trees in the Mediterranean countries.

Fruiting shoot

Broussonetia papyrifera L.
Vent.

A small dioecious tree with villous twigs. The leaves are 7–20cm long, lovate, serrate or sometimes lobed, rough to the touch above, grey-tomentose below. The male flower is a catkin-like inflorescence with a 4-partite perianth; there are 4 stamens, somewhat inflexed in bud; the female flowers occur in dense globose tomentose heads; the perianth has 4 very small teeth and forms a layer of pulp in the ripe fruit. An uncommon E. Asian tree planted in S. Europe for ornament, sometimes becoming naturalized. Fr It Ro Si.

Habit

Fruiting shoot

PROTEA FAMILY PROTEACEAE

Embothrium coccineum
J.R. & G. Forst.
Chilean Firebush
A small evergreen tree up to 12m tall. The bark is slightly flaking, dark purplish to grey. The crown is slender, the branches sinuous, leaning outwards; the shoots are somewhat pendulous, pale green, smooth. The leaves are variable, 5–15cm (rarely up to 22cm) long, elliptic to lanceolate, cuneate or rounded, entire, pale to deep bluish-green; the petiole is *c.* 1cm long, bright green. The inflorescences are axillary or terminal clusters of bright red flowers; the flowers are 5–10cm long, swollen at the apex and divided into 4 segments. The fruit is a capsule, 3 x 1cm, oblong, grooved, on a dark red peduncle and bearing a dark red style up to 3cm long at the tip. Flowering period: late May and June. A S. American species from Chile and Argentina planted for ornament in W. Europe. GB.

Flowering shoot

Habit

PHYTOLACCA FAMILY PHYTOLACCACEAE

Phytolacca dioica L.
Phytolacca
A small evergreen dioecious tree with robust brown glabrous branches. The leaves are 6–12 x 2.5–6cm, entire, elliptical to ovate, acute, glabrous, petiolate, rich green with a prominent vein. The inflorescence is an axillary, drooping cylindrical raceme up to *c.* 12cm with a peduncle up to 1.5cm long; the flowers are green, spotted with white,

pubescent; the males slender, *c.* 1.5cm long with pointed membranous petals; the female flowers are more robust with elliptical, obtuse petals and 7–10 styles. The fruit is a sub-globose berry with 7–10 carpels joined only at the base, compressed, about 3mm long and 7.5mm wide, purplish-black. Flowering period: June to August. A native of temperate and sub-tropical S. America planted for ornament and shade in the Mediterranean region and locally naturalized. Fr Gr It Si Sp.

leafy twig with fruit

KATSURA FAMILY CERCIDIPHYLLACEAE

Cercidiphyllum japonicum
Sieb. & Zucc.
Katsura Tree
A moderate-sized dioecious tree up to 25m with an ovoid-conical crown and a solitary trunk or divided into many stems. The bark is dull greyish-brown, becoming vertically fissured and eventually peeling in strips. The branches are slender, curving upwards, covered with opposite pairs of buds; the buds are dark brown, glossy. The opposite leaves are *c.* 8 x 7cm, ovate or round, obtuse, cordate with small rounded teeth, emerging as a pink colour, becoming green, turning red in the autumn. The flowers occur at the nodes; the male flowers are clusters of red stamens, appearing before the leaves; the female flowers are 5–6mm, with clusters of dark red twisted styles. The fruits are in clusters of 4–6, 1.5–5cm, bluish-grey, later becoming green then brown. Flowering period: April. A Japanese species frequently planted in gardens for ornament.

Fruit

Habit

Leaves

147

MAGNOLIA AND TULIP TREE FAMILY MAGNOLIACEAE

Liriodendron tulipifera L.
Tulip Tree

A large deciduous glabrous tree up to 45m tall. The crown is slender, more or less parallel-sided when young, becoming domed, often with massive lowest branches when old. The bark is grey, becoming brown or somewhat orange at maturity, with a network of low ridges. Buds are c. 1cm, broadest above the middle, glossy, reddish-brown with stipules enclosing the bud and each of the young leaves. The leaves are 7–18 x 15–20cm, with 4 large lobes and a broad squarish or notched apex, shiny green above, somewhat waxy and dull below; the lower lobes project at right-angles, triangular or somewhat oval with pointed tips; the upper lobes are narrowly triangular, spreading either side of the apex; the petiole is slender, 5–10cm long. The flowers are borne at the tips of shoots, at first cup-shaped, later opening wider, the petaloid perianth segments yellowish-green with a pale orange band near the base enclosing a greenish-blue area; the stamens are up to 5cm long, fleshy, yellowish-white, erect becoming spreading; the central conical mass ovaries is yellowish with a green tip. The fruit is conical, 5–8.5cm long, consisting of numerous dark-brown carpels, overlapping, erect and pointed, each with a terminal wing and indehiscent when separating from the axis. A N. American species introduced into Europe in the 17th century, widely planted as a timber tree and for ornament. Au De GB Ge. A close relative, the **Chinese Tulip Tree**, *L. chinense*, is less widely planted.

Flowering shoot

Habit

Magnolia grandiflora L.
Evergreen Magnolia or Bull Bay

A medium to large evergreen tree up to 30m high with large spreading branches. The crown is broadly conical. The bark is dull grey and smooth. The shoot is thickly covered with a reddish-brown down; the buds are up to 1.5cm long, conical with a reddish tip. The leaves are 8–16 x 5–9cm, elliptical or broader above the middle, the margin without teeth but sometimes wavy, thick and leathery, shiny above but rusty-pubescent below; the petiole is 2–2.5cm long, covered with a dense down. The flowers are borne at the tips of shoots, initially conical, later cup-shaped, up to 25cm in diameter with 6 thick creamy-white petal-like segments. The fruit is conical, 5–6 x 2–3cm, comprised of separate carpels on an orange-brown stalk, marked where the stamens and petal-like segments have fallen away. Flowering from July to November. A native of the SE. United States, introduced to W. Europe in the early 18th century and now one of the most popular cultivated trees, commonly grown against walls or as free-standing trees in milder areas. There are some 35 other species of Magnolia, many of which are cultivated.

Habit

Flower on leafy shoot

Drimys winteri
Forst.
Winter's Bark
A small evergreen of the Winter-aceae with glossy green leaves and panicles of white flowers. A S. American species cultivated in gardens of SW. Europe.

Flowering shoot

149

BAY FAMILY LAURACEAE

Male flowers

Female flowers

Laurus nobilis L.
Sweet Bay

A medium-sized evergreen tree or shrub up to 20m high with a broadly conical crown and covered in all parts with aromatic oil glands. The bark is usually smooth, dark grey to black. The branches are ascending, usually dark grey, the twigs slender glabrous, reddish near the tip, green on the lower parts of the shoot. The buds are 3mm long, narrowly conical, dark red. The leaves are 5–10 x 2–4cm (rarely up to 7.5cm), alternate, narrowly lanceolate, leathery, dark green above, paler beneath, the margins crinkled, glabrous, dotted with glands and aromatic when crushed; the petiole is dark red. The inflorescence has a short peduncle; the perianth is deeply 4-lobed and not differentiated into sepals and petals. The flowers are doecious, borne in pairs beneath each leaf, *c.* 1cm in diameter, red and green in bud and yellow when open; the male flowers have 8–12 stamens usually arranged in 4 whorls, each with 2 glands at the base, the anthers opening by 2 valves; the female flowers each have 2–4 staminodes and a simple style. The fruit is an ovoid berry, 1–1.5cm long when mature, shiny green at first, later turning black. Flowering period: June. A native of the Mediterranean region, the Sweet Bay is cultivated in many parts of Europe as far north as Britain, often as a shrub or half-standard, and has become naturalized in some places. The 'Laurel' from which poets' wreaths were made in classical times, it is now widely used as a pot herb. Al Co Cr Fr FY Gr It Pl Sa Sp Tu.

Twig with male flowers

Fruit

Habit

Persea americana Miller
Avocado

A much-branched evergreen tree 7–9m high, although in natural habitats reaching 18m or more, the crown rounded, covered in all parts with aromatic oil glands. The leaves are 10–20cm long, elliptic or ovate, acute or shortly pointed, leathery glabrous, dark green above, bluish-green beneath, entire, pinnately veined or 3-veined. The inflorescence is elongated with many flowers, each about 2cm across, greenish, grey-pubescent; the perianth is 6-lobed, the lobes either equal in length or with 3 smaller outer lobes; the anthers open by 4 valves. The fruit is a berry about 10cm long, pear-shaped, oblong or globose, seated on a persistent perianth tube, the skin thick and sometimes woody, varying in colour from green through yellow to brown or purple; the soft flesh is greenish, becoming bright yellow when ripe; the seed is single, large and shiny. The origin of the Avocado is unknown but it is generally thought to be a native of C. America. It is grown as an orchard tree in many parts of the world including the Mediterranean countries. Cultivated plants are generally much smaller and of a bushier habit than wild plants. There are a number of cultivars with fruits of varying sizes and textures occurring at different times of the year. The Avocado is grown for the soft, edible flesh which surrounds the seed.

Flower

Flowering twig

Fruit

Habit

151

WITCH HAZEL FAMILY HAMAMELIDACEAE

Liquidambar orientalis
Miller
Oriental Sweet Gum
A small deciduous tree up to 7.5m high with a dense spreading crown. The bark is dark orange-brown, fissured and flaking. The young shoots are slender, red-brown above, green beneath, glabrous. The buds are ovoid with about 6 outer scales, red-brown, glossy. The leaves are 4–6cm wide, alternate, usually 5-lobed, the lobes ovate, the margins coarsely toothed and finely glandular, glabrous; petiole is *c.* 3.5cm. The flowers are monoecious; the male flowers are intermixed with small scales in catkins 5–7.5cm long, and consist of stamens only, the female flowers are in greenish or yellowish globose heads and consist only of 2-beaked ovaries in the axils of minute scales. The fruiting inflorescence is about 2.5cm in diameter; the fruit is a dehiscent capsule containing 1 or 2 seeds, with a slender beak. Flowering period: May. Originally from Asia Minor this species is cultivated in Europe for the fragrant resin called liquid storax which is obtained from the inner bark. In N. Europe the plants are usually small.

Twig with male and female inflorescences

Fruiting twig

Habit

Liquidambar styraciflua L.
Sweet Gum
A large tree up to 28m, twigs initially downy; leaves up to 15cm, downy beneath on the veins; the petiole is 10–15cm. A native of E. and S. United States, frequently planted in NW. Europe for ornament.

Hamamelis L.
Witch Hazels

Small deciduous trees or shrubs. The branches are usually spreading, stellate-hairy at least when young. The leaves are alternate, ovate, the margins toothed; the petiole is short; the stipules are large, falling early. The flowers are in few-flowered short-stalked clusters emerging from the leaf axils, in most species appearing before the leaves. The calyx consists of 4 rounded sepals; the 4 petals are long, narrow, strap-like, yellow. The fruit is a capsule containing 2 seeds, exploding when ripe. The seeds are black and shiny. Four species are commonly planted: the spring–flowering species, *H. mollis*, **Chinese Witch Hazel** and *H. japonica*, **Japanese Witch Hazel**, with their hybrid *H. x intermedia* and the autumn-flowering *H. virginiana*, **Virginian Witch Hazel**.

Leaf

Flowering twig

Fruit

Parrotia persica
C.A. Meyer
Persian Ironwood

A small deciduous tree 9–12m high with a spreading crown and a short bole. The bark is smooth, flaking, grey to greyish-brown, revealing pinkish-brown or yellow patches beneath. The twigs are stellate-hairy when young. The buds are purplish-black, hairy. The leaves are 5–25 x 2.5–7.5cm, stipulate, ovate or obovate, rounded to tapering at the base, the margins shallowly or unevenly toothed, sometimes only wavy towards the apex, glabrous above, sparsely stellate, hairy below, becoming glossy green, the petiole is 4–5mm long, hairy. The flowers are borne in crowded short-stalked clusters, opening before the leaves. The fruit is a capsule with 2 recurved beaks each splitting into 2 valves. The seeds are c. 1cm long, pointed at one end, brown and shining. Flowering period: February–March. A native of the Caucasus and N. Persia, frequently planted in parks and gardens as an ornamental.

Fruit

Flowering twig

Leafy twig

Habit

153

PITTOSPORUM FAMILY PITTOSPORACEAE

Pittosporum tenuifolium
Solander ex Gaertner
Pittosporum

A tree up to *c*. 8m high, sometimes with a very stout bole. The bark is dark grey; the twigs and young leaves are more or less pubescent. The leaves are 1–7 x 0.5–2cm (usually 3 x 2cm), entire, oblong to oblong–ovate, obtuse to acute, acuminate, thinly leathery, wavy and crinkled, pale green above, light green below; the petioles are short. The flowers are fragrant, axillary, solitary on short pedicels; or in small cymes; the bracts fall early; the sepals are narrowly ovate-oblong, subacute to obtuse, silky hairy when young; the petals are very dark red to purplish or almost black, *c*. 12cm long, the limb spreading to become deflexed; the ovary is hairy; the style is long. The fruit is a subglobose, 2-valved capsule *c*. 1.2cm in diameter, the valves are glabrous, slightly rough, nearly black and thinly woody when mature. Flowering period: May. A native of New Zealand, cultivated in W. Europe for its attractive leaves. Interesting cultivars include cv. *'Variegatum'* with pale cream variegated leaves and cv. **'Silver Queen'** with silvery-green leaves. *P. colensoi* Hooker fil., with a taller trunk and stouter limbs than *P. tenuifolium*, is cultivated on a lesser scale, as is the fragrant-flowered species *P. eugenioides* and the red-flowered *P. ralphii*.

Habit

Young fruit

Mature fruit

Flowering shoot

Pittosporum crassifolium
Putterlick

An erect evergreen shrub or small tree up to 10m high with black bark and a clustered crown. The leaves are 5–8 x 2–3cm, obovate-oblong, obtuse, dark green above, white-tomentose below, very leathery. The flowers occur in few-flowered cymes; the petals are deep red to purplish-black, oblong. The capsule is 2–2.8cm, long, subglobose, white-tomentose, with 3–4 woody valves. A native of New Zealand cultivated for ornament and shelter in parts of W. Europe and naturalized in the Scilly Isles. *P. tobira* is a species from S. Japan and E. China with leaves of a similar shape but glabrous, and with white or yellowish fragrant flowers, cultivated for ornament in S. and W. Europe.

Flowering shoot (P. tobira)

Flowering shoot (P. crassifolium)

Pittosporum undulatum
Vent.

White Holly or Mock Orange

A glabrous tree up to 20m high with a grey bark and a pyramidal crown. The leaves are 7–13cm (rarely up to 20cm) long by 2–6cm wide, ovate-lanceolate, acute, wedge-shaped at the base, shining green, somewhat wavy, evergreen. The flowers are fragrant and occur in few-flowered flat-topped cymes; the petals are white, lanceolate. The capsule is 1–1.2cm long, obovoid, glabrous, with 2 valves, orange when ripe. Flowering period: May–June. A native of SE. Australia widely cultivated for ornament in S. and W. Europe, becoming extensively naturalized in the Atlantic islands and locally elsewhere.

Flowering shoot

Habit

Fruit

PLANE TREE FAMILY PLATANACEAE

Platanus L.
Plane Trees

Large, very long-lived deciduous trees with scaling bark. The leaves are alternate with thick petioles. The flowers are unisexual catkins arranged on the same tree in dense globose heads.

Platanus orientalis L.
Oriental Plane

A broad, irregularly domed tree up to 30m. The lower branches are often drooping, the lower limbs sometimes resting on the ground. The trunk is often covered with large burrs; the bark is fairly smooth and generally pale brown but flaking and scaling to reveal round yellow patches. The young shoots are yellow-brown, hairy, but becoming darker with age; the older twigs are grey or reddish-brown. The leaves are up to 18 x 18cm, with 5–7 lobes, palmate, yellow-green, with deep, acute sinuses; the lobes are rather narrow and coarsely toothed, the central lobe longer than the rest; the petiole is up to 5cm long, the red base swollen and enclosing the young buds; the male inflorescences are 5–6cm long with 2–7 globose yellowish heads of flowers; the female inflorescences are 6–8cm long with 2–6 flattened

Leaf

Fruiting heads

Bark

Habit

globose, dark red heads of flowers. The fruiting catkins grow to 15cm long with heads up to 3cm in diameter, comprised of many 1-seeded carpels surrounded at the base with long spiny hairs. Flowering period: April–June. W. Asia to the Balkan Peninsula, It is widely planted in parks and gardens elsewhere. Al Bu Cr FY Gr.

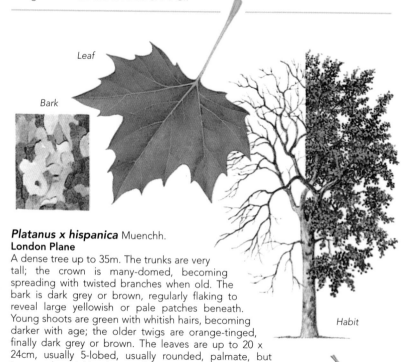

Leaf

Bark

Habit

Platanus x hispanica Muenchh.
London Plane

A dense tree up to 35m. The trunks are very tall; the crown is many-domed, becoming spreading with twisted branches when old. The bark is dark grey or brown, regularly flaking to reveal large yellowish or pale patches beneath. Young shoots are green with whitish hairs, becoming darker with age; the older twigs are orange-tinged, finally dark grey or brown. The leaves are up to 20 x 24cm, usually 5-lobed, usually rounded, palmate, but immensely variable, shiny and smooth except for the woolly veins above, paler below; the sinuses are generally shallow but very variable, cutting one-third to half the length of the blade; the lobes are somewhat triangular with up to 5 for-ward-pointing teeth on each side. The catkins are 2–8cm long; the male flowers are borne on 2–6 yellowish globose heads; the female flowers are borne on 2–5 crimson globose heads. The fruiting heads are brown; the seeds, shed in great abundance in the spring, are cylindrical and surround-ed with whitish hairs. One of the most vigorous-growing trees in almost any environment, due to the shedding bark and shiny short-lived leaves; this makes the London Plane one of the commonest street trees, planted throughout Britain and Europe since the 17th century. Its origins are obscure. It is considered by many writers to be either a hybrid between the **Western Plane** *P. occidentalis* from N. America and the Oriental Plane *P. orientalis*, or simply a cultivar of *P. orientalis*.

Male catkins

Female catkins

157

ROSE FAMILY ROSACEAE

One of the largest families of flowering plants, with some 2000 species of herbs, shrubs and trees.

Cydonia oblonga
Miller
Quince
A small tree 1.5–7.5m high. The shoots are woolly when young but become glabrous at maturity. The leaves are 5–10cm long with entire margins, green-glabrous above, grey-woolly below. The flowers are borne singly in the axils of the leaves, 3.8–5cm in diameter and distinctly bowl-shaped; the sepals are toothed; the petals are usually pink but sometimes white, longer than the sepals; the anthers number 15–25; the female part consists of 5 free styles, and 5-carpellate ovaries with thick, cartilaginous walls at maturity and numerous seeds in each carpel. The fruit is 2.5–3.5cm long, pear–shaped or globose, greenish when young, yellow, woody and sweet-smelling when mature. Flowering period: May. Plants cultivated for eating in much of C. and S. Europe have much larger fruits (5–12cm long) than NW. European plants. A species which originates in SW. and C. Asia, the Quince has become naturalized in hedges and copses in much of Europe but mainly in the Mediter-ranean countries. Al Au Bu Co FC FS FY Ge Gr Hu It Ne Ro Sa Si Sp Tu.

Mature fruit

Flowering twig

Habit

Pyrus L.
Pears

Small to medium-sized deciduous trees and shrubs, usually with spiny lower and young branches. The leaves are alternate, simple or occasionally lobed, the margin toothed or entire, the stipules falling early. The flowers are borne in flat-topped clusters; the petals are distinct, larger than the sepals, tapered at the base, and white or pinkish in colour; there are 15–30 anthers which are conspicuously red or reddish-purple, the outer ones maturing before the inner; the female part consists of 2–5 free styles, with the carpels joined together in groups of 2–5, their walls becoming leathery at maturity and each carpel containing 2 seeds. The fruit is a characteristic pome and may be pear-shaped, top-shaped or globose, the flesh invariably containing stone-cells, giving a gritty texture. The flowering period for most species is April–May.

Pyrus salicifolia
Pallas
Willow-leaved Pear

A small-domed slender tree about 10m high. The main branches are more or less horizontal and the twigs pendulous and densely white-woolly, especially when young. The leaves are 3.5–9cm long, narrowly lanceolate, distinctly pointed, the margins entire, somewhat grey in colour with silvery down on both sides at first, but later becoming glossy green above; the petiole is about 1cm long or less. The flowers are about 2cm in diameter, often opening simultaneously with the leaves; the calyx is persistent, the sepals woolly; the petals are entire or sometimes notched, white; the styles are villous at the base. The fruit is 2.5–3cm long, pear-shaped, top-shaped or cylindrical, brown when mature; the pedicel is white-woolly. A native of the Caucasus, Persia and Siberia, Willow-leaved Pear is cultivated in Europe. A weeping form, cv. '*Pendula*', is the most commonly planted ornamental pear, frequent in parks and gardens.

Fruiting twig

Flower

Flowering twig

Habit

Pyrus cordata
Desf.

A small slender tree or shrub up to 8m high. The branches are usually spreading or at right-angles and usually spiny; the twigs are purplish and more or less glabrous. The leaves are 2.5–5.5cm (rarely as little as 1cm) long, more or less ovate or sometimes heart-shaped, with a toothed margin, and densely hairy when young; the petiole is 2.5cm long. The flowers open with the leaves, The calyx is deciduous, the sepals 2–3 x 1–1.5mm; the petals are 6–8 x 5–7mm, white. The fruit is 0.8–1.8cm long, more or less pear–shaped, red and shiny when mature, covered with brown lenticels; the pedicel is slender: An uncommon, sometimes rare species of woods and hedgerows. Fr GB Pl Sp

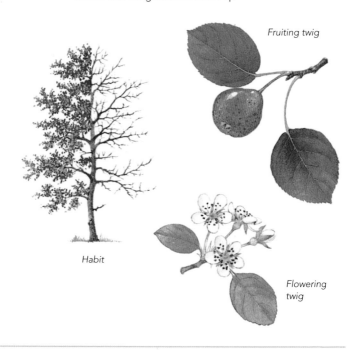

Fruiting twig

Habit

Flowering twig

Pyrus pyraster
Burgsd.

A medium-sized round tree 8–20m high. The branches may be ascending or spreading and are usually spiny; the twigs are grey or brown, glabrous. The leaves are 2.5–7cm long, elliptic to orbicular in outline but sometimes heart-shaped; the margin is toothed, sometimes with the teeth confined to the apex, or absent; glabrous when mature; the petiole is 2–7cm long. The flowers appear with the leaves; the calyx is persistent, the sepals 3–8 x 1–3.5mm; the petals are 1–1.7 x

0.7–1.3cm, pure white. The fruit is 1.3–3.5 x 1.8–3.5cm, top-shaped or globose, yellowish-brown or black, covered with lenticels; the pedicel is slender. This species is sometimes difficult to identify because it consists of a number of variants of wild and naturalized European pears. The trees are usually solitary and grow in thickets and open woods. Al Au Be Bu De FC Fr FS GB Ge Gr Hu It Pl Ro Si Sp Sz.

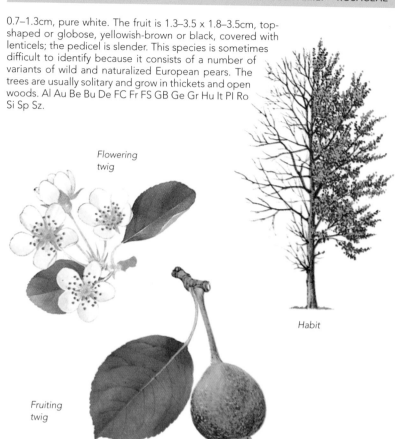

Flowering twig

Habit

Fruiting twig

Pyrus bourgaeana
Decne

A small tree up to 10m high, The lower branches are spiny; the twigs are grey, glabrous and slightly shiny. The leaves are 2–4cm long, usually ovate, sometimes almost heart-shaped, the margins toothed, hairy when young, glabrous or papillose on the lower surface when mature. The flowers appear with the leaves. The calyx is persistent, the sepals 5–7 x 2–2.5mm, the apex with a small point; the petals are 0.8–1 x 0.5–0.7cm, white. The fruit is 1.7–2.5cm in diameter, top-shaped to globose, dull yellow to almost brown when ripe; the pedicel is thick. An uncommon species, usually found near running water. Pl Sp.

Fruiting twig

Pyrus elaeagrifolia
Pallas

A small slender tree or sometimes a shrub. The branches are spreading and often spiny; the twigs are covered with grey hairs. The leaves are 3.5–8cm long, more or less lanceolate, toothed at the apex or entire, with dense grey-white wool; the petiole is 1–1.5cm long. The almost sessile flower clusters appear with the leaves. The calyx is persistent, the sepals 5 x 1.5mm; the petals are 1 x 0.7cm, white; the styles are densely hairy below the middle. The fruit is *c.* 1.3cm long, pear-shaped to globose, green; the pedicel is thick. An isolated tree of dry places. Al Bu FS Gr Ro Tu.

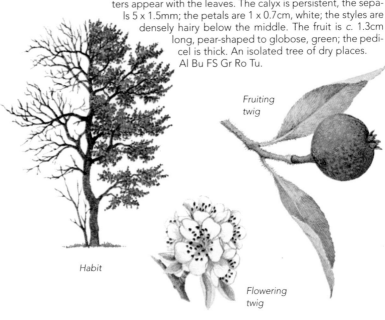

Fruiting twig

Habit

Flowering twig

Pyrus salvifolia
DC.

Sage-leaved Pear or **Aurelian Pear**

A small tree up to 10m high. The branches are thick, somewhat spreading and usually spiny; the twigs are grey, hairy when young, becoming dark brown to black and slightly hairy when mature, The leaves are 4–7cm long, lanceolate to elliptic, with entire margins, becoming glabrous above, grey-woolly beneath; the petiole is 2–5cm long. The clusters of flowers appear with the leaves. The calyx is persistent; the petals are glabrous, white; the styles are more or less glabrous. The fruit is 6–8cm long, pear-shaped or top-shaped, usually woolly when young, yellowish, bitter-tasting; the pedicel is long and woolly. *P. salvifolia* is a very variable species and is thought by some authors to be a hybrid between *P. nivalis* and

Fruiting twig

P. communis. It is often cultivated, the fruit being used in the brewing industry to make perry. It occurs as an isolated tree on sunny, grassy slopes and in dry woods and may be naturalized in parts of Europe. Au Be Fr FS FY Gr Hu Po Ro.

Pyrus amygdaliformis
Vill.
Almond-leaved Pear
A small slender tree or dense shrub up to 6m high. The branches are spreading, sometimes spiny; the twigs are dull grey and slightly woolly when young. The leaves are 2.5–8cm long, of variable shape but usually lanceolate to obovate, sometimes 3-lobed, with a shallowly toothed or entire margin, downy when young, becoming glabrous and shiny above and papillose beneath when mature; the petiole is 2–5cm long. The flower clusters appear with, or slightly before, the leaves. The calyx is persistent, the sepals 5–6 x 1.5mm, white and hairy; the petals are 7–8 x 5–6mm, usually notched, white. The fruit is 1.5–3cm in diameter, globose, yellowish-brown or tawny when mature; the pedicel is thick, about the same length as the fruit. A plant of dry and rough places, appearing as isolated trees. Al Bu Co Cr Fr FY Gr It Sa Si Sp.

Fruiting twig

Flowering twig

Habit

Pyrus nivalis
Jacq.

A medium-sized stout tree 8–20m high. The branches are ascending and usually without spines; the twigs are stout, densely woolly when young, becoming glabrous and darker later. The leaves are 5–9cm long, obovate, the edges of the blade decurrent, running down the petiole, entire or with slightly toothed margins at the apex, sparsely hairy above, but densely greyish and woolly below; the petiole is 1–2cm long, woolly. The flowers open when the leaves are young. The calyx is persistent, the sepals 6–8 x 3–4mm; the petals are 1.4–1.6 x 1.2–1.4cm, white; the styles are hairy at the base. The fruit is 3–5cm long, subglobose to globose, greenish-yellow, spotted with purple dots, the flesh sweet when over-ripe; the pedicel is long. Narrow-leaved varieties with smaller fruits may be found which tend to cause some confusion with the commonly cultivated pear *P. communis*. Grows in sunny places and dry open woods. Au Bu FC Fr FY Hu It Ro Sz.

Fruiting twig

Habit

Flowering twig

Pyrus austriaca
Kerner

A medium-sized to largish tree up to 20m. The branches are stout, somewhat erect, black and without spines; the twigs are thick and black but covered with grey wool when young. The leaves are 6–9cm long, more or less lanceolate, the margin toothed towards the apex, becoming glabrous above but with yellowish-grey wool beneath. The flowers appear with the leaves. The calyx is persistent; the sepals are 5–7 x 3–4mm; the petals are 1.2–1.5 x 1.1–1.3cm, white; the styles are more or less glabrous. The fruit is 2.5–5.5cm long, pear-shaped or top-shaped, greenish-brown when mature; the pedicel is slender. A species of open places, frequently cultivated and may be naturalized in some countries. Au FC FS Hu Sz.

Fruiting twig

164

Pyrus communis L.
Common Pear

A medium to tall tree up to 20m high. The branches are ascending when young, later spreading, and may be spiny; the twigs are reddish-brown, sometimes slightly hairy but soon becoming smooth and shiny. The leaves are 5–8cm long, variable in shape but usually ovate to elliptic, the margins finely toothed, sometimes hairy when young but glabrous and glossy green when mature; the petiole is 2–5cm long. The flowers open before the leaves have fully emerged. The calyx is persistent, the sepals 6–8 x 3–4mm; the petals are 1.2–1.4 x 1–1.2cm, white. The fruit is 4–12cm long, pear-shaped, top-shaped or globose, usually brown, with sweet-tasting flesh; the pedicel is slender. The garden pear, *P. communis* var. *culta*, of which more than a thousand cultivars are known, is probably a hybrid. Many species are thought to be possible parents, including *P. pyraster, P. salvifolia, P. nivalis* and *P. austriaca. P. communis* is a tree of W. Asian origin, now cultivated in orchards throughout most of Europe except the extremely cold northern and dry southern regions. Its cultivated habit is extremely variable and it may be grown in orchards as a standard or half-standard tree or as a cordon. Isolated trees may occur as escapes in hedgerows and woods.

Flowering twig

Fruiting twig

Habit

Malus L.
Apples

A genus of some 25–30 species of north temperate trees and shrubs, with many cultivars and hybrids raised for both fruit and ornament. The genus is separated from *Pyrus*, its nearest relative, by the styles being united at the base rather than free as in *Pyrus*.

Malus florentina (Zuccagni)
C. K. Schneider

A small unarmed tree up to 4m high. The leaves are 3–6cm long, broadly oval or or ovate, truncate or heart-shaped at the base, irregularly sharply lobed with several lobes on each side, dark green above, white-tomentose beneath; the petiole is 0.5–2cm long. The flowers are 1.5–2cm in diameter, white; the sepals are 3–4mm long, deciduous. The fruit is *c*. 1cm in diameter, ellipsoid or obovoid, red, with stone cells. A localized native of the S. Balkan Peninsula. Al FY Gr It.

Malus sylvestris
Miller
Crab Apple

A small tree or shrub up to 10m high with unarmed or, more rarely, thorny branches. The bark is brown and fissured, breaking up into small plates. The leaves are 3–11 x 2.5–5.5cm, ovate to elliptic or suborbicular, broadly wedge-shaped to rounded at the base, acuminate at the apex, crenate or serrate, glabrous when mature: the

Flowers

Habit

Leafy twig with fruit

petiole is 1.5–3cm long. The flowers are white, flushed with pink, 3–4cm in diameter; the calyx-tube and peduncles are glabrous or nearly so; the styles are glabrous or sparsely villous at the base. The fruits are 2.5–3cm in diameter, yellowish-green flushed with red, hard, sour-tasting, subglabrous. Flowering period: late May. A native of much of Europe, but rather localized on the mountains in the south. It is of little horticultural importance except as one of the parents in the hybrid orchard apple. All except Az Bl Cr Fi Ic Sa.

Malus dasyphylla

Borkh.

A small or medium-sized, sparsely spiny tree. The twigs are initially tomentose, later becoming glabrous. The leaves are 3.5–11 x 2.5–5cm, elliptical, crenate, acuminate at the apex, tomentose below; the petiole is 1.5cm long. The flower are are white, *c.* 4cm in diameter, the styles are glabrous. The fruit is *c.* 4cm in diameter, yellowish and occasionally red along one side, sour-tasting; the pedicel is 1–5cm but usually 2.5cm long. Flowering period: May. A native of damp lowland woods along the Danube basin and the northern part of the Balkan Peninsula. Al Au Bu FY Gr Hu Ro.

Flowers

Habit

Leafy twig with fruit

Malus domestica
Borkh.
Cultivated Apple

A small or medium-sized unarmed tree up to 15m tall. The young stems are covered with woolly down. The leaves are 4–13 x 3–7cm, elliptic-ovate, usually rounded at the base, the margins serrate, slightly tomentose above, densely woolly below. The flowers are usually white or pink-tinged, tomentose on the pedicel, calyx tube and on the outside of the calyx. The fruit (apple) is large, invariably more than 5cm in diameter, indented at base, varying in colour, sweet or sour, usually longer than the pedicel. Flowering period: May–June. The apple is of undoubted hybrid origin, probably derived from *M. sylvestris*, *M. dasyphylla*, **M. praecox** (Pallas) Borkh. and an Asiatic species. More than a thousand cultivars have been described and are currently grown for their fruit throughout Europe, often escaping and occasionally becoming naturalized.

flower

Habit

Bramley's Seedling

James Grieve

Cox's Orange Pippin

In addition to edible fruit cultivars there are several species and many hybrids cultivated for their ornamental flowers. The following are some of the most important in Europe:

Malus x magdeburgensis
Schoch
Magdeburg Apple

A hybrid of **M. spectabilis x pumila** Miller. A free-flowering cultivar with pale green leaves and large pink, semi-double flowers. Flowering period: May.

Leafy twig

Malus spectabilis (Aiton) Borkh.
Chinese Crab Apple
A large Chinese tree species up to 12m tall, with twisting, pendent branches and large globose flower buds opening into pink or pale pink semi-double flowers up to 5.5cm in diameter. Flowering period: May.

Malus baccata L. Borkh.
Siberian Crab Apple
A Chinese species with slender leaves; inflorescence crowded with small white flowers; abundant fruit initially green but becoming bright red and persisting on the tree until late spring. Flowering period: April–May.

Malus hupehensis (Pamp.) Rehder
Hupeh Crab Apple
Another Chinese species, similar to *M. baccata* but with spreading flowers, pink buds, cupped flowers and overlapping petals.

Malus x purpurea (Barbier) Rehder
Purple Crab Apple
A garden hybrid, widely planted as a street tree, in parks and small gardens. The buds are deep red; flowers dark pink or purplish, up to 4 cm, opening in April–May; a prolific crop of small red or purplish apples is produced in late summer.

Malus halliana Koehne
Hall's Crab Apple
Another Chinese species. The leaves are dark green; margins and petioles red. The buds are dark pink, opening into petals with paler inner surfaces. The fruits are globose, *c.* 5mm in diameter, crimson.

Flowers

Malus x floribunda
Siebold ex Van Houtte
A Japanese hybrid with an amazing spring profusion of large flowers up to 3cm in diameter, with deep pink buds and flowers paler pink, eventually forming yellow fruits up to 2.5cm in diameter.

Fruit

Habit

169

Sorbus L.
Whitebeams, Rowans and Service Trees

Deciduous trees. The leaves are simple, lobed or pinnately divided. The flowers are in clusters; the petals are white, occasionally pink; there are 15–25 stamens; there are 2–5 carpels, thin-walled in fruit each containing 2 ovules. Although the widespread species are regular outbreeding trees (eg. *S. domestica, S. torminalis, S. aria*) several local species are apomicts, capable of setting seed without fertilization. Also some species, eg. *S. torminalis* and *S. aria*, frequently hybridize, creating variable hybrid populations. Problems of hybridity and variation between local populations make *Sorbus* species difficult to identify in the field. Some of the more widespread and easily recognizable species are described below.

Sorbus domestica L.
True Service Tree

A medium-sized tree up to 20m high with a domed crown. The bark has many small fissures, ultimately shredding, variously shaded orange and brown. The branches are spreading or horizontal; the young twigs are green with silky hairs, becoming glabrous later. The buds are about 1cm long, ovoid, bright, glossy green. The leaves are pinnate, the leaflets in 6–10 pairs; each 3–6cm long, oblong, the margins sharply and doubly toothed towards the apex, hairy beneath when young, becoming glabrous. The flowers are 1.5–1.8cm in diameter, white or creamy. The fruit is 2–3cm long,

Fruit

Flower

Leaf

Habit

more or less ovoid or pear-shaped, greenish or brownish-red, the flesh containing many stone cells. Flowering period: May. A native of S. Europe, N. Africa and W. Asia, often planted throughout Europe as an ornamental and for its fruit. It has become locally naturalized in C. Europe. Al Au Bu Co FC Fr FS FY Ge Gr Hu It Ro Sp Sz Tu.

Fruiting twig

Sorbus vilmorinii
C.K. Schneider
Vilmorin's Rowan
A native of China, with dark green leaves consisting of 9–12 pairs of leaflets; bears dark pink fruits which become whitish when ripe.

Sorbus commixta
Hedl.
Japanese Rowan
A native of Japan with leaves consisting of 6–7 pairs of leaflets, glossy green above, pale bluish-green below, turning dark purple in autumn and bearing reddish-orange fruits when ripe. Flowering period: May; fruits ripening August–September. Both this species and
S. vilmorinii are planted in parks
and gardens or occasionally
as street trees.

Leaf

Fruit

171

Sorbus aucuparia L.
Rowan, Mountain Ash

A small to medium-sized tree up to 20m high with a roughly ovoid, open crown. The bark is smooth or faintly ridged, grey or silvery. The branches are few and ascending; the twigs are greyish or purplish, hairy at first, becoming glabrous later. The buds are about 1.7cm long, narrowly ovoid, curved at the tip, dark purple, covered with dense greyish hairs, those on the outer scales appressed. The leaves are pinnate, the leaflets in 5–8 pairs; the leaflets are 3–6cm long, oblong, sharply toothed, hairy when young, becoming glabrous; the rachis is round in cross-section, becoming grooved between the leaflets. The flowers are 0.8–1cm in diameter, creamy-white; the pedicels are woolly, erect or nodding. The fruit is 6–9mm in diameter, subglobose or ovoid, bright red when ripe, the flesh with a few stone cells. Flowering period: May; fruit ripening in September. It occurs in much of Europe and is commonly planted as a street tree or garden ornamental. All except Bl Cr Fi Sa Tu.

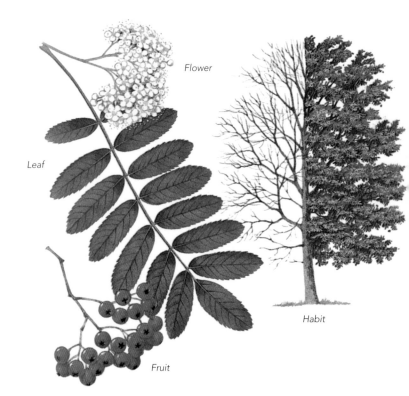

Flower

Leaf

Habit

Fruit

Sorbus hupehensis
C.K. Schneider
Hupeh Rowan

A small tree up to 14m high. The twigs are hairy, becoming glabrous. The buds are up to 1cm long, pointed, dark red. The somewhat pendent leaves are pinnate, the leaflets in 5–6 pairs; the leaflets are 3.5–7.5cm long, oblong, the margins sharply toothed on the outer half; the rachis is grooved, reddish. The flowers are about 0.8cm in diameter; white. The fruit is 6mm in diameter, globose, white or pink when ripe. Flowering period: May; fruit ripening in September. A native of W. China, the Hupeh Rowan is often planted in parks and gardens.

Fruit

Leaf

Sorbus sargentiana
Koehne
Sargent's Rowan

A bushy tree up to about 10m high. The branches are stout, the twigs are dark brown. The buds are up to 1.5cm long, ovoid, dark red, glossy, resiniferous. The leaves are pinnate with leaflets in 4–5 pairs; the leaflets are up to 5cm long, oblong-lanceolate, sharply toothed, softly hairy beneath. The flowers are about 6mm in diameter, white. The fruits are 6mm in diameter, numerous, bright red. Flowering period: June. A W. Chinese species often planted for its colourful autumn foliage. For vigorous growth it is often grafted on to stocks of Mountain Ash.

Leaf

Fruit

173

Sorbus torminalis (L.)
Crantz
Wild Service Tree

A medium-sized spreading or domed tree up to 25m high. The bark is finely fissured, brown or greyish; the twigs are shiny dark brown. The buds are about 5mm long, globose, shiny green. The leaves are simple, 5–10cm long, with 3–5 pairs of triangular-ovate to lanceolate lobes, the margins sharply toothed, dark green on both surfaces, hairy below when young, becoming glabrous later; the petiole is yellowish-green, becoming reddish in autumn. The flowers are 1–1.5cm in diameter, white; the pedicels are woolly. The fruit is 1.2–1.8cm in diameter, usually widest above the middle, brown, covered with numerous lenticels. Flowering period: May–June; fruits ripening in September. A native of much of Europe, occasionally planted in gardens. Al Au Be Bu De FC Fr FS FY GB Ge Gr Hu It Ne Po Pl Sa Si Sp Sz Tu.

Flowering twig

Fruit

Habit

Fruit

Sorbus aria L.
Crantz
Whitebeam

A medium-sized tree up to 25m high, or occasionally a shrub, with a domed or spreading crown. The bark is smooth, sometimes ridged, grey. The branches are divergent; the twigs are brown above, green below, hairy at first, becoming glabrous. The buds are 2cm long, ovoid, green, the tip with white hairs. The leaves are simple, 5–12cm long, ovate or elliptical, rounded at the base, the margins shallowly lobed or shallowly and irregularly toothed, the outer edge of each tooth curved towards the apex, with 10–14 pairs of veins, densely hairy, becoming glabrous above, remaining white or greenish-woolly beneath. The flowers are 1–1.5cm in diameter, white. The fruits are 0.8–1.5cm long, more or less ovoid, bright red when ripe, with numerous small lenticels. Flowering period: May–June; fruits ripening in September. It is found throughout much of Europe but the southern limits of its distribution are unclear because of confusion with other species. It is often found in gardens and two cultivars are commonly used as street trees: cv. '*Decaisneana*' has larger leaves than normal *S. aria* and yellow pedicels with white-flecked fruits; cv. '*Lutescens*' has purple twigs and silvery leaves which are smaller than those of *S. aria*. Al Au Be Bl Bu Co FC Fr FS FY GB Hu Ir It Po Ro Sa Si Sp Sz.

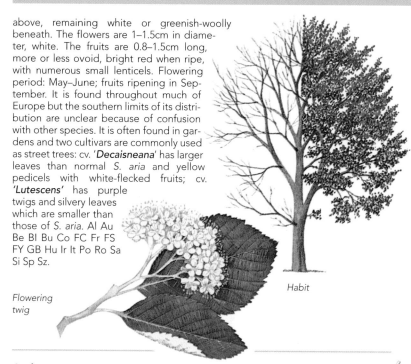

Flowering twig

Habit

Sorbus graeca (Spach) Hedl.

A small tree or sometimes a shrub. The leaves are simple, 5–9cm long, suborbicular or widest above the middle, not lobed, sharply double-toothed, the teeth even and spreading, with 9–11 pairs of veins, rather leathery with thick greenish-white wool beneath. The fruit is up to 1.2cm in diameter, more or less globose, red with large lenticels. It is frequently confused with a number of closely related and very similar species throughout Europe. Al Au Bu Cr FC FS FY Ge Gr Hu It Ro Si.

Leaf

Sorbus rupicola (Syme) Hedl.

A small tree or a shrub. The leaves are simple, 8–14.5cm long, more or less ovate or widest above the middle, not lobed, with sharp, coarse and unequal teeth which are curved on the outer margin and pointed towards the apex, with 7–9 pairs of veins, densely white-woolly beneath. The fruit is 1.2–1.5cm in diameter, more or less globose, bright red with numerous lenticels. Flowering period: May–June; fruits ripening in September. Similar and closely related to *Sorbus graeca*. FS GB Ir No Sw.

Fruit

175

Leaf

Sorbus umbellata (Desf.)
Fritsch in A. Kerner
A small tree or sometimes a shrub. The leaves are 4–7cm long, simple, triangular, broadest above the middle or more or less round, with shallow lobes and coarse teeth towards the apex, the lobes extending up to halfway to the midrib, with 4–7 pairs of veins, densely white-woolly beneath. The flowers are about 1.5cm in diameter, white. The fruit is 1–5cm in diameter, globose, yellowish. Al Bu FS FY Gr Ro Si.

Fruit

Sorbus mougeotii
Soyer-Willemet & Godron

Leaf

A tree up to 20m high or sometimes a shrub. The leaves are 7–10cm long, simple, ovate or widest about the middle, shallow-ly lobed, the large lobes cutting one-quarter of the way to the midrib, more or less smooth above, white or grey, woolly beneath. The flowers are about 1cm in diameter, white. The fruit is about 1cm in diameter, more or less globose or slightly longer than wide, red with a few small lenticels. Flowering period: May; fruits ripening in September. A species of the Alps and Pyrenees, thought to have originated as a hybrid between S. aucuparia and S. graeca. Au Ge It Sp Sw.

Fruit

Sorbus austriaca (G. Beck)
Hedl.
A small tree. The leaves are 8–13cm long, simple, broadly ovate or somewhat elliptical with shallow lobes, the larger lobes extending about one-third of the way to the midrib, the lobes sometimes overlapping, with 8–11 pairs of veins, greyish to white, hairy beneath. The fruit is up to 1.3cm in diameter, more or less globose, red and covered with many large lenticels. A tree of hilly and mountainous regions; there are 4 subspecies but only subsp. *austriaca* is wide-spread in the mountains of Europe. Au Bu FC FS FY Hu Ro.

Fruit

Leaf

Sorbus intermedia (Ehrh.)
Pers.
Swedish Whitebeam

A medium-sized tree up to 15m high. The bole is short, the crown broadly domed. The bark is smooth with shallow and often wide fissures, greyish. The twigs are densely hairy when young, becoming glabrous. The buds are 8mm long, ovoid, green or reddish-brown, covered with grey hairs. The leaves are 0.8–1.2cm long simple, elliptic, lobed below the middle, the lobes cut up to one-third of the way to the midrib, the lobes of vigorous shoots often more pronounced, toothed above the middle, green above, with yellowish-grey wool beneath. The flowers are 1.2–2cm in diameter, white. The fruit is 1.2–1.5cm long, oblong-ovoid, bright scarlet when ripe with few lenticels; the pedicels are glabrous, greenish-brown. Flowering period: May; fruits ripen in September. A N. European species, Swedish Whitebeam is commonly planted as a street tree and as an ornamental in parks and occasionally in gardens. De FC Fi FS Ge No Po Sw.

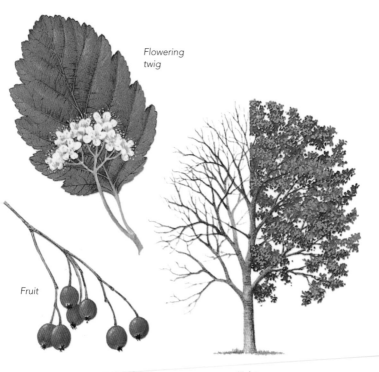

Flowering twig

Fruit

Habit

Sorbus latifolia (Lam.) Pers.
Service Tree of Fontainebleau

A medium-sized tree up to 18m high. The twigs are reddish-brown, hairy when young, becoming glabrous and shiny. The buds are 8mm long, ovoid, pale brown. The leaves are 5–10cm long, simple, broadly elliptical, with 7–9 pairs of veins, more or less triangular lobes, the lobes rounded at the lower edge, unevenly or doubly toothed, hairy, becoming glabrous above, remaining greyish-hairy below. The flowers are about 2cm in diameter, white; the pedicels are woolly. The fruit is 1.2–1.5cm in diameter, more or less globose, yellowish-brown with many large lenticels. Flowering period: May; fruits ripening in September. *S. latifolia* and a number of allied species are now known to be apomictic (capable of setting seed without fertilization) and are thought to have originated as hybrids between *S. torminalis* and *S. aria*. A tree first discovered in the forests of Fontainebleau, now frequently found in C. and W. Europe. Fr Ge Pi Sp Sw.

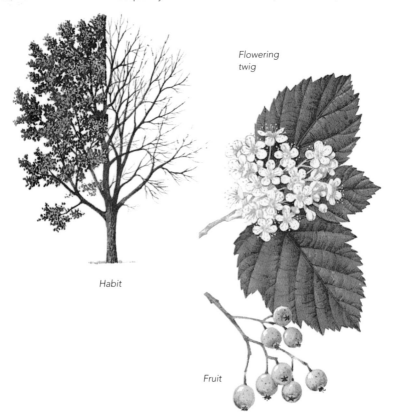

Flowering twig

Habit

Fruit

Sorbus hybrida L.
Bastard Service Tree

A medium-sized tree up to 14m high with a dense ovoid crown. The bark is slightly cracked, grey. The twigs are pinkish, darker towards the tips. The buds are 8mm long with few scales, reddish-brown. The leaves are 7.5–10.5cm long, pinnate with 1–4 (usually 2) pairs of free sessile leaflets towards the base; the remaining portion of the leaf is lobed, the lowest lobes usually cut to the midrib; the margins of the leaflets are toothed towards the tip; somewhat leathery, grey-green above, densely white-woolly beneath. The flowers are about 1cm in diameter, white. The fruit is 1–1.2cm in diameter. globose, bright red with small lentices. Flowering Period: May; fruits ripening in September. Cv. **'Fastigiata'** has erect close branches and is often planted in restricted spaces. Woodlands of S. and W. Scandinavia. De Fi No Sw.

Leaf

Fruit

Habit

Sorbus meinchii (Lindeb.)
Hedl.

A small tree similar to *S. hybrida*. The leaves have 4–5 pairs of free sessile leaflets towards the base, the remaining portion of the leaf being a large lobed terminal leaflet, more or less glabrous above, greyish-hairy beneath. The fruit is up to 1.2cm in diameter, more or less globose, sometimes slightly longer than wide, red. A species confined to Norway.

Leaf

Fruit

179

Eriobotrya japonica (Thunb.) Lindley
Loquat

Small evergreen tree or sometimes a shrub, up to 10m high. The twigs are hairy. The leaves are 10–25cm long, broadest above the middle or more or less elliptic, the margins toothed, conspicuously veined, dark green, leathery, glossy above with dense reddish-brown or greyish hair beneath. The inflorescence is a terminal raceme, tightly branched, covered with dense reddish-brown hair. The flowers are about 1cm in diameter, fragrant; the calyx is persistent in fruit; the petals are ovate to almost orbicular, tapering to a point at the base, usually white but often obscured by dense brown hairs; the stamens number 20; the carpels number 2–5, are thin-walled in fruit, each containing 2 ovules; the styles are joined only at the base. The fruit is 3–6cm long, rounded or elliptical, yellow, fleshy and sweet-tasting. The seeds number one to several. A native of China, the Loquat is cultivated in S. Europe as an orchard tree and sometimes for ornament. It has become naturalized in Cr It Pl Sp.

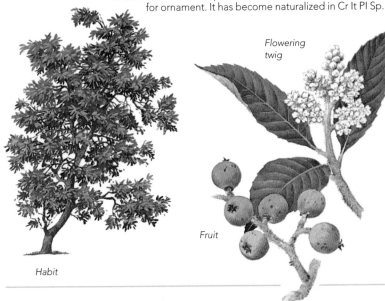

Flowering twig

Fruit

Habit

Amelanchier Medicus
Snowy Mespils

Small trees or shrubs. Branches lacking spines. Leaves alternate. Stipules falling early. The flowers are in terminal racemes, sometimes solitary. The calyx is persistent in fruit; the petals are white or pinkish; stamens number 10–20; carpels number 5, fused or partly free with cartilaginous walls in fruit, each containing 2 ovules. Fruit globose, usually juicy and sweet, edible.

Amelanchier ovalis
Medicus
Snowy Mespil
Usually a shrub but occasionally a tree, reaching 5m. The young twigs are woolly. The leaves are 2.5–5cm long, ovate, coarsely toothed with 3–5 teeth per centimetre, woolly beneath when young. The inflorescence is a raceme, erect and woolly, with 3–8 flowers; the styles are free. The fruit is blue-black. A plant of open woodland, mountains and rocky areas, usually growing on limestone. Al Au Be Bl Bu Co Cr FC Fr FS FY Ge Gr Hu It Pl Po Ro Sa Si Sp Sz Tu.

Young flowering twig

Fruit

Mature leaf

Amelanchier spicata (Lam.)
C. Koch
Similar to *A. ovalis*, being distinguished by the finely toothed leaves, fused styles and hairy apex of the ovary. A N. American species, it is frequently grown as an ornamental in N. Europe where it sometimes becomes naturalized. Fi Fr FS Ge No Sw.

Amelanchier grandiflora
Rehder
A small tree or shrub up to 9m high. The young twigs are hairy. The leaves are 3–7cm long, elliptical, finely toothed with 6–12 teeth per centimetre, purplish and woolly when young, becoming green and glabrous at maturity. The racemes are many-flowered, usually drooping and somewhat hairy. The petals are 1.5–1.8cm long, narrow; the pedicels are 2–2.2cm long. The fruit is dark purple. A species of garden origin, frequently cultivated as an ornamental and occasionally naturalized in W. Europe. Be Fr GB Ge Ne.

Habit

Mature leaf

Young flowering twig

Fruit

Amelanchier laevis
Weig.
Allegheny Serviceberry

Mature leaf

A small tree sometimes reaching 20m high, many-stemmed or with a single bole. The young twigs are nearly glabrous. The leaves are up to 8cm long, ovate, pointed at the apex, finely toothed, pinkish-purple and glabrous when young, becoming green. The racemes are many-flowered, drooping, glabrous. The petals are 1–1.8cm long, narrowly oblong; the pedicels are 3–8cm long. The fruit is 6mm long, more or less glabrous, purple-black when ripe. Thought to be a native of E. N. America, it is commonly grown in gardens for its rich red and gold autumn foliage. A. laevis has frequently been confused with A. canadensis.

Flowering twig with young leaves

Fruits

Habit

Amelanchier canadensis L.
Medicus
Very similar to A. spicata but with leaves more or less oblong and the apex of the ovary glabrous. A native of E. United States sometimes grown in gardens.

Cotoneaster frigidus
Wall.
Himalayan Tree Cotoneaster
A short to medium-sized tree up to 20m. The trunk is usually short or sometimes there are many stems spreading outwards; the arching branches form a broadly domed crown. The smooth young bark is pale greyish-brown. The leaves are 6–12 x 4–6cm, semi-evergreen, elliptical to obovate, with a wedge-shaped base, the upper surface dark green, the

lower surface densely white-hairy. The inflorescence is a dense cluster of white flowers up to 5cm in diameter; the stamens number 20; the styles 2–5. The fruit is about 5mm long, rounded with bright red flesh. A species of Himalayan origin widely planted in large gardens of NW. Europe. *Cotoneaster frigidus* is perhaps less common than its many shrubby relatives. It readily forms hybrids in cultivation with species such as the crinkly-leaved **C. salicifolius** Franchet.

Flowering twig

Fruits

Habit

Mespilus germanica L.
Medlar

A small tree up to 6m, or a spreading, rather tangled shrub. The bark is greyish-brown, becoming fissured between oblong plates. The young shoots are covered with dense white hairs. The leaves are 5–15cm long, broadly lanceolate to obovate, entire or minutely toothed, crinkled with distinct sunken veins, dull, yellowish-green and more or less glabrous on the upper surface, paler with dense white hairs underneath. The solitary flowers are 3–6cm in diameter; the sepals are 1–1.6cm long, longer than the petals and triangular-pointed, the petals are white; the stamens number 30–40 with red anthers. The fruit is 2.3cm long, having 5 carpels with strong walls, brown, somewhat globose with a depressed apex. A woodland species of SE. Europe which has become widely naturalized in C and W. Europe to SE. England. It is frequently cultivated for the fruit which when soft and over-mature becomes edible. Au Be Bu FC Fr FS FY GB Ge Gr It Ne Ro Sa Si Sp Sz.

Flowering twig

Fruit

Habit

Crataegus L.
Hawthorns

A widespread group of some 400 northern hemisphere species. Nearly all species can assume the shrubby habit, but several European natives are either true trees or can grow into a tree form. True tree species are widely used in horticulture.

Crataegus crus-galli L.
Cockspur Thorn

A small spreading tree up to 10m high with a low-domed, rather flattened crown and a short bole. The bark is grey or brown, that of young trees smooth, in mature trees finely fissured. The twigs are glabrous, purple-brown and carry numerous spines, 7–10cm long. The leaves are 5–8 x 2–3cm, 3 times as long as broad, widest above the middle, rounded at the tip, the margins sharply toothed, somewhat shiny dark green, turning orange in autumn, glabrous on both surfaces. The inflorescence is a loose cluster of few white flowers, each up to 1.5cm in diameter. Flowering period: May. Fruiting: late October, the fruits persisting on the twigs for some time. A species native to NE. America, frequently planted as a street tree or ornamental, particularly for its unique orange autumn foliage. Two hybrids with other American species, *C. x lavallei* Hérincq. the **Hybrid Cockspur Thorn**, with downy shoots and inflorescences and narrower leaves; and *C. x prunifolia* (Poir.) Pers., the **Broad-leaved Cockspur Thorn**, with glabrous, dark purple-brown twigs, shorter spines (1.5–2cm), villous inflorescences and broad leaves, are similarly cultivated for ornament.

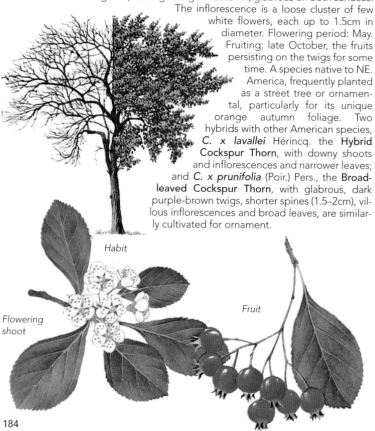

Habit

Flowering shoot

Fruit

Crataegus laevigata (Poiret)
DC.
Midland Hawthorn

A large shrub and more rarely a tree up to 10m high. The bark is divided into rectangular plates, with a grey surface layer cracking to reveal brown below. The occasional axillary spines are up to 1.1cm long. The leaves are 1.5–6cm long, about three-quarters as broad as long, with 3–5 shallow lobes or more or less entire, the sinuses reaching halfway to the midrib, the lobes somewhat rounded with distinct teeth down to the base, dark shining green, somewhat paler below; petiole is 0.6–2cm long. The inflorescences are few, lax corymbs with up to 9 flowers but often less; the flowers are 1.5–2.4cm in diameter, usually white; there are 2–3 styles. The fruit is 0.6–1.3cm long, more or less globose, deep red. Flowering period: May–June. Fruiting: August–October. A species most often found in shady places on moist clay soils, usually in woodlands and particularly oakwoods, although it can also occur on dry limestone slopes. It is much less common and grows in shadier places than *C. monogyna* with which it often forms hybrids. It also produces hybrids with *C. calycina* and its identity is therefore frequently confused. A widespread native of C. Europe but not found in extreme conditions. Au Be De FC Fr FS GB Hu Ne Po Ro Sw Sz.

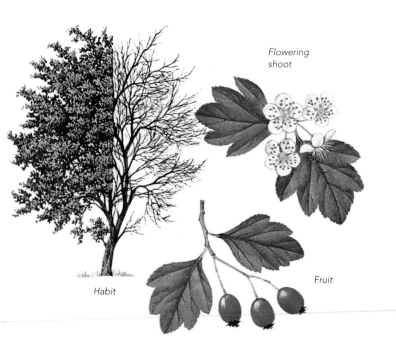

Flowering shoot

Habit

Fruit

Crataegus monogyna
Jacq.
Common Hawthorn or **Quickthorn**

A small tree or shrub up to 18m tall. The bole can be simple or much branched from the base, spreading out into a rather variable crown. The bark is usually cracked or fissured into a regular pattern, revealing an orange or pinkish layer beneath the silvery-grey surface layer. Axillary spines are common, up to 1.5cm long, some developing into short lateral branches terminating in spines. The leaves are 1.5–4.5cm long and up to one and a half times as long as broad, ovate, with 3–5 (rarely 9) lobes, the sinuses usually reaching more than halfway to the midrib, the lobes somewhat pointed with more or less entire margins or a few apical teeth, somewhat leathery, dark shining green above, dull and paler below, with tufts of white hairs in the axils of the veins; the petiole is 1–2cm long, dark pink. The inflorescence is a dense to lax corymb of 9–18 flowers; the flowers are white to pink, 0.8–1.5cm in diameter, usually in groups of 3; there is 1 style. The fruit is globose to ovate, bright red to maroon, 0.7–1.4cm long. Flowering period: March–June. Fruiting period: May–September. A very common native growing in hedgerows, scrub, thickets or woodlands in a variety of habitats but particularly on calcareous soils. It is found throughout Europe and invariably forms hybrids when growing with other species, particularly *C. nigra* and *C. pentagyna*. It is particularly difficult to identify when it forms hybrids with shrubby forms of the Balkan endemics **C. heldreichii** and *C. orientalis*. It is commonly planted as a park and street tree. All except Ic.

Habit

Fruit

Flowering shoot

Crataegus calycina
Peterm.

A shrub or small tree up to 11m with occasional axillary spines 4–11cm long, and rarely with short lateral branches terminating in spines. The bark is grey with a brown-red or purple under layer. The leaves are 2.5–6.5cm long, about as long as broad, oval, with 3–7 lobes; the lobes are acute, the sinuses extending about one-third of the way to the midrib, the basal lobe often cut and finely toothed more or less to the base, bicoloured, usually somewhat villous on the veins below, In the axils and on the petiole; the petiole is about half the length of the blade. The inflorescence is a lax, raceme-like, villous umbel of 4–9 flowers; the flowers are white, 1.2–2cm in diameter; there are 5 sepals and petals, *c.* 20 red anthers, and 1 style. The fruit is large, dark red, 0.9–1.5cm long, ellipsoid. Flowering period: May–June. Fruiting: June–September. A shade-tolerant species usually growing in deciduous woods but sometimes also in pine forests. It is more tolerant of extreme continental climates than *C. monogyna* which it replaces in N. and E. Europe. Al Au Be Bu De FC Fr FS FY Ge Gr Hu No Po Ro Sw Sz Tu.

Flowering shoot

Fruit

Habit

Crataegus pentagyna
Waldst. & Kit. ex Willd.

A small tree or shrub up to 8m high with graceful, arching upper branches. The bark is pale brown on the outside and yellow-brown below. There are occasional stout axillary spines c. 9mm long. The leaves are 2–5cm long and the same wide, broadly or narrowly ovate, laciniate, with 3–7 lobes, the lowest lobes sometimes widely spaced with acute open sinuses, leathery, olive-green above, paler below; the petiole is half to three-quarters the length of the blade. The inflorescence is a lax many-flowered cluster; the flowers are white; there are 5 sepals and petals, about 20 anthers and 3–5 styles. The fruit is globose or occasionally ovate, dull black or dark red-black, 0.7–1 x 0.6–1.1 cm. Flowering period: late May–June. A species of open places, in scrub or forest mainly in E. Europe and the Balkan Peninsula. Bu FS FY Hu Ro Tu.

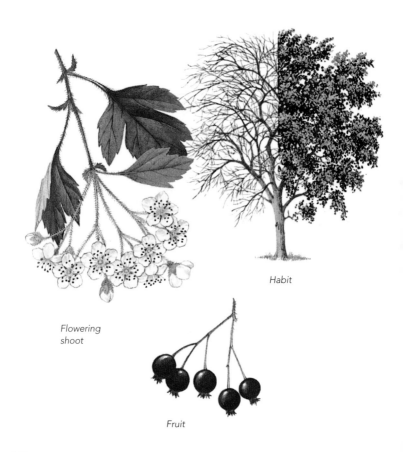

Habit

Flowering
shoot

Fruit

Crataegus nigra
Waldst. & Kit.

A small tree up to 6m high with occasional axillary spines 0.7–1cm long. The bark is ridged and purple-red. The leaves are 2.5–10cm long x 2–8cm wide, usually slightly longer than broad, ovate to lanceolate, with 5–11 lobes; the lobes are generally shallow, although the lowermost is frequently cut to the midrib, toothed, bicoloured, tomentose; the petiole is one-quarter to one-third as long as the blade. The inflorescence is a somewhat lax cluster of 10–20 flowers; the flowers are 1.2–1.7cm in diameter, white but often turning pink before falling; there are 5 sepals and petals, c. 20 anthers and 4–5 styles. The fruit is globose or occasionally ovoid, 0.8–1.3 x 0.9–1.1cm, black with green flesh. Flowering period: late April–early May. Fruiting: May–June. One of the rarer hawthorns, *C. nigra* is a species from the islands and banks of the river Danube and its tributaries, occurring in marshy open woodlands. Hu FY Ro.

Flowering shoot

Fruit

Habit

189

Crataegus orientalis
Pallas ex Bieb.
Oriental Thorn

A shrub or small tree up to 5m with strong lateral branches terminating in spines up to 1cm long. The bark is grey-brown, cracking to reveal a reddish-brown under layer. The young twigs are hairy. The leaves are 1.5–4cm long, ovate to triangular, usually slightly longer than broad, with 3–7 lobes, deeply divided with acute sinuses, sometimes slightly fan-shaped, the lobes narrow, dull green, tomentose on both surfaces; the petiole is short, up to 5mm long. The inflorescence is a compact corymb with up to 16 flowers; the flowers are 1.5–2cm in diameter, white; the sepals have a characteristic hooked tip; there are sometimes 3, usually 4–5 diverging styles. The fruit is flattened-globose, brick-red to yellow–orange, 1.5–2 x 0.6–1.2cm, usually broader than long. Flowering period: June; fruiting: August–September. A pioneer species from a variety of soils in scrub or degraded forest margins, especially towards mountain tops between 580 and 2000m. A Balkan species, frequently forming hybrids with less well-known Crimean shrubby endemics and other European species, particularly *C. monogyna* and *C. pentagyna*. Al Bu FS FY Gr.

Fruit

Flowering shoot

Habit

190

Crataegus azarolus L.
Azarole

A shrub or small tree up to 8m high with stout axillary spines up to 1cm long. The young branches are tomentose, later becoming glabrous. The leaves are up to 5cm long, ovate to triangular, usually narrower than long, laciniate, with 3–5 lobes; the lobes are forward-projecting, entire with rounded apices or dentate with a few large teeth; the leaf-base is cuneate and often decurrent on the short petiole which is *c.* 3–8mm long. The inflorescence is a compact corymb with 3–18 flowers; the flowers are 1.2–1.8cm in diameter; there are 2–3 styles. The fruit is globose, slightly flattened at the base and conspicuously angled longitudinally. Flowering period: March–April. Fruiting: June–September. A species of humid maquis and sometimes found in oak scrub on limestone. It is native to the E. Mediterranean region and SW. Asia, but as it has been cultivated in France and Italy since Roman times the natural European distribution is somewhat confused. Cr Fr FY GB It Si Sp.

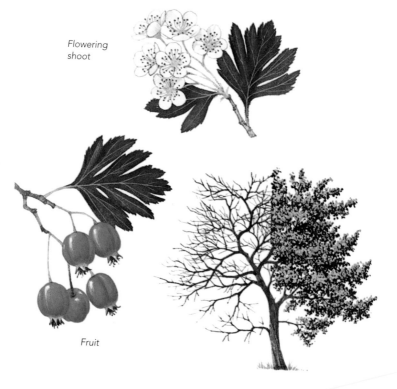

Flowering shoot

Fruit

Habit

Prunus L.
Cherries and **Plums**

Deciduous or evergreen trees or shrubs. Leaves alternate, simple with rounded or sharp teeth, petiolate; stipules free, narrow, more or less papery, usually failing early. The flowers are solitary or in clusters, corymbs or racemes of up to 100 flowers, pink or white; the 5 petals are joined with the lower part of the sepals to form a tube. The fruit usually has an outer fleshy layer and a single seed contained in the inner stony layer. A temperate genus of *c.* 200 species, of which many are cultivated for fruit and ornament. Natural hybrids are sometimes formed where the parent species grow together. Many artificial hybrids and cultivated varieties have been produced. Some species have been cultivated for so long that their wild origins are not definitely known.

Prunus persica L.
Batsch
Peach

A rounded, deciduous, bushy tree up to 6m high, but often trained against a wall or as an espalier in orchards. The bark is grey-brown, finely fissured. The branches are straight; the twigs are smooth, reddish, angular in cross-section. The leaves are 5–15 x 2–4cm, narrow, oblong-lanceolate to elliptical, long-pointed with small teeth along the margin, almost smooth; the petiole is *c.* 1.5cm long, glandular. The flowers are short-stalked, solitary or sometimes in pairs, appearing before the leaves fully develop; the flower tube is about as long as wide; the petals are 1–2cm long, usually deep pink, sometimes pale pink or white.

Habit

Leafy twig with fruit

Flowers

The fruit is 4–8cm long, globose, covered with a velvety down or rarely smooth, yellow or pale green flushed with red; the fleshy layer is succulent and sweet; the stone deeply grooved. Flowering period: March–May. The peach or nectarine of commerce, it has been cultivated for so long for its fruit that its natural origins are obscure. It is probably a native of China. It is grown as a field crop or in gardens and is occasionally naturalized in the south. Al Au Bu Co Cr FC Fr FS FY Ge Gr Hu It Pl Sa Si Sz Tu.

Prunus dulcis (Miller)
D.A. Webb
Almond

A small deciduous tree up to 8m, upright-branching when young but becoming broad and bushy. The bark is blackish and deeply cracked into small rectangles. The branches are spiny in wild trees, straight and without spines in cultivated trees; the twigs are usually smooth. The leaves are 4–13 x 1.2–4cm, oblong-lanceolate, long-pointed, the margins with small rounded teeth, smooth; the petiole is c. 2cm

Leafy twig with fruit

long, glandular. The flowers are very short-stalked, mostly produced in pairs before the leaves appear; the flower tube is broadly bell-shaped; the petals are 1.5–2.5cm long, bright pink or rarely white, fading to almost white. The fruit is 3.5–6cm long, oblong-ovoid, slightly flattened and covered with a velvety down, grey-green; the fleshy layer is rather leathery; the stone has a ridge around the margin, and fine pits. Flowering period: February–April. The Almond is a tree cultivated for its seeds and ornamental flowers. It is probably native to C. and SW. Asia and perhaps N. Africa. Al Au Bu Co Cr FC Fr FS FY Ge Gr Hu It Pl Ro Sa Si Sz Tu.

Flowers

Habit

Prunus armeniaca L.
Apricot

A deciduous shrub or a small, round-headed tree 3–10m high. The bark is greyish-brown and finely fissured. The branches are tortuous; the twigs are smooth and reddish. The leaves are 5–10 x 5–9cm, broad, ovate to almost circular, abruptly pointed, the margin with small sharp teeth, squarish or almost heart-shaped at the base; the petiole is 2–4cm long. The flowers are very short-stalked, solitary or in pairs, appearing before the leaves; the flower tube is broadly bell-shaped, hairy; the petals are 1–1.5cm long, white or pale pink. The fruit is 4–8cm long, almost globose, downy, reddish-orange or yellow, the fleshy layer acid becoming sweet, the stone lens-shaped and smooth with 3 narrow ridges along one edge. Flowering period: March–April. Widely cultivated as a field crop in S. Europe for its fruit, becoming naturalized in a few localities. It is native to C. Asia and China. Al Au Bu Co Cr FC Fr FS FY Ge Gr Hu It Pl Ro Sa Si Sp Sz Tu.

Flowers

Leafy twig with fruit

Habit

Prunus cerasifera
Ehrh.
Cherry Plum or Myrobalan

A deciduous shrub or round-headed tree up to 8m high. The bark is dark brown with rows of lenticels, becoming finely fissured. The branches are numerous, fine, sometimes spiny. The twigs are green, smooth and glossy. The leaves are 4–7 x 2–3.5cm, oblong-obovate, tapering at the base, the margins with regular rounded teeth, smooth and glossy above, the veins downy beneath; the petiole is *c.* 1cm long, grooved, pinkish. The flowers are mostly solitary, appearing with or slightly before the leaves; the pedicel is 0.5–1.5cm long, smooth; the flower tube is broadly bell-shaped; the petals are 0.8–1cm long, usually white. The fruit is 2–3.5cm long, globose, smooth, red or yellow, the fleshy layer becoming sweet; the stone is almost globose, with a thickened margin, smooth. Flowering period: March. The Cherry Plum is commonly cultivated for its fruit, which is used for cooking. *P. cerasifera* var. *pissardii* is very commonly planted in gardens and streets of suburban areas for its dark reddish leaves and pale or rosy-pink flowers. A native of the Balkan Peninsula and the Crimea but much planted elsewhere. Al Au Bu De Fr FS FY GB Ge Gr Hu It Ro Tu.

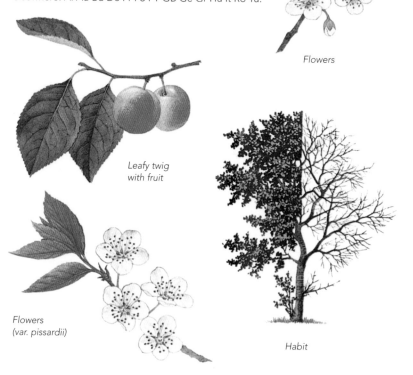

Flowers

Leafy twig with fruit

Flowers (var. pissardii)

Habit

Prunus brigantina
Vill. in L.
Rather smaller than *P. cerasifera* with spreading branches and larger, sharper teeth on the leaf margins. The flowers are in clusters of 2–5, appearing before the leaves; the petals are white. The fruit is *c.* 2.5cm long, almost globose, smooth, yellow. Native to the SW. Alps on dry slopes up to 1800m. Fr It.

Leaf

Prunus spinosa L.
Sloe or **Blackthorn**

A thickly-branched, deciduous shrub or small tree up to 6m, spreading by suckers. The bark is blackish-brown. The branches are numerous, spreading widely; the twigs are much branched, spiny, usually downy. The leaves are 2–4.5cm long, obovate to ovate, pointed at the tip, the margins with rounded pointed teeth, tapering at the base, dull green and smooth above, usually downy underneath the veins; the petiole is *c.* 1cm long. The flowers are mostly solitary, appearing before the leaves; the pedicel is *c.* 5mm long, smooth; the flower tube is broadly bell–shaped; the petals are 5–8mm long, white. The fruit is 1–1.5cm long , globose or slightly elongated, bluish-black with a blue-grey bloom on the surface; the fleshy layer is very acid and astringent; the stone smooth or slightly rough. Flowering period: March–April. A native of much of Europe except the extreme N. and NE. It is commonly found in hedges and thickets. The fruit is sometimes used for making jams and wines. It occasionally hybridizes with *P. domestica* subsp. *institia*, except Cr Ic.

Leafy twig with fruit

Flowers

Habit

Prunus domestica L.
Plum

A deciduous, suckering shrub or tree up to 10m high. The bark is dull brown. The branches are straight; the twigs are spiny in wild plants but usually without spines in cultivated plants, dull, usually downy. The leaves are 3–8 x 1.5–5cm, elliptical to obovate, the apex rather blunt to pointed, the margins with regular rounded teeth, smooth and dull green above, downy to almost smooth beneath; the petiole is *c.* 1.5cm long, glandular and downy. The flowers usually occur in clusters of 2–3, appearing with the leaves; the pedicel is 0.5–2cm long, the flower tube broadly bell-shaped; the petals are 0.7–1.2cm long, white. The fruit is 2–7.5cm long, globose to oblong, usually pendent, purple, red, yellow or green; the fleshy layer is sweet or acid but not astringent; the stone is rough, rather flattened, slightly pitted. Flowering period: March–May. Widely cultivated for its fruit as a field crop in all except the extreme N. and NE. of Europe. It is often naturalized in hedgerows. The **Bullace**, *P.* **domestica** subsp. *institia*, usually has spiny branches and dense down on the young twigs and pedicels, and globose fruits up to 5cm long. The Mirabelle group of plums, damsons and greengages all probably belong with this subspecies, All except Ic.

Flowers

Fruit
(subsp. *institia*)

Leafy twig
with fruit

Habit

Prunus cocomilia

Ten.

A tree or shrub rather smaller than *P. domestica* with leaves 2.5–4 x 1.2–2.5cm long, flowers borne on pedicels 2–4mm long with white petals *c.* 6mm long and the fruits 1.2–4cm long, oblong, yellow suffused with purplish-red. A native of the mountainous parts of S. Italy, Sicily and the S. Balkan Peninsula. Al FY Gr It Si.

Prunus avium L.
Gean

A deciduous broad-crowned tree up to 30m high with a well–developed bole. The bark is reddish-brown, shiny with horizontal rows of lenticels, peeling in papery strips or later becoming fissured. The branches are widely spreading; the young twigs are smooth, reddish above. The leaves are 8–15 x 4–7cm, ovate to oblong-obovate with a long tapering point, the margin with deep irregular forward-projecting teeth, smooth and dull above, persistently downy on the veins beneath; the petiole is 2–5cm long with

Flowers

2 conspicuous reddish glands near the blade. The flowers usually occur in clusters of 2–6, appearing just before the leaves; the pedicel is 2–5cm long; the flower tube is urn-shaped, constricted at the mouth; the petals are 0.9–1.5cm long, white. The fruit is 0.9–2cm long, globose with a depression at the apex, dark purple–red, rarely yellow or black; the fleshy layer is sweet or bitter; the stone is globose, smooth. Flowering period: April–May. Much of Europe except the extreme N. and E. and rather rare in the Mediterranean region. The Gean is the parental species of the sweet cherries which are widely cultivated for their fruit and often naturalized in Europe. All except Cr Fi Ic.

Habit

Bark

Leafy twig with fruits

Prunus cerasus L.
Sour Cherry

Usually a deciduous shrub, but sometimes a small rounded tree up to 8m tall with an ill-defined trunk, often suckering. The bark is reddish-brown. The branches are spreading, rather untidy; the twigs are smooth. The leaves are 3–8 x 1.7–5cm long, ovate to elliptical, abruptly pointed at the tip, the base broad and tapering, the margins with rounded, rather small teeth, smooth and glossy above, sometimes slightly downy beneath when young; the petiole is 1–3cm long with or without glands near the blade. The flowers occur in clusters of 2–6, appearing just before the leaves; the pedicel is 2–3.5cm long; the flower tube is broadly bell-shaped; the petals are 0.8–1.5cm long, white. The fruit is *c.* 1.8cm long, almost globose but slightly depressed above, bright red to blackish; the fleshy layer is soft and acid; the stone almost globose, smooth. Flowering period: April–May. A species cultivated for its fruit, the sour or Morello cherry, used mainly for preserving rather than as a dessert fruit. Double-flowered cultivars are planted for ornament. Native to SW. Asia but widely naturalized in Europe. Al Au Bu De FC Fi Fr FS FY GB Ge Gr Hu Ir It Ne No Pl Po Ro Sp Sw Sz.

Flowers

Leafy twig with fruits

Habit

Prunus sargentii
Rehder
Sargent's Cherry

A deciduous tree up to 25m high in the wild but usually smaller in cultivation. The bark is purplish-brown, rather glossy, with horizontal rows of lenticels. The branches are ascending, spreading at a wide angle; the twigs are slender, dark red, smooth. The leaves are 9–15 x 4–8cm long, oblong-elliptic to oblong-obovate with a long tapering point, the margins with sharply pointed teeth, smooth; the petiole is 2–4cm long, grooved, deep red, usually with 2 reddish glands near the blade. The flowers usually occur in clusters of 2–4, appearing slightly before the leaves; the pedicel is 1–2cm long, the flowertube is rather narrowly bell-shaped; the petals are 1.5–2cm long, rosy-pink. The fruit is 0.7–1.1cm long, ovoid, blackish-crimson, rarely appearing in cultivation. Flowering period: April. Sargent's Cherry is a native of N. Japan, where it never descends below 750m, and the Sakhalin Islands where it grows at much lower altitudes. The species is widely cultivated for ornament in gardens, parks or as a street tree in various European countries, and is often grafted on to a stock of *P. avium* to improve its performance. Hybrids with *P. subhirtella* and other cherries are occasionally grown.

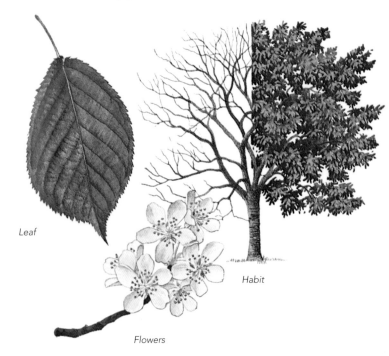

Leaf

Habit

Flowers

Prunus serrulata
Lindley
Japanese Cherry
A deciduous tree up to 15m though usually much smaller. The bark is purplish-brown with horizontal rows of lenticels. The branches are usually ascending, spreading widely; the twigs are smooth. The leaves are 8–20 x 4–9cm, broadly ovate to oblong-obovate with a tapering tip; the margins with sharp, long-pointed spreading teeth; the petiole is 2–4cm long, smooth except for 1–4 reddish glands near the blade. The flowers usually occur in clusters of 2–4, appearing just before the leaves; the pedicel is 1.5–8cm long; the flower tube is narrowly bell-shaped; the petals are 1.5–4cm long, notched, white or pink. The fruit is c. 7mm long, almost globose, purplish-crimson, rarely appearing in cultivation. Flowering period: April–May. The Japanese Cherries have long been cultivated in the parks, streets and gardens of Europe for their showy flowers. Their origins are somewhat obscure but they probably originated in C. China and became early introductions to Japan, giving rise to the 'Sato Zakura' or domestic cherries.

'Amanogawa' habit

'Amanogawa' leaf

'Kanzan' bark

'Kanzan' flowers

Flowers

Leaf

Prunus x yedoensis
Matsum.
Yoshino Cherry
Rather similar to P. serrulata but with twigs downy at first, becoming smooth: the leaves glossy above; the flowers usually occurring in clusters of 5–6 with pedicels c. 2cm long; petals 1.2–1.8cm long, deeply notched, pale pink; the fruits c. 1cm long, red and yellow, smooth. Flowering period: March–April. A Japanese hybrid probably between P. subhirtella and **P. speciosa** (Koidz.) Ingram (the **Oshima Cherry** which is also sometimes cultivated in European parks and gardens) it is commonly planted as an ornamental street tree in suburban areas.

201

Prunus subhirtella
Miq.
Spring Cherry
A deciduous tree up to 20m high in the wild but usually much smaller in cultivation, with a rather dense crown. The bark is greyish-brown. The branches are slender; the twigs are crimson, downy and dense. The leaves are *c.* 6 x 2.5cm, ovate to oblong-lanceolate, long-pointed, the margins with sharp and irregular teeth, the veins downy beneath; the petiole is 0.7–1.2cm long, slightly downy, crimson. The flowers occur in clusters of 2–5, sometimes on a short stalk, appearing before the leaves; the pedicel is 0.7–1.3cm long; the flower tube is urn-shaped with a rather constricted mouth; the petals are 0.8–1.2cm long, notched, pinkish-white to rose-pink. The fruit is 7–9mm, globose to ellipsoid, purplish-black. Flowering period: March–April. A Japanese species widely cultivated for ornament in gardens and sometimes as a street tree. Weeping and double-flowered cultivars are often grafted onto *P. avium*. *P. subhirtella* cv. *'Autumnalis'*, the **Autumn Cherry**, is the most widespread cultivar, differing principally in producing flowers almost continuously from October to April.

Flowers

Leaf

Habit

Prunus serrula
Franchet
Tibetan Cherry
Like *P. subhirtella* but with blackish-purple bark, peeling into strips to reveal a glossy mahogany colour, large wide-spreading branches; leaves 4–12 x 1–3cm, lanceolate with a long tapering point; petioles 6–7mm long; the flowers occurring at the same time as the leaves; pedicels *c.* 4cm long; white petals 0.8–1cm long; bright red fruits 0.4–1.2cm long. Flowering period: April–May. A species fairly widely cultivated in parks and gardens for its ornamental bark.

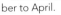

Bark (after peeling)

Prunus mahaleb L.
Saint Lucie Cherry

A deciduous shrub or occasionally a small tree up to 12m high. The bark is grayish-brown with rows of lenticels. The branches are loosely spreading. The young twigs are covered with short greyish glandular hairs. The leaves are 3–7 x 2–5cm, broadly ovate to almost round, with a short point, the base rounded or almost heart-shaped, the margins with rounded teeth, smooth and glossy above, slightly downy beneath, especially on the midrib; the petiole is 1.2–1.5cm long with 2 glands near the base. The fragrant flowers occur in rounded corymbose racemes of 3–10 flowers at the end of short leafy shoots; the pedicel is 0.8–1.5cm long, the flower tube is bell–shaped; the petals are 5–8mm long, white. The fruit is 0.6–1cm long, egg-shaped to rather rounded, blackish; the fleshy layer is thin and bitter, the stony layer almost globose, smooth. Flowering period: April–May. A species native to C. and S. Europe, occurring in open woods and thickets or on dry hillsides. Several varieties are cultivated for ornament and are naturalized in N. Europe.
Al Au Be Bu Co FC Fr FS FY Ge Gr Hu It No Pl Ro Si Sp Sw Sz.

Flowers

Leafy twig with fruit

Habit

Prunus padus L.
Bird Cherry

A deciduous tree, more rarely a shrub, up to 17m high. The bark is smooth and dark greyish-brown with a strong, rather fetid smell. The branches are ascending, slender. The young twigs are finely downy or almost smooth. The leaves are 6–10 x 3.5–7cm, elliptic to obovate with a tapering apex, the base rounded to almost heart-shaped, the margins with fine sharp teeth, dull green and smooth above, paler beneath, smooth or sometimes downy; the petiole is 1.2–2cm long with 2 or more glands. The flowers occur in elongated crowded heads, each 7–15cm long with 15–35 flowers carried at the end of short leafy shoots; the pedicel is 0.8–1.6cm long; the flower tube is broadly bell-shaped; the petals are 6–9mm long, white, often irregularly toothed at the margin. The fruit is 6–8mm long, almost globose, black and shiny; the fleshy layer is bitter, astringent; the stone is almost globose, grooved. Flowering period: May. A native of much of Europe and N. Asia on most soils, but especially in limestone areas. It is planted as a garden ornamental or occasionally as a street tree. Au Be Bu FC De Fi Fr FS FY GB Ge Ir It Ne No Po Ro Sp Sw Sz.

Leafy twig with flowers

Bark

Fruits

Habit

Prunus serotina
Ehrh.
Rum Cherry or **Black Cherry**

A deciduous tree up to 30m high with a stout trunk. The bark is smooth, peeling in strips but later becoming fissured, greyish, bitter and aromatic. The branches are spreading; the twigs are slender, purplish-brown above. The leaves are 5–14 x 2.5–4.5cm, obovate to elliptic-oblong with a tapering point, the margins with tiny forward-projecting teeth, dark green and shining above, paler and slightly downy beneath; the petiole is 0.7–2.5cm long with glands near the leaf-blade. The inflorescence is an elongated head of *c.* 30 flowers, up to 15cm long; the pedicel is 0.3–1.2cm long; the flower tube is broadly cup-shaped; the petals are 3–5mm long, creamy-white, with small teeth at the margins. The fruit is 0.7–1cm long, calyx persisting at base, globose but slightly flattened, purplish-black, the fleshy layer bitter; the stone is almost globose, smooth. Flowering period: May–June. A native of N. America, planted for timber in C. Europe and ornament elsewhere, occasionally becoming naturalized. Au De FC Fr FS FY GB Ge Hu Ne Po Ro Sw.

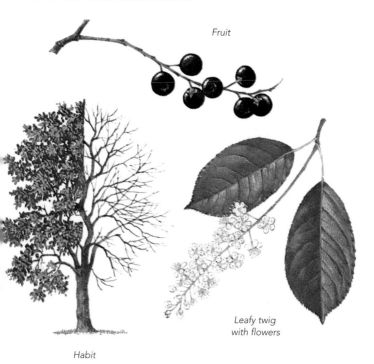

Fruit

Leafy twig
with flowers

Habit

Prunus virginiana L.
Choke Cherry
Like *P. serotina* but only up to 5m tall, more commonly occurring as a shrub than a tree; the bark is not aromatic; the leaves are dull green, the margins with sharply pointed spreading teeth; the calyx falling from the ripening dark red fruit. Flowering period: May. A native of E. to C. N. America, sometimes planted and naturalized in C. and W. Europe. FC Fr FS.

Prunus lusitanica L.
Portugal Laurel

An evergreen shrub or a tree 3–8m (or rarely up to 20m) high. The bark is black and smooth or somewhat scaly. The branches spread widely. The twigs are often flushed dark red, smooth. The leaves are 8–13 x 2.5–7cm, ovate to oblong-lanceolate with a tapering point, the base rounded, the margin with regular, shallow, pointed or rounded teeth, smooth and rather leathery, the upper surface very dark green and glossy, the underside yellowish–green; the petiole is c. 2cm long, flushed dark red, without glands. The inflorescence is an elongated head, 15–28cm long with up to 100 fragrant flowers, exceeding the leaf in the axil of which it grows; the pedicel is 0.5–1cm long; the flower tube is bell-shaped; the petals are 4–7mm long, creamy-white. The fruit is 0.8–1.3cm long, ovoid or cone-shaped to almost-globose slightly pointed, purplish-black, smooth; the stone is almost globose, with a faintly keeled margin, smooth. Flowering period: June. A native of Spain, Portugal and SW. France, and much planted for ornament or as a hedge plant elsewhere in W. Europe, occasionally becoming naturalized. Fr Pl Sp.

Flowering shoot

Ripening fruit

Habit

Prunus laurocerasus L.
Cherry Laurel

An evergreen shrub or a small tree up to 8m high. The bark is dark grey-brown with many lenticels. The branches are widely spreading; the twigs are pale green, smooth; the leaves are 10–20 x 3–6cm, oblong to lanceolate with a short tapering tip, the base rounded or tapering, the margins more or less entire or with a few minute teeth, smooth and leathery, the upper surface dark glossy green, the underside yellowish-green; the petiole is *c.* 1.2cm long with 1 or more stalkless glands beneath. The inflorescence is an elongated upright head 8–13cm long with *c.* 30 fragrant flowers, equalling or very slightly exceeding the leaf from the axil of which it grows; the pedicel is *c.* 6mm long; the flower tube is funnel-shaped to bell-shaped; the petals are *c.* 4mm long, creamy-white. The fruit is 1.1–2cm long, somewhat conical to almost globose, smooth, initially turning from green to red, then becoming blackish-purple; the stone is more or less globose with a faintly keeled margin, smooth. Flowering period: April. A native of the E. Balkan Peninsula, widely planted for ornament since the 16th and 17th centuries in the S. and W. parts of Europe and frequently becoming naturalized. Many different cultivated varieties have been raised, differing in habit, leaf shape and colour. Bu Co Fr FY GB Ir Pl Tu.

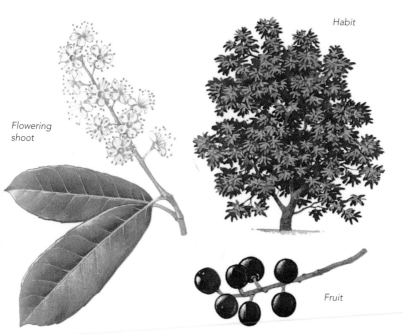

Habit

Flowering shoot

Fruit

PEA FAMILY LEGUMINOSAE

Albizia
Durazz.
Siris
Unarmed deciduous trees or shrubs with twice-pinnate leaves and panicles of rather narrow flower heads. The bisexual or polygamous flowers are in 5 parts, with a tubular 5-toothed calyx and funnel-shaped corolla. The numerous stamens greatly exceed the corolla in length and have the filaments fused at the base to form a tube. The fruit (legume) is long, broadly linear and flat.

Albizia lophantha
Bentham
Plume Albizia
A small tree or shrub up to 7m high with dense, evenly hairy branches. The leaves have 16–20 pinnae, each pinna bearing 40–60 leaflets; the petiole is velvety-hairy; each leaflet is *c.* 6mm long, curved, glabrous above, silky and hairy below. The inflorescence is a loose cylindrical axillary spike, 3.5–7cm long, the Peduncle densely hairy; the bright yellow flower is *c.* 5mm long, the calyx shortly lobed and less than half as long as the corolla. The stamens are *c.* 1.2cm long, the filaments united at the base to form a tube about as long as or slightly shorter than the corolla. The legume is 7.5cm long, *c.* 1cm broad or sometimes larger, flattened and containing ovate or orbicular seeds. A native of SW. Australia, planted for ornament in the Mediterranean area.

Leaf and inflorescence

Legume

Albizia julibrissin
Durazz.
Pink Siris

A small tree rarely exceeding 13.5m high with a rounded or rather flattened crown and smooth bark. The spreading branches are glabrous. The leaves are 20–30cm (sometimes up to 46cm) long with 10–25 (occasionally 30) pinnae, each pinna bearing 35–50 (occasionally 80) leaflets; the rachis and rachilla are slightly hairy above, the leaflets 1–1.5cm long, narrowly ovate, curved, green above, whitish beneath, the margins and lower surface with short hairs; the petiole has a cup-shaped gland on the upper surface. The young panicles are hairy with about 10 spreading branches, each terminating in a 20-flowered head; the flowers are 7–9mm long, sessile, pinkish; the stamens are 3.5–4cm long and also pink. The legume is 8–15cm long, brown when ripe, somewhat constricted between each of the 10–15 seeds. Flowering period: July–August. A woodland and riverside species in lowland Asia, frequently planted as an ornamental and shade tree in S. Europe. In N. Europe it is sometimes used as an annual garden plant.

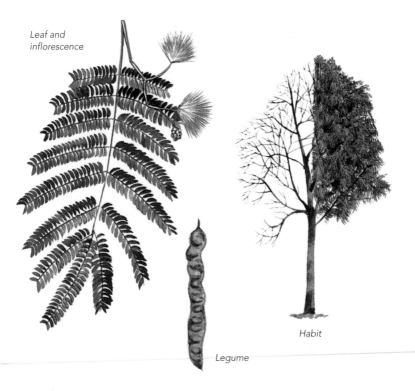

Leaf and
inflorescence

Legume

Habit

Cercis siliquastrum L.
Judas Tree

A small deciduous tree or shrub up to 10m high, with a rounded or irregular crown and often more than one bole. The branches are ascending and spreading, the twigs and buds red-brown or crimson. The leaves are 7–12cm long, simple, alternate, suborbicular, obtuse or notched at the tip, heart-shaped at the base, glabrous and rather glaucous when young, becoming dark or yellowish-green above, paler and glaucous beneath, digitately veined. The flowers are borne in clusters usually appearing before the leaves; the calyx is regularly 5-toothed, brown; the corolla is 1.5–2cm long, pink, the 3 upper petals much smaller than the lower 2. The legume is 6–10cm long, compressed and narrowly winged on the ventral suture, glabrous, becoming red-purple, eventually brown when mature, dehiscent. Flowering period: May. Typically in dry rocky places in the Mediterranean region, frequently planted as an ornamental and may become naturalized. Al Bu Cr Fr FY Gr It Pl Si Sp Ro Tu.

Fruiting twig

Flowering twig

Habit

Ceratonia siliqua L.
Carob, Locust Tree

A small, monoecious or dioecious, evergreen tree or shrub up to 10m high with a low, dense, domed crown. The leaves are pinnate with no terminal leaflet, 2–5 pairs of leaflets, the rachis brown or greenish. Each leaflet is 3–5cm long. The inflorescence is a short axillary raceme; the calyx has 5 short teeth which fall early; corolla is

Habit

Flowering twig

absent. The legume is 10–20cm long, compressed, pendent, green at first, brownish-violet when ripe, indehiscent. A native of dry areas in the Mediterranean region, widely cultivated as a fodder crop and naturalized in many places. Al Bl Co Cr Fr FY It Pl Sa Si Sp.

Male flower

Immature fruit

Gleditsia triacanthos L.
Honey Locust

A tall, deciduous, armed tree up to 45m high with a spreading crown. The bole and branches have stout, simple or branched spines, those on the bole often very large and forming clusters. The leaves are 10–20cm long, pinnate or twice-pinnate; pinnate leaves with 7–18 pairs of leaflets and twice-pinnate leaves with 8–14 pinnae. The inflorescence is a long axillary raceme: the flowers are fragrant, polygamous, 2.5–3mm long; the calyx has 3–5 lobes, the corolla only slightly zygomorphic with 3–5 greenish-white petals. The legume is 3–4.5cm long, compressed, thick-edged, sickle-shaped or spirally twisted, pale green when young, dark brown when ripe, virtually indehiscent. Flowering period: June. A native of Mississippi basin in N. America, used as an ornamental and for hedging especially in S. and C. Europe where it occasionally becomes naturalized. Spineless cultivars are used as park and street trees. Au Bu Fr FY Ge It Ro Sp.

Flowering twig

Fruit

Detail of bole

Flower

Habit

211

Acacia
Miller
Wattles or **Mimosas**

Acacia cyanophylla
Lindley
Golden Wreath, Willow Wattle
A dense shrub or small tree up to 10m tall with a solitary or
dividing trunk frequently suckering at the base. The bark is
smooth, initially grey, later becoming greyish-brown and fissured. The twigs are often pendulous, somewhat flexible,
finely ribbed and glabrous. The phyllodes are variable,
10–20cm (rarely 35cm) long by 0.6–3cm wide (and up to 8cm
wide on suckers), linear to lanceolate, straight or sickle-
shaped, often pendulous, glabrous, green to glaucous, dull
to shiny, with a conspicuous midrib; a gland is usually present on the upper margin near the base. The inflorescences
are large heads, 1–1.5cm in diameter, with 25–70 flowers per
head occurring on pendulous racemes of 2–8; the flowers
are bright yellow. The legume is 6–12 x 0.4–0.8cm, linear
compressed, distinctly constricted between the seeds,
glaucous when young, later brownish. Flowering period:
March–May. A native of W. Australia planted widely in
S. Europe for stabilizing sand dunes and for ornament. Co Fr
Gr It Pl Sa Sp.

Legume

Phyllodes

Habit

Flowers

Acacia dealbata
Link
Silver Wattle, Mimosa

A handsome medium-sized tree up to 30m high. The bark is smooth and greenish-grey. The twigs, young shoots and foliage are all silvery-white to creamy-yellow due to a dense covering of fine, very short hairs. The leaves are tripinnate; the leaflets occur in 25–50 pairs, each about 5mm long; the glands are numerous and occur irregularly at the point of insertion on to the rachis. The large terminal and smaller axillary inflorescences are long, spreading racemes or panicles of 20–30 flower heads; the peduncles are rather short and covered with short white or yellowish hairs; the flower heads are bright yellow, 5–6mm in diameter with 30–40 flowers per head. The legume is 4–10 x 1–1.2cm, compressed, and not constricted between the seeds. A native of SE. Australia and Tasmania planted in many warmer parts of Europe for ornament, for timber and for soil stabilization. It has become widely naturalized in the Mediterranean region. Fr FY GB It Pl Ro Sa Sp.

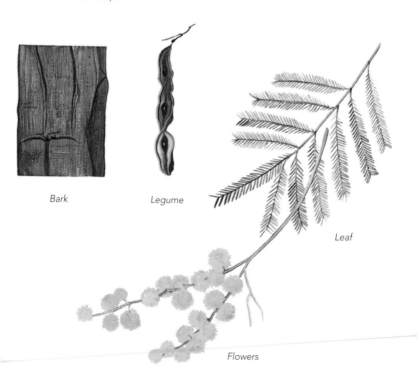

Habit

Bark

Legume

Leaf

Flowers

213

Acacia longifolia (Andrews)
Willd.
Sydney Golden Wattle

A shrub or small slender tree up to 10m tall, spreading to about 10m in open conditions, with a dense bushy crown and bright green shiny foliage. The bark is smooth and dull grey. The twigs are stiff, glabrous. The phyllodes are 7–15 x 0.8–3cm, oblong to oblong-lanceolate, straight, striped with prominent longitudinal veins. The inflorescence is a large fluffy cylindrical spike up to 5cm long; the flowers are bright yellow and strong-smelling. The legume is 7–15 x 0.4–0.5cm, linear, terete, almost straight to curled and twisted, distinctly constricted between the seeds, brown when mature. The stalk of the seed is white. Flowering period: April–May. A native of coastal areas of New South Wales, Australia, widely planted in SW. Europe for ornament and sand dune stabilization. Fr It Pl Sp.

Habit

Legume

Phyllodes with inflorescence

Acacia mearnsii
De Wild.
Green Wattle

A similar species to *A. dealbata* but rarely attaining more than 15m in height. It is softly yellow, villous; the leaves are dark green with 8–14 pairs of pinnae; there are 25–40 pairs of leaflets; the rachis has glands between the pinnae; the legume is 5–7mm wide, distinctly constricted between the seeds and blackish-brown at maturity. Another SE. Australian

and Tasmanian native planted for ornament and tan bark in the Iberian Peninsula; naturalized in some areas.
Co It Pl Sp.

Leafy twig with inflorescence

Legume

Acacia melanoxylon
R. GB.
Blackwood
A stout tree with straight erect trunk, up to 40m high although not usually attaining more than 15m. The bark is dark grey-brown, rough and furrowed and very persistent even on smaller branches. The branches begin well down the main trunk, usually horizontal or even pendulous; the crown is dense and rounded; the young twigs are hairy. The phyllodes are 6–13 x 0.7–2cm, lanceolate to oblanceolate, slightly curved, bluntly pointed at the apex and tapering at the base, dull, dark green with 3–5 veins, twice-pinnate leaves sometimes occur on young trees, the pinnae with 14–20 oblong leaflets 5–7mm long. The inflorescence is a short axillary raceme bearing yellow or creamy-white heads, *c.* 1cm in diameter, The legume is 7–12 x 0.8–1cm, compressed, contorted, reddish-brown. The stalk around the seed is scarlet. Another SE. Australian and Tasmanian native, planted for its valuable 'blackwood' veneer timber in SW. Europe, where it has become locally naturalized. Fr GB It Pl Sp.

Phyllodes with inflorescence

Legume

Habit

215

Acacia pycnantha
Bentham
Golden Wattle

A small tree or shrub up to 12m tall; the bole is usually short and thin, suckering freely from the base, the crown shade-giving with the branches curving upwards. The bark is dark brown and smooth. The twigs are glaucous. The phyllodes are 8–20 x 1–3.5cm (up to 10cm wide on suckers), initially very broad and large, later becoming sickle-shaped, bright, shining green, leathery, 1-veined. The inflorescence is a large raceme of 20–30 deep yellow, fluffy, highly perfumed flowering heads on thick peduncles; the heads are 0.8–1cm in diameter. The legume is 8–13 x 0.5–0.6cm, almost straight, compressed, dark brown and slightly constricted between the seeds; the stalk of the seed is short and white. The Golden Wattle is the floral emblem of Australia and native to temperate regions of Victoria and S. Australia. It is widely planted in S. Europe for tanning and sometimes ornament and has become locally naturalized in S. Portugal and C. and S. Italy. It Pl Sa Sp.

Phyllodes with inflorescence

Young legumes

Acacia retinodes
Schlecht.
Swamp Wattle

A small glabrous tree or shrub up to 10m tall; the bole is short and the branches tend to curve upwards. The bark is smooth and grey, later greyish-brown; the twigs are usually brown and not pendent. The phyllodes are 6–15 x 0.4–1.8cm, acute to obtuse, with a straight or curved apex, light green. The inflorescence consists of 5–10 heads in short, branched racemes; the heads are 4–6mm in diameter; the flowers are pale yellow. The legume is usually straight and with an almost straight edge, and slightly constricted between the seeds; the scarlet stalk encircles the seed and is bent back upon itself in a double fold. Flowering time: June–July, native of S. Australia, widely planted for ornament in S. Europe and locally naturalized. Fr FY GB It Pl Ro Sp. Shrubby members of the genus are also frequently planted in Europe, ie. *A. farnesiana* from the Dominican Republic, *A. karoo* from S. Africa and *A. cyclops*, which can sometimes be confused with the tree species (see key on pp. 30–31 for distinctions between them).

Phyllodes

Inflorescence

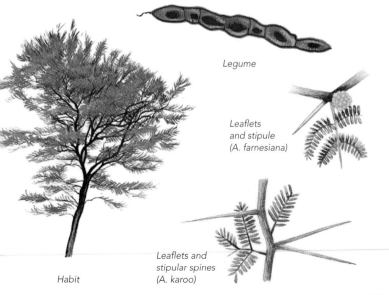

Legume

Leaflets and stipule (A. farnesiana)

Leaflets and stipular spines (A. karoo)

Habit

Laburnum
Fabr.
Laburnums

Deciduous, unarmed trees or shrubs, the leaves having 3 leaflets. The inflorescences are axillary or apparently terminal in pendulous leafless racemes. The calyx is bell-shaped, 2-lipped, the lips sometimes slightly toothed; the corolla is yellow and the stamens are monodelphous. The fruit is a legume, slightly constricted between each of the numerous, compressed seeds.

Laburnum alpinum (Miller)
Berchtold & J. Presl
Alpine Laburnum or **Scotch Laburnum**
A very small tree or shrub up to 5m high with a short bole. It is similar to *L. anagyroides* but differs in a number of features. The green twigs are hairy only when young. The leaflets are green, slightly glossy on both surfaces and more or less glabrous. The racemes are 15–40cm long, slender and rather dense. The corolla is 1.5–2cm long. The legume is 4–5cm long, glabrous, with a narrow wing 1–2mm wide on the upper suture. The seeds are brown. Flowering period: June. A montane species from C. S. and SE. Europe, sometimes planted as a roadside tree. Cultivated specimens may reach 10m in height. Al Au FC Fr FY GB It Sz.

Flowering twig

Ripe fruit

Fruit cluster

Habit

Laburnum anagyroides
Medicus
Common Laburnum

A small tree or shrub up to 7m high with a narrow, open, rather irregular crown and slender bole. The bark is greenish or brown, smooth, with small warts or flakes. The branches are ascending, the smaller ones arching; the twigs are greyish-green with long silky appressed hairs. The leaflets are 3–8cm long, elliptical or wider above the middle, rather blunt with a shortly pointed tip, greyish-green on both surfaces with appressed hairs beneath when young; the petiole is 2–6cm long. The racemes are 10–30cm long and rather loose. The corolla is about 2cm long, golden-yellow and often with brown markings. The legume is 4–6cm long, appressed hairy when young, becoming glabrous and dark brown when mature, the upper suture unwinged. The seeds are black. Flowering period: May–early June. A self-seeding, rapidly growing but short-lived species, the Common Laburnum is one of the most poisonous native European trees. A montane species of S. and C. Europe, of woods and scrub up to 2000m. It is one of the most commonly planted ornamental trees sometimes becoming naturalized. Au Co FC Fr FY GB Ge Hu Ir It Ro Sz.

Habit

Ripe fruit

Flowering twig

Laburnum x watereri
Dippel
Voss's Laburnum

A hybrid between L. anagyroides and L. alpinum, with large flowers, combining the early flowering period of L. anagyroides and the long dense racemes of L. alpinum. The hybrid and its various cultivated forms have replaced L. anagyroides as the most commonly planted Laburnum in some areas.

Sophora japonica L.
Pagoda Tree

An unarmed, deciduous tree up to 25m high with an irregular, rather open crown. The bark is wrinkled and furrowed, dark or grey-brown. The branches are contorted, the twigs glaucous and hairy at first, becoming green and glabrous. The leaves are 15–25cm long, alternate, pinnate with a terminal leaflet, and 3–8 pairs of leaflets. The inflorescence is a large, finely hairy, terminal panicle, 15–25cm long. The white or pale pink flowers appear only on old trees; the calyx is tubular and slightly 2-lipped; the corolla is strongly zygomorphic, 1–1.5cm long. The legume is 5–8cm long, conspicuously constricted between the seeds, glabrous, greenish, indeh iscent or dehiscing very late. There may be many seeds or as few as one. Flowering period: August–September. A montane plant of thickets and thin woods in E Asia, it is often planted as an ornamental and may become naturalized in places. Au Fr Ro

Habit

Pods

Flowering twig

Robinia L.
Locust Trees

Deciduous trees with alternate pinnate leaves having a terminal leaflet and usually with spinose stipules. The inflorescence is a pendulous axillary raceme of white, pink or purple flowers. The bell-shaped calyx is somewhat 2-lipped and the stamens are diadelphous. The legume is linear-oblong, flat and dehiscent with 3–10 seeds.

Robinia pseudacacia L.
Locust Tree

A medium-sized tree up to 25m high with a broad, rather open crown and short, frequently multiple boles, spreading by root suckers and sometimes forming thickets of young stems. The bark is smooth and dark brown in young trees, becoming grey and deeply furrowed into broad twisting ridges in mature trees. The branches are twisted and brittle, the young twigs dark and reddish, with short woody stipular spines on strong shoots. The leaves are 15–20cm long with 3–10 pairs of opposite or subopposite leaflets, each leaflet 2.5–4.5cm long, elliptical or ovate, entire, yellowish-green and glabrous above, slightly hairy but becoming glabrous below, usually with a secondary stipule at the base of the short petiolule. The dense racemes are many-flowered, 10–20cm long; the sweet-scented flowers are 1.5–2cm long, white, rarely pink, with a yellow base to the upper petal. The legume is 5–10cm long, glabrous, often remaining on the tree for some time after reaching maturity. Flowering period: June. An introduced species, native to thin woods and open places in E. and C. N. America, widely planted in Europe as an ornamental and soil-stabilizer. It has become naturalized in many areas, particularly in S. and W. Europe. Al Au Be Bu FC Fr FY GB Ge Gr Hu It Ne Ro Sa Si Sp Sz Tu.

Flowering twig

Pods

Habit

Robinia viscosa
Vent.
Clammy Locust

A sticky, hairy relative from the SE. of N. America, frequently planted in C. and S. Europe as an ornamental.

Pods

Flower

221

CITRUS FRUIT FAMILY RUTACEAE

Citrus L.

Small trees. The leaves are usually simple, alternate, leathery and thin; the petiole is often more or less winged or with narrow margins, with an articulated joint at the meeting of the blade. The flowers are solitary or in small spikes emerging from the leaf-axils; the sepals number 4–5; the petals number 4–8; there are 4–10 times as many stamens as petals. The fruit is a large berry with a thick leathery skin and a soft flesh of large juice-filled hair-cells growing from the inside of the skin. There are more than 60 described species originating from China, SE. Asia and Indomalasia. Those below are widely cultivated in the Mediterranean region for their edible fruits and for essential oils for the perfume industry extracted from the flowers and fruits.

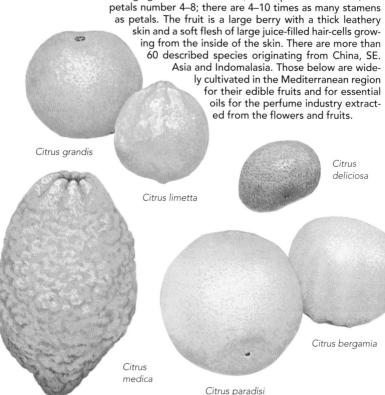

Citrus grandis

Citrus limetta

Citrus deliciosa

Citrus medica

Citrus paradisi

Citrus bergamia

Citrus aurantium L.
Seville Orange

A small to medium tree up to 10m high with a rounded crown. The leaves are 7.5–10cm long, broadly elliptical. The flowers are large, and fragrant with the oil of Neroli. The fruit is about 7.5cm in diameter with a thick skin, orange when ripe.

Citrus aurantium

Citrus sinensis L.
Osbeck
Sweet Orange
A moderate-sized tree up to *c.* 10m with a rounded crown. The leaves are more or less elliptical. The flowers are small and very fragrant. The fruit is the edible orange. The closely related **C. bergamia** Risso & Poiteau is cultivated in Calabria for the Bergamot oil from the fruit rind. It is a small tree with winged petioles, oblong-ovate leaves and a thick-skinned yellow fruit 7.5–10cm in diameter.

Flowering twig

Habit

Citrus sinensis

Citrus deliciosa
Ten.
Tangerine
A small spiny, spreading tree up to 8m. The leaves are narrowly elliptical. The flowers are medium-sized. The fruit is 5–7.5cm in diameter, almost globose, with a thin, easily detachable bright orange rind when ripe.

Citrus paradisi Macfadyen in Hooker
Grapefruit
A relatively large, densely leafy tree up to 12m with a rounded crown. The leaves are 10–15cm long and broadly elliptical; the petiole has very broad wings. The flowers are large. The fruit is 10–15cm in diameter, almost globose, with a thick rind, pale yellow when ripe. The closely related **C. grandis** L. Osbeck, the **Shaddock** or **Pomelo**, has a broader petiole and a fruit up to 25cm in diameter.

Citrus limon L.
Burm.
Lemon
A small thorny, rounded tree. The leaves are *c.* 10cm long, broadly elliptical and minutely toothed; the petiole is narrowly winged and distinctly articulated with the leaf. The flowers are small. The fruit is 6.5–12.5cm in diameter, oblong or ovaid, with a broad protruding apex, a thick, rough to almost smooth, bright yellow rind when ripe. The origin of the lemon is rather obscure but probably derived from **C. medica**, the **Citron**, a small tree with a thick-skinned yellow fruit, 15–25cm in diameter. **C. limetta**, the **Sweet Lime**, is probably a mutant of the lemon with a shorter, greenish-yellow, sweeter fruit.

Flowering twig

Habit

Fruit

223

QUASSIA FAMILY SIMAROUBACEAE

Leaf

Ailanthus altissima (Miller) Swingle
Tree of Heaven

A fast-growing deciduous tree up to 20m (rarely 30m) high with an irregular crown and straight cylindrical bole, suckering freely. The bark is smooth and grey in young trees, becoming paler and slightly scaly in old trees. The branches are stout and ascending; the twigs are smooth, stout and brown, with prominent leaf-scars. The small ovoid buds are scarlet. The leaves are alternate, pinnate, 45–60cm long, more or less glabrous, with 13–25 leaflets; each leaflet is 7–12cm long, lanceolate-ovate, pointed at the tip, unequally cordate at the base, the margin with 2–4 teeth towards the base, each with a large raised gland beneath, fringed, deep red when unfolding, shiny green above when mature and at leaf-fall, pale green beneath, smelling unpleasant when crushed; the petiolule is 0.5–1.5cm long, red. The inflorescence is a large terminal panicle. The flowers are greenish, strong-smelling, 7–8mm in diameter, in 5 parts, polygamous though usually with males and females on separate trees; stamens 10 in male flowers, 2–3 in hermaphrodite flowers; female flowers with 2–5 joined styles. The fruit is a group of samaras, each samara 3–4cm long with a twisted wing, reddish when young. Flowering period: July. A native of China, widely planted in Europe for ornament, especially in parks and as a street tree but also for shade and soil conservation, and it has become widely naturalized. Al Au Be Bu Co FC Fr FS FY GB Ge Gr Hu It Pl Ro Sa Si Sp Sz.

Male inflorescence

Fruit cluster

Habit

MAHOGANY FAMILY MELIACEAE

Melia azedarach L.
Indian Bead Tree or Persian Lilac

A short-lived deciduous tree or shrub up to 15m high with a rather open, spreading often short bole. The bark is shallowly furrowed and dark grey. The young twigs are sparsely covered in deciduous stellate hairs. The leaves are alternate, up to 90cm long, twice-pinnate, with numerous leaflets; each leaflet is 2.5–5cm long, ovate-lanceolate to elliptical, the margin toothed or lobed, dark, somewhat glossy green. The inflorescence is a large loose axillary panicle 10–20cm long, sparsely stellate-hairy when young. The flowers are fragrant, lilac, usually in 5 parts, the petals about 1.8cm long, free-spreading or slightly reflexed; there are twice as many stamens as petals, united to form an almost complete tube with only the anthers free. The fruit is a drupe, 0.6–1.8cm in diameter, more or less globose or somewhat ovoid, yellow or creamy, containing a hard seed. Flowering period: June. A native of dry montane regions of E. Asia, widely planted in S. Europe as an ornamental and shade tree naturalized in the Balkan Peninsula. Cr FY Gr.

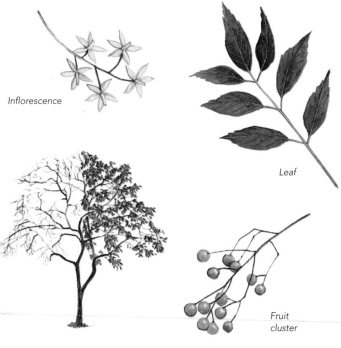

Inflorescence

Leaf

Habit

Fruit cluster

CASHEW FAMILY ANACARDIACEAE

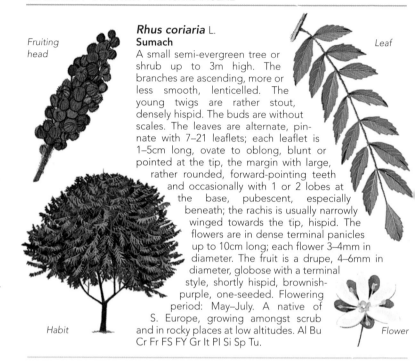

Fruiting head

Leaf

Rhus coriaria L.
Sumach

A small semi-evergreen tree or shrub up to 3m high. The branches are ascending, more or less smooth, lenticelled. The young twigs are rather stout, densely hispid. The buds are without scales. The leaves are alternate, pinnate with 7–21 leaflets; each leaflet is 1–5cm long, ovate to oblong, blunt or pointed at the tip, the margin with large, rather rounded, forward-pointing teeth and occasionally with 1 or 2 lobes at the base, pubescent, especially beneath; the rachis is usually narrowly winged towards the tip, hispid. The flowers are in dense terminal panicles up to 10cm long; each flower 3–4mm in diameter. The fruit is a drupe, 4–6mm in diameter, globose with a terminal style, shortly hispid, brownish-purple, one-seeded. Flowering period: May–July. A native of S. Europe, growing amongst scrub and in rocky places at low altitudes. Al Bu Cr Fr FS FY Gr It Pl Si Sp Tu.

Habit

Flower

Rhus typhina L.
Stag's Horn Sumach

Like *R. coriaria* but deciduous, up to 10m high, often suckering; the leaflets 5–12cm long, oblong-lanceolate, toothed; the rachis unwinged; the flower head 10–20cm in diameter, dense; the female flower heads downy; the fruit covered with crimson hairs. A native to E. N. America, commonly planted for ornament in parks and gardens, becoming naturalized in favourable localities of C. and N. Europe. Bu FC Fr FY GB It Ro Sz. **R. verniciflua**, the famous **Varnish Tree** of Japan, is also occasionally cultivated for ornament.

Leaf and fruiting head

Schinus molle L.
Pepper Tree

An evergreen tree or shrub up to 12m high. The branches are slender, pendent. The young twigs are glaucous. The leaves are alternate, pinnate with 7–13 pairs of leaflets, each leaflet 2–6 x 0.3–0.8cm long, linear-lanceolate with a slender spine-like tip, often toothed towards the apex, pubescent when young, becoming glabrous, strongly aromatic when crushed; the rachis is often flattened but not conspicuously winged, sometimes terminating the leaf with a spine-like tip, glabrous. The flowers are in lateral or terminal, lax panicles up to 25cm long, each flower *c.* 4mm in diameter with 5 yellowish-white petals. The fruit is a drupe, 6–7mm in diameter, globose, shiny, rose-pink, with a solitary seed and a pedicel 2–3mm long. Flowering period: June–December. A native of the mountains of C. and S. America, planted for ornament in S. Europe and more or less naturalized in some localities. Fr Gr It Pl Sa Si Sp. The **Brazilian Pepper**, *S. terebinthifolia*, differing in its erect branches, oblong–ovate leaflets, winged rachis and bright red fruit 4–5mm in diameter, is also planted for ornament.

Flower

Leaf

Fruiting head

Habit

Pistacia terebinthus L.
Turpentine Tree

A deciduous shrub or small tree up to 10m high. The bark is greyish-brown, coarsely fissured. The twigs are grey, resiniferous. The leaves have 3–9 leaflets; each leaflet is 2–8.5 x 1–3.5cm long, broadly ovate to oblong with a small spine-like tip, smooth, rather leathery, shiny dark green; the rachis is rounded in cross-section, unwinged; the petiole is smooth. The flower heads are 5–15cm, lax, with long branches, appearing with the young leaves; the flowers are greenish to brownish. The fruits are 5–7 x 4–6mm, obovoid with a slender pointed tip, coral-red when young, becoming purplish-brown. Flowering period: March–April. A native of the Mediterranean region, Portugal and SW. Asia, growing in thickets and open woodland, usually on dry calcareous rocky slopes. Al Bu Co Cr Fr FY Gr It Pl Sa Si Sp Tu. The similar *P. atlantica* Desf. has lanceolate leaflets with rounded tips, a narrowly winged rachis and a shortly pubescent petiole. A native of SE Europe and N. Africa. Gr FS Tu.

Fruiting head

Habit

Leaf and flower head

Pistacia lentiscus L.
Mastic Tree

Usually a spreading evergreen shrub or occasionally a tree up to 8m. The twigs are warted, glabrous. The leaves have rarely 4, usually 6–12 leaflets without a terminal leaflet; each leaflet is 1–5 x 0.5–1.5cm, lanceolate to oblong with a short spine-like tip, leathery, dark green; the rachis is broadly winged, continued as a spine-like tip to the leaf, the petiole is smooth. The flower heads are in the axils of leaves, 2–5cm long, dense and spike-like; the flowers are yellowish or purplish. The fruits are c. 4mm long, globose with a slender pointed tip, very aromatic, red when young, becoming black. Flowering period: April. A native of the Mediterranean

region and Portugal, growing in scrub or woodland margins on dry stony slopes. Hybrids
between *P. lentiscus* and *P. terebinthus* occur
in parts of France, Italy, Portugal and Sardinia
and are known as ***P. x raportae***.

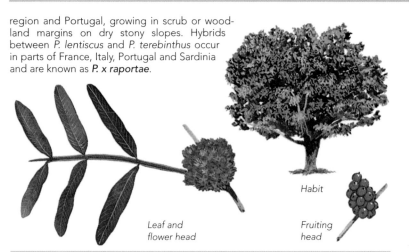

Leaf and
flower head

Habit

Fruiting
head

Pistacia vera L.
Pistachio

A small deciduous tree up to 6m high. The bark is greyish-
brown, rough, with many short ridges. The twigs are grey.
The leaves are simple or pinnate, usually with 3 (rarely 5)
leaflets; each leaflet is 3.5–9cm long, broadly ovate to
oblong-ovate, thin-textured, somewhat downy on both surfaces while young, becoming smooth grey-green; the rachis
is very slightly winged; the petiole is downy. The flower
heads are 7–10cm long, lax, with long branches; the flowers
are greenish. The fruit is 2–2.5cm long, ovoid with a pointed
tip, pale reddish-brown with a hard outer layer and an edible
seed. Flowering period: April. Native to W. Asia, widely cultivated around the Mediterranean countries for its edible nuts
and naturalized in a few localities. Fr Gr Si Sp.

Fruiting
head

Habit

MAPLE FAMILY ACERACEAE

Acer L.
Maples and Sycamores

Deciduous trees or sometimes shrubs, with long-petioled leaves. The flowers are green or yellowish. The fruit is a samara, winged on the outer side.

Acer campestre L.
Field Maple

Usually a small tree, occasionally up to 26m high, or a shrub, with a domed crown and a sinuous bole. The bark is grey or brown with orange fissures. The branches are somewhat pendulous but upturned towards the tips; the twigs are brown and covered with fine hairs, darker above than below, often corky, the older ones winged. The buds are 3mm long, grey or reddish-brown, hairy towards the apex. The leaves are 4–12cm long, 5-lobed (occasionally 3-lobed), the 2 basal lobes smaller than the upper 3, the upper lobes more or less oblong or wedge-shaped with 2 rounded teeth towards the apex, fringed, hair tufted in the axils of the veins beneath, thick and sometimes leathery, pinkish when young, becoming dark green at maturity; petiole about 5cm, slender. The flowers are few, appearing with the leaves in erect hairy heads containing both male and female flowers. The fruits are in clusters of four, 5–6cm in diameter, hairy or glabrous, the wings horizontal, green, sometimes tinged with red. Flowering period: late April–early May. A very varied species, perhaps due to hybridization. Common in N. Europe, it is cultivated for its autumn foliage; occasionally naturalized. Al Au Be Bu Co De FC Fr FS FY GB Ge Gr Hu Ir It Ne Po Ro Sa Si Sp Sw Sz Tu.

Flowering twig

Fruits

Habit

Acer heldreichii
Orph. ex Boiss.
Heldreich's Maple

A medium-sized tree up to 25m high with a high-domed crown. The bark is smooth, finely cracked in older trees, grey. The branches are ascending, with a few reddish-brown twigs. The buds are ovoid, pointed and dark brown. The leaves are 5–17cm long, with 3–5 deep lobes, the middle lobe free almost to the base, all lobes with 2–3 large teeth on each side, green above, bluish-green below with white or brownish hairs on the veins beneath. The flowers are few, appearing with the leaves, in more or less erect, hairless, yellow panicles. The fruits are 2.5–5cm long, the curved wings usually forming an obtuse angle, reddish, glabrous. Flowering period: late May. A montane species of the Balkan Peninsula. Al Bu FY Gr.

Fruits

Habit

Leaf

Among the commonest non-European species planted in parks and gardens are two Chinese species: ***Acer griseum***, the **Paper-bark Maple**, grown for its unusual reddish-brown bark which peels in broad papery strips; and *A. davidii*, **Père David's Maple**, one of the Snake-bark Maples with olive-green young bark marked with a bright network of whitish lines. Paper-bark Maple has hairy twigs and petioles and dark green leaves composed of 3 leaflets, the two lateral ones almost sessile. Père David's Maple has glabrous twigs and either unlobed or up to 5-lobed leaves which are heart-shaped at the base with finely toothed margins. Other commonly planted species include *A. hersii*, *A. cappadocicum*, *A. macrophyllum*, *A. saccharum* and *A. rufinerve*, all from Asia or N. America.

*Leaf
(A. griseum)*

*Leaf
(A. davidii)*

Acer hyrcanum Fischer & C.A. Meyer
Balkan Maple

A small tree up to 16m high with a domed crown. The bark is grey-brown, fissured into square plates. The branches are ascending or spreading. The buds are grey and brown with few scales. The leaves are up to 10cm long, with 3 or usually 5 lobes cut halfway to the base, the 3 main lobes parallel-sided with obtuse apices, shallowly toothed on the margins, green above, the lower surface more or less glabrous except for the veins; the petiole is very slender, pinkish or yellowish. The flowers are few, opening before the leaves, in subsessile heads with slender pedicels, yellowish. The fruit is 1.5cm long, the wings diverging at an acute angle or nearly parallel, green, on slender pedicels, in clusters of 6–8. Flowering period: April. A woodland species from the Balkan Peninsula and the Caucasus. Al Bu FY Gr.

Fruits

Flowering twig

Leaf

Habit

Acer granatense Boiss.

A species very similar to the Balkan Maple, but differs in having leaves up to 7cm long. The lower surfaces of the leaves, the young petioles and young twigs are all rather densely hairy. It is confined to S. Spain, Mallorca and N. Africa. Bl Sp.

Leafy twig

Acer monspessulanum L.
Montpelier Maple

A small tree up to 12m high or sometimes a shrub, with a broadly domed crown. The bark is fissured and cracked, grey or black. The twigs are slender, brown, smooth. The buds are 3mm long, ovoid, orange-brown. The leaves are 3–8cm long, leathery, 3-lobed, the lobes wide-spreading, ovate, the margins entire, dark green and shiny above, slightly bluish beneath with tufts of hairs in the axils of the lower veins; the petiole is slightly orange. The flowers appear after the leaves, erect at first, becoming pendent, in yellowish-green heads with long slender pedicels. The fruit is 1.2cm long, the wings parallel or overlapping, green becoming crimson-tinged, glabrous. Flowering period: June. A S. European species, growing as far north as S. Germany in rather local populations. It is occasionally planted in large parks. Al Au Bu Co Fr FY Ge Gr It Pl Ro Sa Si Sp Tu.

Leaf

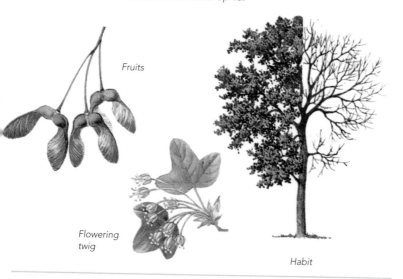

Fruits

Flowering twig

Habit

Acer sempervirens L.
Cretan Maple

A small evergreen up to 12m high, but often a shrub, with a low crown. The bark has few fissures and is dark grey with a few orange patches. The branches are twisted; the twigs are brown and shiny. The leaves are 2–5cm long, 3-lobed, irregularly lobed or undivided with entire wavy margins; the petioles are short, yellowish. The flowers are few, erect, in glabrous greenish heads. The fruits have green or occasionally red wings which are almost parallel or spreading at an acute angle. Flowering period: April. Similar to the Montpelier Maple, but confined to Crete and Greece. Cr Gr.

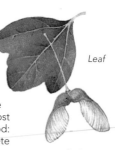

Leaf

Fruits

233

Acer negundo L.
Box-elder

A rather small, fast-growing tree up to 20m high. The crown is domed but often irregular due to numerous shoots sprouting from the bole and branches. The greyish bark is smooth at first but becoming shallowly fissured and a darker colour as the tree matures. The buds are small, with only 2 scales, white or somewhat silvery, The leaves are 5–15cm long, pinnate, with 3–5 (sometimes 7) ovate leaflets, the lower with short stalks, the upper sessile and occasionally incompletely divided, but all with shallow, irregularly toothed margins. The flowers are dioecious, without petals, appearing before the leaves; the male flowers occur in pendent corymbs of 12–16, green or pinkish with red anthers; the females occur in loose pendent racemes of 6–12, 5cm long, greenish. The fruit is 2cm long, glabrous, the wings diverging at an acute angle, brown, maturing early and persisting after leaf-fall. Flowering period: March. A native of E. N. America, widely planted as an ornamental or occasionally to provide shelter and sometimes becoming naturalized. The cultivar **'Variegatum'** is most commonly used as a street tree and is a female form with yellow and green variegated leaves, although it often reverts to the normal green colour. Au Bu Fr FS Ge Hu Sp Sz.

Female flowers

Male flowers

Habit

Fruit

Leaf

Acer opalus
Miller
Italian Maple
A small tree up to 15–20m high, but often a shrub, with a broad crown. The bark is pink-tinged, broken into square plates in young trees, the plates peeling away and leaving orange patches below; in more mature trees the plates curl but do not fall away. The branches are twisted and often low and spreading; the twigs are brown with pale lenticels. The buds are 5mm long, brown, conical and pointed, The leaves are up to 10cm long, though usually less, with 3–5 short, broad, acute lobes, if 5 then the 2 basal lobes smaller and less deeply cut than the others; the leaves are at first dark green, glabrous above and generally hairy below, the hairs later becoming confined to the veins; the petiole is red above, green below, The pendulous flowers are large and relatively few in number, pale yellow with slender yellow petioles, forming subsessile clusters with glabrous peduncles, opening just before the leaves emerge. The fruit is about 2.5cm long, the wings almost parallel, 8–15 in each pendulous cluster, the wings green and pink, the seeds green at first, ripening to red or brown. Flowering period: April. A montane species of the W. Mediterranean and S. Alps, sometimes planted in parks. Co Fr Ge It Sp Sz.

Fruits

Leaf

Flowering twig

Habit

Acer obtusatum
Waldst. & Kit.
Closely related and very similar to *A. opalus*. It is distinguished by the leaves which are up to 12cm long with sometimes 3, but usually 5, broad blunt lobes. The lower leaf surfaces and the petiole are densely and persistently hairy, as are the peduncles. It has a more easterly distribution than *A. opalus*. Al Co FY Gr It Si.

Leaf

235

Fruits

Acer palmatum
Thunb.
Smooth Japanese Maple
A small tree up to 16m high, the crown domed, the bole usually very short and often rather twisted. The bark of young trees is smooth and deep brown, often with paler markings, but becoming more uniform in old specimens. The spreading branches end in slender horizontal twigs which are usually reddish above and green below. The buds are 2–3mm long, ovoid, often with a reddish tinge. The leaves are 7–9cm long with 5–7, rarely up to 11 lobes divided halfway or more to the base, all with sharply toothed margins. The flowers are clustered, 12–15 together in upright heads, each flower 6–8mm in diameter, dark purplish; the slender pedicels are about 4cm long, green or red. The fruits are usually in pendulous clusters, each pair 2cm across, the angle between the wings obtuse, in erect or pendulous clusters, becoming reddish when mature. Flowering period: April–May. A species of lowland; and mountain woods in its native Japan. Cultivars are extremely common in gardens and parks, particularly those forms with purple leaves such as cv. **'Atropurpureum'** or with scarlet autumn leaves and fruits such as cv. **'Osakazuki'**. Also, it is grown as a small, dense, strongly domed shrub.

Flowering twig

*Leaf and fruit of
cv. 'Atropurpureum'*

Habit

Acer japonicum
Thunb.
Downy Japanese Maple

A small tree up to 14m high with a high-domed crown and a very short bole usually little more than 1m high. The greyish-brown bark is smooth. The branches are horizontal or slightly curved upwards; the twigs are often reddish or brownish above. The buds are ovoid, pointed, the scales red with a greyish margin. The leaves are 7–13cm, somewhat broader than long, with 7–11 sharply pointed lobes divided less than halfway to the base, hairy when young but becoming glabrous except on the veins beneath; the margins of the lobes have sharp forward-pointing teeth; the petiole is 3–5cm long, hairy when young, becoming glabrous. The flowers are purple, about 1.5cm in diameter, appearing before the leaves in pendulous clusters on long stalks. Each pair of fruits is 4–5cm across, the angle between the wings obtuse or horizontal, the seed and the margins of the wings green, hairy at first becoming glabrous; the reddish pedicel is about 2cm long. Flowering period: April–May. This Japanese species is similar to *A. palmatum* and is also grown in gardens. The cultivar **'Vitifolium'** is planted for its bright red autumn foliage.

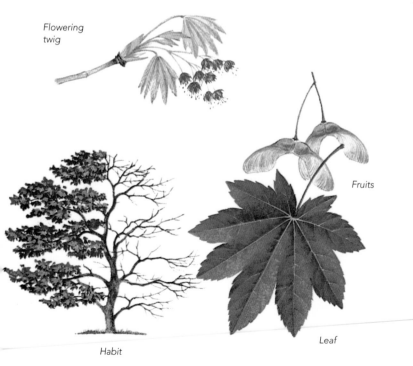

Flowering twig

Fruits

Leaf

Habit

237

Acer platanoides L.
Norway Maple

A tall tree up to 30m high with a domed spreading crown and rather short bole. The bark is grey and smooth or with low ridges. The branches are rather sparse, the twigs dull green or tinged with red. The buds are ovoid, those at the tips of shoots often with a red tinge. The leaves are 10–15cm long, with 5–7 pointed, toothed lobes, the basal pair smaller and more narrowly triangular than the rest; bright green and glabrous above, paler beneath with white hairs in the axils of the veins; the petiole is up to 20cm long. The flowers are in upright clusters of 30–40, each flower up to 8mm in diameter, a strong greenish-yellow, opening before the leaves, and persisting until the leaves are fully open. The pairs of yellowish fruits are 6–10cm across, the angle between the wings wide or horizontal. Flowering period: March–April. A forest tree native to much of Europe but only as a montane species in the south. It is planted as an ornamental in parks and gardens and frequently as a street tree. Numerous cultivars are known, many with red, purple or variegated foliage. Al Au Be Bu FC Fi Fr FS FY GB Ge Gr Hu It Ne No Po Ro Sp Sw Sz Tu. The very similar *A. lobelii* Ten., **Lobel's Maple**, from the mountains of C. and S. Italy, can be distinguished by its columnar habit and leaves with entire lobes.

Leaf

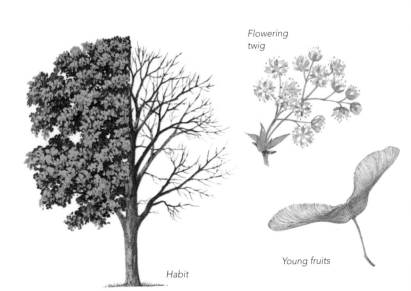

Flowering twig

Young fruits

Habit

Acer pseudoplatanus L.
Sycamore

A large tree up to 35m, the crown domed and so widely spreading as often to be broader than tall. The grey bark is fissured into irregular rectangles which sometimes flake away leaving slightly orange patches. The branches are often stout, the twigs short and rather sinuous, greyish-green with pale lenticels. The buds are 0.8–1cm long, ovoid, surrounded by reddish scales which gradually curve back and open. The leaves are 10–15cm long, 5–lobed, the lobes cut about halfway to the base, acute and coarsely toothed, dark green above, paler beneath with hairs around the main veins. The size and lobing of the leaves varies with age: immature trees have larger, more deeply cut leaves and longer scarlet petioles; mature slow-growing trees have smaller leaves and shallow lobes, the lower 2 often smaller than the others, and with shorter pink or green petioles. The flowers are numerous, yellowish, in narrow pendulous heads, 6–12cm long, appearing with the leaves. The pairs of fruits are 6cm across, the wings spreading at right-angles, green tinged with red, or brownish when ripe, glabrous. Flowering period: April. A native montane species of woods and hedges in C. and S. Europe. It is widely planted for shelter and as an ornamental, seeding freely and often becoming naturalized. Al Au Be Bu Co De FC Fr FS FY GB Ge Gr Hu Ir It Ne Pl Po Ro Si Sp Sw Sz Tu.

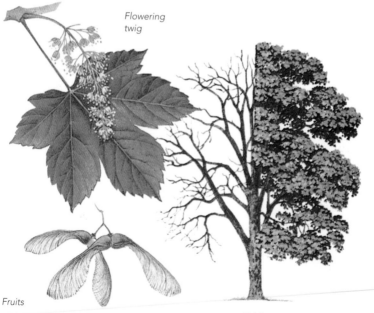

Flowering twig

Fruits

Habit

Acer saccharinum L.
Silver Maple

A tall monoecious tree up to 30m high with a spreading crown. The bark is grey and smooth, becoming shaggy as the plant matures, often covered with shoots and suckers. The branches are numerous, slender and arching with pendulous brownish or purple twigs. The leaves are 9–16cm long, 5-lobed, the lobes cutting more than halfway to the base and deeply and unevenly toothed, orange or red above becoming green, silvery with thick white hair beneath; the petiole is slender, pink. The flowers appear before the leaves in clusters of 4–5 at the nodes, similar to those of *A. rubrum* but without petals and borne on dark red pedicels. The fruit is 5–6cm long, the wings diverging at a narrow angle, green, with prominent veins. Flowering period: March. A N. American species planted in gardens and as a street tree. Cv. *'Laciniatum'* is often used in town centres.

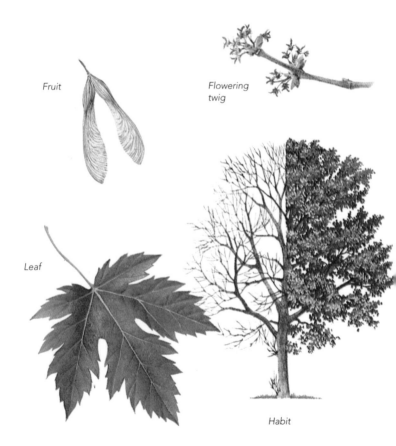

Fruit

Flowering twig

Leaf

Habit

Acer rubrum L.
Red Maple

A fast-growing monoecious or dioecious tree, up to 23m high with an irregular crown and ascending, somewhat arching branches, The twigs are slender and reddish or copper-coloured. The leaves are 8–10cm, about as broad as long, with 3–5 lobes cut less than halfway to the base, the basal lobes small, the larger lobes projecting forwards, coarsely toothed, reddish-green above at first, becoming dark green, silvery below; the petiole is red. The flower buds circle the stem, the pedicels lengthening as the flowers mature, the females becoming longer than the males; the flowers are red and appear before the leaves. The fruit is 1cm long, bright red, the wings diverging at a narrow angle. Flowering period: March. A N. American species commonly planted as an ornamental in parks, gardens and churchyards.

Fruit

Leaf

Female flowers

Acer tataricum L.
Tartar Maple

A small, usually monoecious tree up to 10m high, often a shrub. The smooth bark is brown with pale stripes. The leaves are 6–10cm long, with 3–5 lobes or more usually undivided, oblong, heart-shaped at the base, the margin finely and sharply toothed; the petiole is up to 3.5cm long, whitish or red. The flowers are greenish-white, 20–30 in suberect panicles appearing after the leaves. The fruit is 2.5cm long, the wings more or less parallel, deep red with a thick green outer edge to the wing, hairy at first but later becoming glabrous. Flowering period: May. A S. and C. European species, on rare occasions found in gardens. Al Au Bu FC FS FY Gr Hu Ro.

Habit

Flowering twig

Fuit

241

SOAPBERRY FAMILY SAPINDACEAE

Koelreuteria paniculata Laxm.
Pride of India or **Golden Rain Tree**

A graceful deciduous tree up to 15m high with a gaunt habit when young, becoming more compact at maturity, with soft pithy wood. The bark is brown with short fissures down to the orange-coloured underbark. The young shoots are minutely downy. The leaves are alternate, 15–40cm long, pinnate, sometimes twice-pinnate at the base, with 9–15 ovate-oblong leaflets each 3–8cm long, coarsely and irregularly toothed or pinnately-lobed, dark green and hairless above, paler beneath. The flowers are in large terminal pyramidal panicles up to 40cm long and 1cm in diameter, yellow, with 4 petals, 8 or fewer stamens and a 3-celled ovary. The fruit is a conical, inflated, 3-valved capsule up to 5.5cm long with acute or acuminate valves containing black seeds. A native of E. Asia widely planted in S. Europe in parks and on roadsides and perhaps naturalized in E. Europe.

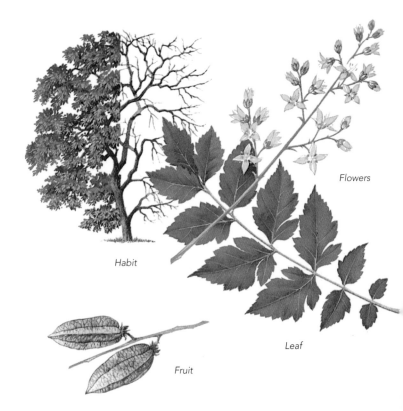

Flowers

Habit

Fruit

Leaf

HORSE CHESTNUT FAMILY HIPPOCASTANACEAE

Aesculus hippocastanum L.
Common Horse Chestnut

A stout tree up to 25m high with a huge domed crown. The bark is greyish-brown, sometimes with a red tinge, scaling or cracking to form large plates or scales. The twigs are reddish-brown with pale lenticels. The winter buds are strikingly large, up to 3.5cm long, very resiniferous and sticky. The leaves have 5–7 leaflets; each leaflet is 10–25cm long, obovate, but with a prolonged wedge-shaped base, doubly toothed, glabrous above, tomentose or glabrescent below. The flowers are in cylindrical or pyramidal panicles, 15–30cm long; the petals are *c.* 1cm long, white and blotched with pink or yellow at the base. The fruit is spiny, globose, up to 6cm in diameter, containing a single rounded seed (conker) or 2–3 flattened seeds, each one brown with a large pale scar. Flowering period: May. Fruiting period: September. A native of mountain woods, particularly in the Balkan Peninsula, but is extensively planted for ornament, for timber and as a shade tree in much of Europe except the extreme north. It is frequently locally naturalized in thickets and hedges in W. and C. Europe. A related species, *Aesculus x carnea*, the **Red Horse Chestnut** is also often planted in Europe. It is like the Common Horse Chestnut but is usually smaller in all of its parts, with pink or red petals and a fruit without spines. It is a hybrid between *A. hippocastanum* and *A. pavia* L., a N. American native.

*Flower
(A. x carnea)*

*Fruit
(A. x carnea)*

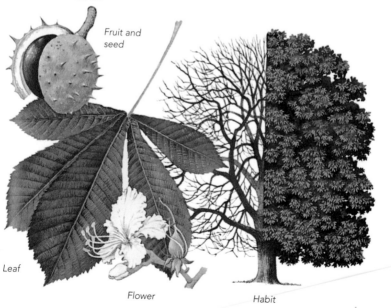

Fruit and seed

Leaf

Flower

Habit

HOLLY FAMILY AQUIFOLIACEAE

Ilex L.
Hollies

A large genus of evergreen and deciduous shrubs and trees occurring throughout the world, except in Australasia and W. N. America.

Flowering twig

Ilex aquifolium L.
Common Holly

An evergreen shrub or tree up to 10m (exceptionally up to 25m) high with a narrow, rather conical crown. The bark is smooth, silvery-grey, becoming warted with age. The young twigs are usually bright green, slightly downy, becoming smooth and shiny. The leaves are 5–12cm long, up to 3 times as long as wide, ovate to oblong-elliptic, usually spiny-tipped, the margin undulate with widely spreading, spine-tipped teeth, becoming flat and entire in the upper parts of large trees, smooth, glossy dark green above, matt dull green beneath: the petiole is *c.* 1cm long, stout, grooved above. The flowers are fragrant, 6–8mm long, the male flowers have large anthers and an abortive ovary; the female flowers have a large ovary and small anthers. The fruit is 0.7–1cm long, globose, scarlet; the pedicel is 4–8mm long. Flowering period: May–June. A native of W. Asia and W. and S. Europe, commonly forming an under-storey tree in beech or oak woodland. The Holly is widely cultivated for ornament or shelter and many varieties exist, differing in habit, leaf colour and leaf shape. Al Au Be Bu Co De Fr FY GB Ge Gr Ir It Ne No Pl Ro Sa Si Sp Sw Sz.

Fruiting twig

Habit

Bark

Ilex x altaclarensis
Dallim.
Highclere Holly

An evergreen tree up to 20m high with a dense, often domed crown The bark is purplish-grey. The branches are rather spreading. The twigs are lined with purple or some-times green. The leaves are 5–14 x 3–10cm, ovate to oblong, flat, entire or with up to 10 (rarely 20) small spines directed towards the tip, usually glossy, dark green above, paler beneath. The flowers are *c.* 1.2cm long, the base of the petals are often tinged purple. The fruit is *c.* 1.2 x 1cm, oblong-elliptic to globose, scarlet; the pedicel is up to 1.2cm long. Flowering period: May. The Highclere Holly is one of a group of vigorous hybrids derived from the Common Holly and the Canary Holly. They are commonly planted for orna-ment near the coast, and, being pollution-tolerant, in indus-trial towns. *Ilex perado*, the **Canary Holly** is similar but with leaves 2.5–6cm long, elliptic-oblong to almost orbicular, the margin entire or with up to 3 short spines directed towards the rounded tip, petiole slightly winged, flowers pinkish; fruit 7–9mm long, pedicel *c.* 1cm long. A native of the Azores, Madeira and the Canary Islands, occasionally planted for ornament in park and gardens.

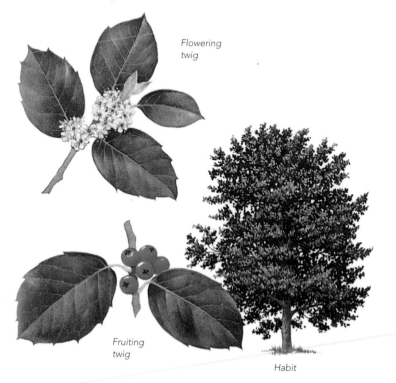

Flowering twig

Fruiting twig

Habit

SPINDLE TREE FAMILY CELASTRACEAE

Euonymus L.
Spindle Trees

Unarmed trees or shrubs with opposite leaves and flowers in 4–5 parts. The fruit is a dehiscent capsule, the seeds almost completely enveloped by a fleshy orange aril.

Euonymus europaeus L.
Common Spindle Tree

A small, much-branched, monoecious or dioecious deciduous tree or shrub up to 6m high. The bark is smooth and grey at first, becoming shallowly fissured and pink-tinged in older specimens. The twigs are green and 4-angled, becoming terete as they mature. The buds are 2–4mm long, ovoid and pointed. The leaves are up to 10cm long, ovate-lanceolate or elliptical with a pointed apex and shallow, sharply-toothed margins, turning purple-orange in autumn. The inflorescence is an axillary cyme with 3–8 yellowish–green flowers in 4 parts. The capsule is pink, 10–15cm wide, with 4 paired rounded segments. Flowering period: May–June. A common species in much of Europe except for the extreme north and south, growing in hedges and thickets on lime-rich soils. A number of cultivars are known and planted mainly for their large colourful fruits. All except Bl Cr Fi Fr Ic Ro Sz.

Fruit

Flower

Habit

Flowering twig

Euonymus latifolius (L.)
Miller
Broad-leaved Spindle Tree

Similar to *E. europaeus*, but the twigs are less obviously 4-angled and the buds are 7–12cm long, slender and more pointed, and the leaves are up to 16cm long, sometimes with finely toothed margins; the cymes have 4–12 flowers, the flowers in 5 parts with broad, rounded, pinkish petals; the capsule is 15–20cm wide, 5-celled and more angular.
Flowering period: May–June. A common species in woods and thickets of S. C. and SE. Europe. Al Au Bu Fr FS FY Ge Gr It Ro Sz Tu.

Flower

Flowering twig

Fruit

Euonymus japonicus L. fil.
Japanese Spindle Tree

An erect evergreen tree or large shrub up to 6m high with weakly 4-angled grey twigs. The leaves are thick and somewhat leathery, up to 7cm long, elliptical or widest above the middle, pointed or blunt at the tip, with very finely toothed margins. The greenish-yellow flowers are small and in 4 parts, in rather long axillary clusters. The capsule is c. 8mm wide, pinkish, with rounded angles. Flowering period: June–July. A common and variable species of coastal woodland, native to E. Asia. There are numerous cultivars with a wide range of foliage colours; widely planted for ornament, becoming naturalized in some parts of Europe. Bu Fr FY It Sp.

Flowering twig

Flower

BOX FAMILY BUXACEAE

Buxus sempervirens L.
Box

A small tree or shrub up to 5m (occasionally 8m) high, rather narrow, often leaning and with more than one bole. The bark is smooth and brown at first, becoming corky and finely fissured into small squares, turning grey in old trees. The twigs are 4-angled and green, at least when young, with persistent whitish hair. The buds are very small, 1–2mm long, terete, pale orange-brown and densely hairy. The leaves are 1.5–3cm long, ovate, oblong or elliptical, usually notched at the tip, the margins revolute, dark glossy green above, paler beneath, the proximal part of the leaf with persistent white hair; the petiole is very short, *c.* 1mm long, pale orange and hairy. The inflorescence is a terminal cluster of 5–6 sessile male flowers, *c.* 5mm in diameter, yellow, the bracteoles ovate and acute. The capsule is *c.* 7mm long, subglobose to broad-oblong, brown or grey, the styles 2.5mm long, spreading at right-angles, straight. The seeds are 5–6mm long, hard, black and shiny. Flowering period: April. A species of dry hills, usually on base-rich soils in SW. and W. C. Europe, although it is rather local. There are many different cultivars, mainly used for hedging and topiary and sometimes for timber. Al Au Be Co Fr FY GB Ge Gr It Pl Ro Sa Sp Sz Tu.

Flowering twig

Fruit

Habit

Male flower

Female flower

Buxus balearica
Lam.
Balearic Box
Similar to *B. sempervirens* but more upright and with pinkish bark; the twigs are stouter, rather stiffly erect and flattened at the nodes, glabrous or quickly becoming so; the leaves are 2.5–4cm long, the pairs more distant from each other, paler and less glossy; the inflorescence is *c.* 1cm in diameter. Flowering period: May. A species of damp rocky places in Sardinia, the Balearic Islands and parts of E. and S. Spain, although cultivated in gardens in S. Europe. BI Sa Sp.

MALLOW FAMILY MALVACEAE

Corynabutilon vitifolium (Cav.)
Kearney
Flowering Maple
A small tree or shrub 4–9m high, the young shoots covered with white hairs. The leaves are alternate, simple, grey-tomentose, usually 10–15cm long, heart-shaped at the base, the margins with 3–5 rather shallow lobes, each lobe pointed and coarsely toothed. The inflorescence is a long-pedunculate, few-flowered axillary cyme, rarely with one, usually 3–5 flowers; each flower is *c.* 7cm in diameter, in 5 parts, the petals rounded and overlapping, usually pale blue or whitish in colour. The fruit splits into several single-seeded segments. Flowering period: May–July. A native of coastal Chile, cultivated for ornament in Europe in sheltered areas with mild winters.

Flowering twig

Habit

BUCKTHORN FAMILY RHAMNACEAE

Paliurus spina-christi
Miller
Christ's Thorn
A small, profusely branched tree or shrub up to 3m high. The twigs are flexible, zigzagging, glabrous or finely hairy. The leaves are alternate, in 2 rows along the stems, 2–4cm long, ovate, the margins entire or with small sharp teeth; the stipules are spinose, the spines alternately hooked and straight. The flowers are hermaphrodite, 2mm in diameter, yellow, in loose axillary pedunculate cymes. The fruit is woody, 1.8–3cm in diameter with a broad, spreading and undulate wing. Flowering period: July. A species native to the dry slopes in the Mediterranean region, particularly the Balkan Peninsula, and sometimes grown as a hedge plant due to its resistance to grazing. Al Bu Co Fr FS FY Gr Hu It Ro Sp Tu.

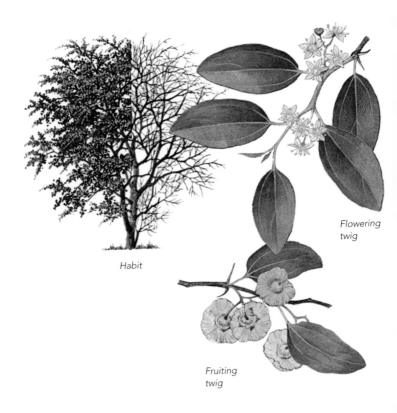

Habit

Flowering twig

Fruiting twig

Zizyphus jujuba (L.)
Miller
Common Jujube

A small, profusely branched tree or shrub up to 8m high, similar in appearance to *Paliurus*. The green twigs are flexible, zigzagging, glabrous, the sterile ones armed with spinose stipules, the flowering ones usually unarmed. The leaves are alternate, 2–7cm long, oblong with a blunt apex and shallow bluntly-toothed margins, bright shiny green and glabrous above, slightly hairy below, especially on the veins; the petioles are very short. The 2 spiny stipules are unequal in length, one long and straight, the other short and curved. The inflorescence is a small, few-flowered, axillary cyme with a peduncle shorter than the cyme; the greenish-yellow flowers are inconspicuous, about 3mm in diameter. The fruit is an ovoid-oblong drupe, 1.5–3cm long, reddish-brown or black when ripe, the flesh sweet. Flowering period: June–July. An Asian species which is cultivated in S. Europe for the edible fruits. It is sometimes naturalized in hedgerows and orchards. Al Bu Fr FY Gr It Ro Si Sp Tu.

Flowering twig

Twig with young fruits

Habit

Rhamnus catharticus L.
Buckthorn

A deciduous dioecious tree or shrub up to 10m high. The bark of old trees is nearly black, fissured and scaling to reveal orange patches. The branches are opposite, spreading at right-angles to the bole, some of the lateral branches ending in spines, the others forming short spurs bearing the leaves and flowers. The twigs may be glabrous or densely hairy, grey or brown, and have prominent leaf scars. The buds are dark with scales. The leaves are 3–7cm long, opposite or nearly so, ovate to elliptical, the apex blunt or slightly notched, the margins finely toothed, with 2–4 pairs of conspicuous lateral veins, green, turning yellow in autumn; the petiole is much shorter than the blade; the stipules are soft and fall early. The sweet-scentend flowers are in 4 or occasionally 5 parts, unisexual, on slender pedicels, solitary or in clusters on the short shoots of the previous year's wood. The fruit is a globose drupe, 6–8mm in diameter, with 2–4 yellow stones, black when ripe. Flowering period: May–June. A species of chalky soils, in hedges, thickets and on the edge of woods in much of Europe except the Mediterranean area.
Al Au Be Bu De FC Fi Fr FS FY GB Ge Gr Hu Ir It Ne No Pl Po Ro Si Sp Sw Sz.

Winter twig

Fruiting twig

Habit

Male flower

Female flower

Frangula alnus
Miller
Alder Buckthorn

A small unarmed deciduous tree or shrub up to 5m high. The bark is thin, smooth in older trees, brown with a network of purplish markings. The branches are ascending, subopposite, forming an acute angle with the bole but not distinctly differentiated into long and short shoots. The young twigs are green at first, becoming brown with age, slightly hairy and with paler lenticels. The buds are without scales but are covered with dense brownish hairs. The leaves are widest above the middle, bluntly pointed, entire, hairy beneath when young, but becoming glabrous, with 7–9 pairs of inconspicuous lateral veins, green in summer, turning yellow and red in autumn. The flowers are solitary or in clusters on the new wood, in 5 parts, hermaphrodite. The fruit is a globose drupe 0.6–1cm in diameter, yellow at first, ripening red, eventually black. Flowering period: May–June (September). Common in marshy woodlands throughout Europe except the extreme north and parts of the Mediterranean region. Al Au Be Bu De FC Fi Fr FS FY GB Ge Gr Hu Ir It Ne No Pl Po Ro Sp Sw Sz Tu.

Flower

Habit

Fruiting twig

Winter twig

253

LIME TREE FAMILY TILIACEAE

Tilia tomentosa
Moench
Silver Lime

A broad pyramidal or domed tree up to 30m tall. The bark has a network of shallow flattish ridges and is dark greenish-grey. The branches are variable, usually rather straight, ascending; the young twigs are whitish-tomentose, becoming dark greyish-green above, bright green beneath. The buds are 6–8mm long, ovoid, brown and green, pubescent. The leaves are 8–12cm long, suborbicular, abruptly narrowing to a tapering tip, the base heart-shaped on one side, the margin sharply toothed or slightly lobed, dark green, rather wrinkled and almost smooth above, white-tomentose with stellate hairs below; the petiole is 1.8–5cm long, usually less than half as long as the leaf blade, densely whitish-pubescent. The bracts are lanceolate to oblong-obovate, yellowish-green, pubescent. The flowers are dull white, 5–10 carried together in a pendent cyme; staminodes are present; the peduncles are *c.* 3cm long. The fruit is 0.6–1.2cm long, usually ovoid, slightly 5-angled, the surface minutely warted, downy. Flowering period: July–August. A species of SW. Asia and the Balkan Peninsula, extending northwards to the W. Ukraine and N. Hungary. It is frequently planted for ornament in city and town parks. Al Bu FS FY Gr Hu Ro Tu.

Fruit

Flowering shoot

Habit

Bark

Tilia petiolaris
DC.
Weeping Silver Lime

A rather narrowly domed tree up to 30m tall. The bark is dark and pale grey with narrow, shallow ridges and furrows. The branches are initially ascending and rather sinuous, becoming conspicuously pendent towards the ends; the young twigs are pale greyish-green, densely pubescent. The buds are *c.* 5mm long, ovoid, dull green, pubescent. The leaves are 5–12cm long, rounded-ovate with a short tapering point, deeply cordate or sometimes truncate at the base, sharply toothed, dark green and slightly downy, densely white-tomentose below; the petiole is 6–12cm long, usually about as long as the leaf blade, densely white-pubescent. The bracts are spathulate to narrowly obovate with minute tufts of down. The flowers are dull white, 3–10 occurring in a pendent cyme; staminodes are present; the peduncle is *c.* 3cm. The fruit is *c.* 1.2cm long, depressed-globose, slightly 5-angled, the surface minutely warted, nearly always sterile. Flowering period: July. Some authors consider this species to be an extreme variant of *T. tomentosa*, perhaps most appropriately treated as a cultivar. The origin is not known, but the Weeping Silver Lime may have come from the Caucasus. It is frequently planted in large gardens, churchyards, parks and urban streets.

Flowering shoot

Fruit

Habit

255

Tilia platyphyllos
Scop.
Large-leaved Lime

A tall, narrowly domed tree up to 40m high. The bark is dark grey, with fine fissures and sometimes flattish ridges. The branches spread at narrow angles; the young twigs are reddish-green, glabrous or pubescent, the hairs often confined to the tip of the twig. The buds are c. 6mm long, ovoid, dark red, pubescent or glabrous. The leaves are 6–9cm (rarely 15cm) long, broadly ovate, abruptly narrowed into a short tapering tip, symmetrically or obliquely deeply heart-shaped at the base, the margins with regular sharp teeth, soft, dark green above, paler and usually hairy or sometimes almost smooth beneath; the petiole is 1.2–5cm long, often pubescent. The bracts are oblong-obovate, whitish-green, minutely pubescent or glabrous. The flowers are yellowish-white, occurring in clusters of 2–6 in a pendent cyme; staminodes are absent; the style is smooth; the peduncles 1.5–3.5cm long. The fruit is 0.8–1.2cm long, almost globose to pear-shaped with 3–5 strong ridges, tomentose; the shell is woody. Flowering period: June. A variable species occurring on lime-rich soils in C. and S. Europe, extending eastwards to the W. Ukraine and Asia Minor. It may have been introduced to some parts of NW. Europe. It is frequently planted in parks and as a street tree. Al Au Be Bu Co De FC Fr FS FY GB Gr Hu It Ne Po Ro Si Sp Sw Sz Tu.

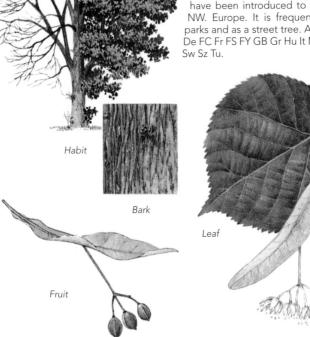

Habit

Bark

Leaf

Fruit

Flowers

Tilia rubra
DC.
A species very similar to and often confused with
T. platyphyllos but with firmer, smoother leaves with a
more oblique base, and teeth ending in a hair-like
point. S. and CE. Europe. Al Bu FS FY Gr Hu Ro.

Leaf

Tilia cordata
Miller
Small-leaved Lime
A tall, irregularly domed tree up to 32m high with
a dense crown. The bark is grey, very smooth on young trees,
becoming dark grey or brown with large cracks and flakes on
old trees. The branches are ascending, becoming down-
wardly-arched on old trees; the twigs are smooth or almost
smooth, brownish-red above, olive below. The buds are *c.*
5mm long, ovoid, smooth, dark red. The leaves are 3–9cm
long, more or less round, abruptly narrowed into a tapering
point, heart-shaped at the base, the margin with fine, sharp
teeth, dark shiny green and smooth above, pale beneath,
often glaucous with reddish-brown tufts of hairs
in the axils of the veins; the petiole is 2.5–4cm
long, smooth. The bracts are oblong-lanceolate to obovate, bright, pale green, petiolate. The
flowers are translucent white, 4–15 carried together
in an obliquely erect cyme, staminodes are absent;
the style is smooth; the peduncle is 1–2.5cm long. The
fruit is *c.* 6mm long, globose, sometimes slightly ribbed,
downy at first, but often becoming smooth; the shell is thin
and rather membranous. Flowering period: July. A
native commonly occurring on base-rich soils in
much of Europe except the extreme N. and S. It
is frequently planted in parks or as a street
tree. Al Au Be Bu Co De FC Fi Fr FS FY GB
Ge Gr Hu It Ne No Po Ro Sp Sw Sz Tu.

Fruit

*Flowering
shoot*

Habit

257

Tilia x vulgaris
Hayne
Common Lime

A tall, irregularly domed tree up to 46m high. The bark is dull grey, smooth on young trees, becoming finely fissured or with flattish ridges at maturity; the bole often with dense sprouts and burrs. The branches are ascending, becoming arched on old trees; the young twigs are green, smooth or (rarely) slightly downy. The buds are *c.* 7mm long, ovoid, reddish-brown, usually smooth. The leaves are 6–10cm long, broadly ovate with a short tapering tip, the base obliquely heart-shaped or nearly truncate, the teeth rounded with a sharp point, dull green above, paler beneath, smooth except for tufts of whitish hairs in the axils of the veins beneath; the petiole is 2–5cm long, green, smooth. The bracts are oblong, yellowish-green, slightly downy on the midrib. The flowers are yellowish-white, occurring in clusters of 5–10 in a pendent cyme, staminodes are absent; the style is smooth; the peduncle is 1.5–3.5cm long. The fruit is *c.* 8mm long, broadly ovoid to almost globose, rounded at the ends, slightly ribbed, downy, the shell thick and woody, often sterile. Flowering period: July. The Common Lime is a hybrid between *T. cordata* and *T. platyphyllos*. These two species commonly hybridize where they grow together in Europe, and the cultivated plant probably originated from a wild hybrid. It is very widely planted for ornament or as a shade tree and in many regions is more abundant than either parent. Au FC Fr FS GB Ge Gr Hu It Po Ro Si Sp Sw Sz.

Fruit

Habit

Bark

Flowering shoot

Tilia x euchlora
C. Koch
Caucasian Lime

A medium-sized, irregularly domed tree up to 20m high. The bark is smooth, dull grey, becoming brown and cracked on old trees. The branches are ascending at first, rather sinuous, curving downwards and becoming pendulous at the tips of old trees; the twigs are bright green, occasionally reddish-brown above, usually smooth. The buds are 3–6mm in diameter, yellow and reddish, smooth. The leaves are 5–10cm long, broadly ovate, abruptly narrowed into a short tapering tip, obliquely heart-shaped at the base, the teeth fine and ending in a slender hair-like tip, dark shining green above, paler beneath with conspicuous tufts of reddish-brown hairs in the axils of the veins; the petiole is *c.* 3.5cm long, smooth. The bracts are rather narrowly obovate to elliptic-oblong, greenish-white. The flowers are rich yellow, occurring in pendent cymose clusters of 3–7; staminodes are absent; the peduncle is 2.5–5.5cm long. The fruit is *c.* 1.2cm long, ovoid to elliptic, tapered at both ends, slightly 5-ribbed, downy; the shell is thick and woody. Flowering period: July. The Caucasian Lime is a rare hybrid between *T. cordata* and *T. dasystyla* Steven, from Crimean oak woodlands. *T. dasystyla* has downy young twigs, tufts of yellowish hairs in the leaf vein axils and a pubescent style. It is rarely cultivated, whereas the hybrid is frequently planted in various parts of Europe for ornament in parks or as a street tree.

Fruit

Leaf

Flowers

Habit

259

TUPELO OR SOUR-GUM TREE FAMILY NYSSACEAE

Nyssa sylvatica
Marsh
Black Gum, Tupelo or **Pepperidge**

A deciduous dioecious tree up to 30m high in the wild, with a bole up to 1.5m in diameter and a broadly conical crown. The bark is brownish-grey, with cracks separating broad ridges. The leaves are 5–15cm long x 4–8cm wide, usually ovate or obovate with a tapering base, entire or rarely somewhat toothed, usually glabrous except on the petiole and midrib; the petiole is 1.5–2.5cm long, frequently reddish-tinged. The flowers are unisexual, on separate trees, up to 1.5cm in diameter, greenish, produced on slender downy peduncles up to 3cm long; the male flowers are numerous, in rounded heads; the females are in few-flowered clusters, with 2–4 in each head. The fruit is a drupe, 1–2cm long, in a cluster, egg-shaped, bluish-black with a 1-seeded stone.

A swamp species in E. N. America introduced as an ornamental into European gardens for its brilliant red and yellow autumn foliage.

Shoot with male flowers

Autumn shoot with fruits

Habit

Female flower

Male flower

Davidia involucrata
Baillon
Pocket-handkerchief Tree, Ghost Tree or Dove Tree

A slender deciduous tree 12–20m high, with stout branches and a conical crown becoming narrowly domed at maturity. The bark is greyish-brown or purplish-brown with small vertical cracks, and occasionally flaking. The shoots are smooth and dull brown. The buds are ovoid, smooth and dark red. The leaves are 8–18cm long, broadly ovate, heart-shaped at the base, tapering to a slender tip, with 5–9 pairs of veins, the margin with triangular teeth tapering to sharp tips, deep shiny green above, pale and softly pubescent beneath; the petiole is up to 15cm long, pink, yellow-green or sometimes dark red. The flowers are small, lack petals, in dense heads, each with numerous male flowers and 1 bisexual flower; they are conspicuous by the stamens and a large pair of white bracts up to 16cm long x 10cm wide, hanging from the base. The fruits when ripe are 3.5cm in diameter, rounded, green with a purple bloom. Flowering period: May. A species native to China commonly planted in parks and gardens in NW. Europe.

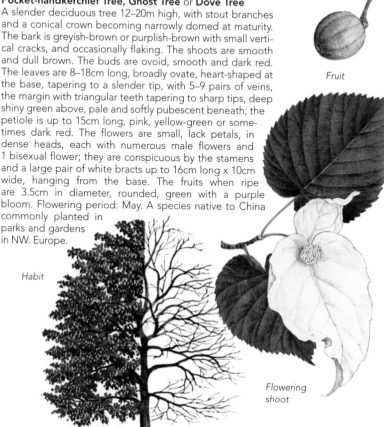

Fruit

Habit

Flowering shoot

EUCRYPHIA FAMILY EUCRYPHIACEAE

Several species of *Eucryphia*, a genus of southern hemisphere shrubs, are grown in Europe for their showy flowers. The following 2 cultivars are perhaps the most important: ***Eucryphia x nymansensis*** Bausch, a hybrid between **E. glutinosa** and **E. cordifolia** with evergreen leaves and large white flowers 6–8cm in diameter; and ***Eucryphia x intermedia***, a hybrid between *E. glutinosa* and **E. lucida** with glossy evergreen leaves and white flowers 6cm in diameter.

BUCKTHORN AND OLEASTER FAMILY ELAEAGNACEAE

Hippophäe rhamnoides L.
Sea Buckthorn

A much-branched deciduous dioecious shrub or small tree up to 11m tall, suckering freely from the bole. The bark is fissured and scaling on old stems. The twigs are covered with silvery scales. The leaves are 1–6 x 0.3–1cm, more or less sessile, simple, entire, covered on both sides with silvery or reddish-brown scales. The greenish flowers are *c.* 3mm in diameter, rather inconspicuous, appearing before the leaves on previous year's growth; the male flowers have 4 stamens, the lower flowers sessile, and the flower tube is shorter than the 2 lobes; all of the female flowers are pedicellate with a flower tube longer than the lobes. The fruits are 6–8mm in diameter, berry-like, bright orange, and contain a single seed. Flowering period: March–April. Fruiting period: September onwards. A coastal species of stable sand dunes and sea-cliffs, and on river gravel and alluvium in montane regions. It is a native of much of Europe, particularly the NW. It is often planted for ornament, or as a sand dune stabilizer, and has become naturalized in many places. Au Be Bu De FC Fi Fr FS FY GB Ge Hu It Ne No Po Ro Sp Sw.

Flowering shoot

Scales from leaf surface
(greatly magnified)

Habit

Fruit

Elaeagnus angustifolia L.
Oleaster

A dioecious deciduous shrub or small tree up to 13m high, occasionally with spiny branches. The young shoots are covered with glistening silvery scales, becoming glabrous and dark in the 2nd year. The leaves are 4–8 x 1–2.5cm, oblong or linear-lanceolate, dull green above and covered with silvery scales beneath. The flowers are 0.8–1cm long, fragrant, appearing either solitary or in twos or threes in each leaf axil, before the leaves; each flower is a bell-shaped tube, silvery outside and yellow inside; the peduncle is 2–3mm long. The fruit is oval, 1–2cm long, succulent, yellowish and covered with silvery scales. Flowering period: June. A native of W. Asia, planted for ornament and widely naturalized in S. Europe, northwards to Czechoslovakia and C. Russia. Al Au Bu Cr FC Fr FS Gr Hu It Ro Sp. A related species *Elaeagnus commutata*, the **Silver Berry** from N. America, is often confused with the Oleaster. It differs in having brown twigs and dry mealy fruits. It is cultivated and has become naturalized in many parts of Europe for its silvery foliage and delightfully fragrant flowers.

Fruit

Flowering shoot

Habit

263

TAMARISK FAMILY TAMARICACEAE

Tamarix L.

Shrubs or small trees with small, scale-like, clasping or sheathing alternate leaves with sunken, salt-secreting glands. The flowers are small, white or pink, in spike-like racemes which may be borne on the current year's growth, the previous year's growth, or both; there are 4–5 sepals and petals; there are 4–15 stamens, 4–5 opposite the sepals and 0–10 opposite the petals; there are 4–5 short styles. In species without stamens opposite the petals there is a more or less fleshy, nectar-secreting disc with 4–5 lobes between the stamens and the ovary. The seeds have a tuft of hairs.

Tamarix africana
Poiret
African Tamarisk

A slender tree up to 8m high. The bark is black or dark purple-black, and glabrous. The leaves are 1.5–4mm long, with narrow papery margins, acute. The racemes are 3–6 x 0.5–0.8cm, solitary, usually appearing in spring, but frequently summer in Spain and Portugal; the bracts are triangular, obtuse to acuminate, sometimes exceeding the calyx; the flowers are subsessile, white or pale pink, the flower parts in fives, without stamens opposite the petals; the sepals are 1.5mm long, angular-ovate, acute; the petals are 2–3mm long, angular-ovate, some of them persistent; the stamen filaments are expanded at the base and joined with the lobes of the disc. A species of coastal salt marshes and river banks in SW. Europe but introduced and occasionally naturalized elsewhere. BI Co Fr GB It Po Sa Si Sp.

Flowering shoot

Flower

Habit

Tamarix canariensis
Willd.

A more or less bushy shrub or tree up to 10m high with reddish-brown bark. The leaves are 1–3mm long. The racemes are 1.5–4.5 x 0.3–0.5cm, solitary or clustered, dense, with a papillose axis, usually appearing in summer, but sometimes spring in Spain; the bracts are linear to triangular-acuminate, entire, equalling or somewhat exceeding the calyx; the flowers are pink, with 5 parts, and with 5 stamens opposite the petals; the sepals are 0.5–0.75mm long, finely and deeply divided; the petals are 1.25–1.5mm long, obovate and falling early; the stamen filaments are expanded at the base and joined with the lobes of the disc. A maritime species in dry places of the W. Mediterranean region and Portugal. Bl Fr Po Sa Si Sp.

Flower

Flowering shoot

Habit

Tamarix gallica L.
French Tamarisk

A small tree or often a shrub up to 8m. The bark is purplish-brown to blackish-brown, without papillae. The leaves are 1.5–2mm long. The racemes are 2.5 x *c.* 0.5cm, loosely clustered, appearing in spring; the bracts are ragged-edged, shorter than the calyx, the lowermost oblong and blunt, the upper narrowly triangular with a slender tapering point; the flowers are pink and in 5 parts without stamens opposite the petals; the sepals are 0.7–1.3mm, angular-ovate, acute; the petals are 1.5–2mm long, elliptic to somewhat ovate, falling early; the stamen filaments are not conspicuously swollen at the base but are joined with the lobes of the disc. A common species in SW. Europe, extending to NW. France but frequently cultivated and occasionally becoming naturalized elsewhere. BI Co Fr GB It Si Sp.

Flowering shoot

Flower

Habit

Tamarix parviflora
DC.

A feathery, slender shrub or small tree up to 6m high, with a dark brown or purple smooth bark. The leaves are 3–5mm long, acute, with a papery margin. The racemes are 3–5 x 0.3–0.5cm, solitary, dense, mostly produced in the spring; the bracts are oblong, obtuse and almost entirely scarious, the flowers are white or pale pink, with 4 (occasionally 5) parts with 0–4 stamens opposite the petals, the sepals are 2–2.5mm long, ovate or somewhat angular, denticulate, the outer keeled and acute, the inner obtuse and shorter; the petals are *c.* 2mm long, the filaments of the stamens opposite the sepals are inserted in shallow sinuses between the lobes of the conspicuous fleshy disc. A native of river banks, hedges and roadsides of the Balkan Peninsula and the Aegean region, but now widely cultivated for ornament in C. and S. Europe. Al Co Cr FY Gr It Sp Tu.

Flower

Flowering shoot

Habit

Tamarix tetrandra
Pallas ex Bieb.

A remarkably similar species to *T. parviflora* but with black bark, longer and broader racemes, herbaceous bracts and larger flowers (with petals 2.5–3mm long). A montane species, particularly of damp places in SE. Europe and the Balkan Peninsula. Bu FS FY Gr Tu.

Flower

Tamarix dalmatica
Baum

A small glabrous tree with dark brown or blackish bark. The leaves are 2.5–4mm, long, acute. The racemes are 2–6 x 0.8–1cm, solitary, usually appearing in spring. The bracts are broadly triangular, obtuse to acuminate, often thin and papery usually exceeding the pedicels and calyx; the flowers are subsessile, white, in 4 (sometimes 5) parts with up to 3 stamens opposite the petals; the sepals are 3.5mm long, keeled, the outer ones angular-ovate, acute, the inner ones obtuse; the petals are 2.5–5mm long, narrowly obovate; the bases of the stamen filament suddenly expand to surround the disc. A common species of coastal marshes and river banks in the E. Mediterranean. Al Cr FY Gr It Si.

Flowering shoot

Flower

Habit

268

Tamarix smyrnensis
Bunge

A small tree or shrub with reddish-brown bark. The leaves are 1.5–3.5mm long, acute. The racemes are 1.5–7 x 0.3–0.4cm long, loosely clustered, the uppermost without flowers at the base, usually appearing in summer, the bracts are narrowly triangular, acute, denticulate, exceeding the pedicels, the pedicel is shorter than the calyx; the flowers are pink, in 5 parts, without stamens opposite the petals; the sepals are *c.* 1mm long, angular-ovate, obtuse or sometimes ragged at the tip, the petals are *c.* 2mm long, ovate-orbicular, strongly keeled, especially towards the base; the stamen filaments are slender and attached between the slightly notched lobes of the fleshy disc. A species of coastal salt-marshes and mountain streams in SE. Europe, extending from the Aegean region to the S. Ukraine. Al Bu Cr FS Gr Ro Tu. The similar Chinese species, *T. chinensis* Louv., the **Chinese Tamarisk**, is widely planted in Europe for ornament. It has smaller flowers than *T. smyrnensis*.

Flowering shoot

Flower

Habit

269

MYRTLE FAMILY MYRTACEAE

Eucalyptus
L'Her

Eucalyptus and Gum Trees

Large to medium-sized trees. The bark is of 3 kinds: (i) soft and brittle, shedding in short irregular flakes, lacking in fibre; (ii) hard and long-fibred, shedding in long, broad, thick flakes or strips; (iii) very thin and finely fibred, shedding in ribbons. The leaves are of 3 kinds, passing through juvenile, intermediate and mature stages. The inflorescences are either solitary or in umbels. The buds are surrounded by an operculum of fused calyx segments. The fruit is a capsule consisting of an enlarged calyx tube with a flat disc surrounded by a rim and opening by valves.

Eucalyptus botryoides
Sm.
Bangalay

A dense, shade-giving tree, 12–24m high. The bark is slightly fibrous and persistent on the trunk and main branches. Juvenile leaves are 5–8 x 3–4cm, opposite for 3–4 pairs, broadly lanceolate to ovate, with short petioles, thin and somewhat wavy, with very fine veins; mature leaves are 10–14 x 3–6cm, alternate, lanceolate to oval, dark green, leathery, pointed, with long petioles; the veins are faint to conspicuous and the intramarginal vein is close to the margin. The inflorescence

Flowering twig

Habit

Bark

Cluster of fruits

is axillary, in 6 to 10-flowered umbels on peduncles 7–10cm long. The buds are 1–1.2 x 0.5–0.6cm, slightly angled or 2-ribbed, sessile; the operculum is hemispherical or bluntly conical; the anthers are oblong, with an ovate dorsal gland about half the length of the cells. The fruit is 7–9 x 7–9mm, sessile, cylindrical or barrel-shaped, with a small disc and 3–4 triangular valves, which are enclosed or only slightly project-ing above the rim. A timber, shade or ornamental tree which will grow on a variety of soils but in particular well-suited to gravelly, sandy or even marshy soils. A native of SE. Australia (New South Wales and Victoria) now cultivated in It Pl Si Sp.

Juvenile leaves

Eucalyptus citriodora
Hooker
Lemon-scented Spotted Gum

A tall graceful slender tree 25–40m high. The bark is smooth and deciduous throughout, white or pinkish. The juvenile leaves are 7–15 x 3–6cm, opposite for 4–5 pairs, oblong or lanceolate, rough and bristly; the adult leaves are 10–25 x 1–4cm, alternate, narrowly or broadly lanceolate, strongly lemon-scented; the veins are moderately conspicuous but the intramarginal vein is not distinct from the margin. The inflorescence is an axillary branched flattened spike, with 3–5 flowers on peduncles 5–7mm long. The buds are 1–1.2 x 0.7–0.8cm, pedicellate; the operculum is hemispherical; the anthers are somewhat club-shaped, with a gland about half as long as the long cells. The fruit is *c.* 1 x 1cm, globose or subcylindrical, shortly pediceilate, but strongly contracted at the mouth with a wide disc and 3–4 enclosed valves. An adaptable tree found on a variety of soils but particularly suitable for poor soils. A native of Queens-land, this species is cultivated as an ornamental in It Pl Sp.

Cluster of fruits

Flowering twig

Juvenile leaves

Bark

Habit

271

Eucalyptus robusta
Sm.
Swamp Mahogany, Swamp Messmate, Iron Bark
A medium-sized shady tree up to 30m high. The bark is rough, rather fibrous and persistent throughout, dark in colour. The juvenile leaves are up to 11 x 7cm long, opposite for 4–5 pairs, stalked, thick, broadly lanceolate to elliptic-lanceolate; adult leaves are 10–18 x 4cm, alternate, lanceolate to oval, with long apical points, lustrous dark green above, dull green below, the veins are moderately conspicuous. The inflorescence is an axillary umbel of 5–10 flowers, supported by a flat peduncle 2–3cm long, the buds are 1–2 x 0.7–1cm, on short pedicels; the operculum is beak-like; the anthers are somewhat club-shaped with a large oval dorsal gland. The fruit is 1.2–1.5 x 1–1.2cm, pedicellate, cylindrical to urn-shaped, with an oblique disc and deeply enclosed valves. A lowland plant from marshes, shores of estuaries and brackish water. A native of E. Australia, it is now planted as a plantation tree for its foliage, as a shade tree and a windbreak in Fr It Pl Sa Sp.

Flowering twig

Cluster of fruits

Juvenile leaves

Bark

Habit

272

Eucalyptus resinifera
Sm. in White
Red Mahogany

A large tree with trunk up to 1.2m in diameter at maturity. The bark is rough, very fibrous with distinct longitudinal fissures, shedding below but persistent on the branches, reddish in colour. The juvenile leaves are 4–6 x 1.5–2cm, opposite for 3–4 pairs, lanceolate to ovate with short petioles; the adult leaves are 10–16 x 2–3cm, alternate, lanceolate, dark green above, paler below, the veins moderately conspicuous. The inflorescence is an axillary umbel with 5–10 flowers on flattened peduncles 1.5–2cm long. The buds are 1.2–1.7 x 0.5–0.6cm, pedicellate; the operculum is very long and pointed, 2–3 times as long as the calyx tube; the anthers are club-shaped to oblong, opening in parallel slits. The fruit is 5–8 x 5–8mm, ovoid to hemispherical with a small, slightly domed disc and 4 strongly projecting valves. A species which is grown on a variety of soils but mostly suitable for sandy coastal areas with subsoil moisture. A native of E. Australia (Queensland and New South Wales) the Red Mahogany is grown widely in sheltered places of the Mediterranean region as a timber tree, for its hard, heavy, fine-grained timber, Fr It Pl Sa Sp. The N. African hybrid *Eucalyptus x trabutii* is similar in general appearance to *E. resinifera* and grown in similar places, but has more oval mature leaves, a shorter operculum and a fruit more tapered at the base.

Valve arrangements

teeth

E. botryoides

deflexed teeth / raised septum

pore

E. citriodora   *E. robusta*

E. camaldulensis

E. maidenii

Flowering twig

Cluster of fruits

Juvenile leaves

Habit

Bark

273

Eucalyptus gomphocephala
DC.
Tuart

A medium-sized to large tree up to 43m high. The bark is fibrous and persistent throughout, light grey. The juvenile leaves are 5–7 x 4–5cm, opposite for 3–4 pairs, broadly lanceolate, the mature leaves are up to 17 x 2cm, alternate, distinctly stalked, thick, narrowly lanceolate, pointed. The inflorescence is an axillary umbel with 3–7 flowers suspended on strap-shaped peduncles, 2.5–3.5 x 1–1.5cm long. The buds are 2–2.5 x 1.2–1.5cm, sessile. The operculum is hemispherical or bluntly conical, mushroom-like and broader than the calyx tube, the anthers are oblong, opening in longitudinal slits and with a large oblong dorsal gland. The fruit is 1.3–2 x 1.1–1.5cm, sessile, bell-shaped, with a disc forming a conspicuous rim around the strong, shortly projecting valves. Occurring on low-lying coastal plains on sandy loam and calcareous soils. A coastal species of Australia, planted experimentally for reafforestation of sand dunes, since it is resistant to drought, and, owing to its short bole, resistant to wind. It Si Sp.

Juvenile leaves

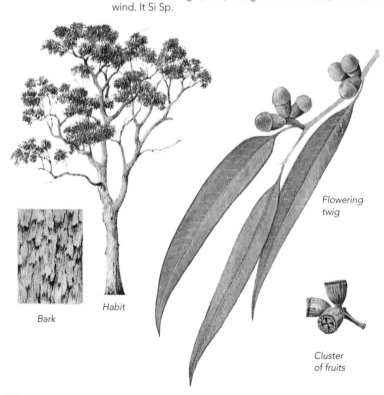

Bark

Habit

Flowering twig

Cluster of fruits

Eucalyptus camaldulensis
Dehnh.
Red Gum or Murray Red Gum

A tall tree growing up to (rarely) 40m with a short trunk and a spreading crown. The bark is smooth, shedding in plates or strips, mottled buff and grey. The juvenile leaves are 6–9 x 2.5–4cm, opposite for 3–4 pairs, broadly lanceolate to ovate, waxy and bluish, the adult leaves are 12–22 x 0.8–1.5cm, alternate, lanceolate, long-pointed, thin, dull and pale green; the veins are conspicuous. The inflorescence is an axillary 5 to 10-flowered umbel on a slender round peduncle 0.6–1.5cm long. The buds are 0.6–1 x 0.4–0.5cm, on slender 3–8mm pedicels. The operculum is beaked, or a long cone; the anthers are obovate, opening in parallel slits, with a small globose dorsal gland. The fruit is 6–8 x 5–6mm, hemispherical to broadly top-shaped, with a sharp domed disc and 4 sharp triangular curved valves. One of the most variable and widespread species of Australia, it is one of the most widely planted trees in the world's eucalypt plantations. It is usually planted on heavy soils and in Spain is particularly valuable as a timber tree for making mine props and for use as firewood. It was introduced to the Mediterranean region in the early 19th century. Al Co Gr It Pl Sa Si Sp

Valve arrangements

horizontal teeth

E. gunnii   *E. resinifera*

horizontal teeth

E. gomphocephala

erect teeth

E. globulus   *E. viminalis*

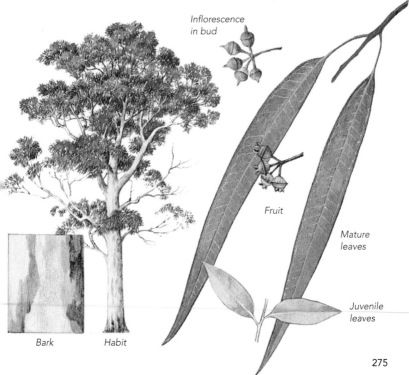

Inflorescence in bud

Fruit

Mature leaves

Juvenile leaves

Bark   Habit

275

Eucalyptus globulus
Labill.
Tasmanian Blue Gum

A medium-sized to large tree, reputed to attain 65m. The bark is smooth, mostly deciduous but persistent at the base, blue-grey. The juvenile leaves are 7–16 x 4–9cm, opposite for many pairs, broadly lanceolate to ovate, heart-shaped at the base, sessile and even clasping the stem; the adult leaves are 10–30 x 3–4cm, or longer, alternate, narrowly lanceolate to lanceolate, sickle-shaped, lustrous dark-green all over, leathery, distinctly petiolate; the veins are only moderately conspicuous. The inflorescence consists usually of a single axillary flower but can have an umbel with up to 3 flowers on very short peduncles. The buds are up to 3 x 2cm glaucous, sessile, the operculum is a flattened hemisphere, peaked, thick and warty; the anthers are obovate, opening in broad parallel slits with a globose gland. The fruit is 1–1.5 x 1.5–3cm, a flat globe-shape to broadly top-shaped, roughly 4-angled, warty, with one or more short irregular ribs, and with a large, thick smooth disc completely extending over 3–6 valves arranged more or less at disc level. An Australian endemic from SE. Tasmania and Victoria. Planted on a tremendous scale in the Mediterranean region. It is grown for its yellow timber, used as a pulp in the paper industry, and as a source of oil from the leaves. It occurs particularly in Sp and Pl, but also in Co Gr It and as an ornamental in GB. In addition to *E. globulus* and the species described on pages 270–279 which have been largely planted in S.C. and SW. Mediterranean Europe, some 30 other species of Eucalyptus have been occasionally planted for ornamental purposes in parks and gardens and in small coastal plantations in many parts of NW. Europe. Important examples include ***E. rudis, E. cladocalyx, E. diversicolor, E. maculata, E. sideroxylon, E. amygdalina, E. pauciflora, E. punctata, E. tereticornis, E. urnigera*** and ***E. coccifera***.

Habit

Flowering twig

Fruit

Juvenile leaves

Bark

Eucalyptus maidenii
Mueller
Maiden's Gum

A medium-sized to tall tree 15–46m high. The bark is smooth, shedding annually, bluish-white. The juvenile leaves are 4–16 x 4–12cm, opposite for a large number of pairs, ovate to almost orbicular, often heart-shaped at the base, distinctly greyish in appearance; the mature leaves are up to 20 x 2.5cm, alternate, narrowly lanceolate to lanceolate, sickle-shaped, dark lustrous green, leathery, petiolate: the veins are conspicuous. The inflorescence is an axillary 3–7 (or more) flowered umbel on a flattened peduncle, 10–15cm long. The buds are *c.* 1.5 x 0.8cm, sessile or pedicellate, the operculum is a peaked hemisphere or beak-shaped. The anthers are obovate, opening in narrow parallel slits with an ovate gland, half the length of the cells. The fruit is 0.8–1 x 1–1.2cm, subsessile to shortly bedicellate, bell-shaped or conical, waxy on the surface, with a thick, smooth, flat or convex disc partly fused to the strongly projecting valves. A species of good, somewhat heavy soils. A SE. Australian tree cultivated for timber. It Pl Sa Si Sp

Fruit

Flowering twig

Bark

Habit

Juvenile leaves

Eucalyptus viminalis
Labill.
Ribbon Gum

A large tree up to 50m high. The bark is rough and persistent at the base or quite smooth throughout, deciduous, often hanging from the branches in long ribbons. The juvenile leaves are 5–10 x 1.5–3cm, slender, lanceolate, opposite for an indefinite number of pairs, sessile to semi-clasping, pale green; the intermediate leaves are 8–27 x 4–5cm, broadly lanceolate, pointed, pale green; the mature leaves are 11–18 x 1.5–2cm, narrowly lanceolate, alternate, petiolate, flat or undulate, pale green; the veins are faint to moderately conspicuous. The inflorescence is an axillary, usually 3-flowered umbel on an angular 3–6mm peduncle. The buds are c. 7 x 5mm, oval to cylindrical, sessile or on short pedicels; the operculum is hemispherical to conical, usually longer than the tube; the anthers are obovate with an ovate gland. The fruit is 5–6 x 7–8mm, spherical or top-shaped, sessile or with a very short pedicel with a prominent convex or upwardly contracted disc and 3–4 projecting and spreading valves. Flowering period: August–September. A fairly useful shade and shelter tree with a light, serviceable timber. It grows in Riviera towns and Mediterranean sandy areas. A S. and E. Australian and Tasmanian tree cultivated in It Pl Sp.

Fruit

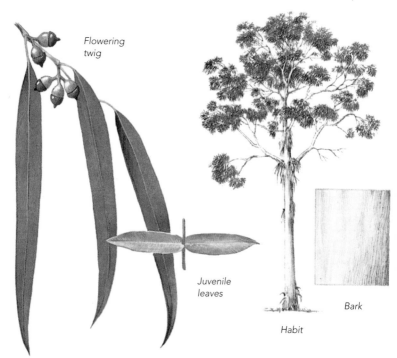

Flowering twig

Juvenile leaves

Bark

Habit

Eucalyptus gunnii
Hooker fil.
Cider Gum
A medium-sized to large tree up to 30m high. The bark is quite smooth, deciduous, green and white or pink-tinged. The juvenile leaves are 3–4 x 2–4cm or larger, elliptical to obovate in outline and somewhat heart-shaped at the base, sessile, glaucous or green; the mature leaves are 4–7 x 1.5–3cm, narrow to broad lanceolate, petiolate, distinctly green; the veins are faint to moderately conspicuous. The inflorescence is an axillary 3-flowered umbel on a slightly flattened or rounded peduncle 3–8mm long. The buds are 6–8 x c. 5mm, club-shaped or subcylindrical, sessile or on short pedicels, the operculum is peaked-hemispherical and much shorter than the flask-shaped calyx-tube, the anthers are oblong to orbicular with a large globose dorsal gland. The fruit is 0.7–1 x 0.8–0.9cm, hemispherical or bell-shaped, with a small depressed blunt disc and 3–5 narrow, slightly projecting valves. A subalpine species planted in cooler parts of Europe, since it is tolerant to cold weather and wet soils. A native species from the highlands of Tasmania, it has been vigorously cultivated from seed in Britain and France.

Juvenile leaves

Habit

Bark

Flowering twig

Fruit

Myrtus apiculata
Niedenzu
Orange-bark Myrtle
A moderate-sized evergreen tree with a loosely conical crown. The orange bark flakes readily to leave tapering white streaks below. The leaves are 2.5 x 1.5cm, alternate, subsessile, oval with a distinct mucronate tip, with a sweet spicy smell when crushed. The flowers are solitary in the axils of the leaves; they are globose in bud, red and green in colour, producing masses of white flowers up to 2cm in diameter. The fruit is a berry, initially red, becoming black. Flowering period: August–September. A S. American species planted in gardens.

Flower

POMEGRANATE FAMILY PUNICACEAE

Punica granatum L.
Pomegranate

A deciduous shrub or sometimes a small tree up to 8m high. The branches are numerous, slender, mostly ascending or erect. The twigs are spiny or unarmed, somewhat 4-angled, glabrous. The leaves are opposite, 2–8 x 0.8–2.5cm, oblong-lanceolate to obovate, entire, smooth and shiny, without glands; the petiole is very short; stipules are absent. The flowers are hermaphrodite, terminal, often on short side-shoots, solitary or in pairs, each 2.5–4cm in diameter; the sepal tube is funnel-shaped at the base, leathery, persistent, reddish with 5 or more thick, pointed lobes; the 5–7 petals are scarlet or sometimes white, crumpled in bud; the stamens are numerous. The fruit is 5–8cm in diameter, globose to somewhat oblong, reddish-brown or yellowish, the outer layer leathery, containing several cells each with many seeds; the fleshy layer surrounding each seed is translucent, purplish-yellowish or white, acid, usually becoming sweet; the pedicel is very short. Flowering period: June–September. A native of SW. Asia but cultivated from antiquity in S. Europe for its edible fruit and often naturalized in the Mediterranean region. Al Bl Bu Co Cr Fr FY Gr It Pl Ro Sa Si Sp Sz Tu.

Flowers

Fruit

Habit

DOGWOOD FAMILY CORNACEAE

Cornus mas L.
Cornelian Cherry

A small deciduous tree or shrub up to 8m (occasionally 15m) with an open crown. The branches are spreading, greyish. The young twigs are greenish-yellow, covered with minute grey hairs. The leaves are opposite, 4–10 x 2–4cm, ovate to elliptic, acuminate at the apex, the base rounded or acute, entire, dull green, pubescent; the petiole is *c.* 6mm long. The flowers are in small umbellate flower-heads, *c.* 2cm in diameter, each containing 10–25 flowers, appearing before the leaves on the previous year's growth; the bracts are 0.6–1 x 0.3–0.6cm, yellowish, pubescent, 4 at the base of each flower cluster, falling readily; each flower is c. 4mm in diameter, yellow. The fruit is a berry, 1.2–2cm long, oblong-ovoid with a sunken apex, pendulous, fleshy, bright red when ripe, acid-tasting; the pedicel is *c.* 6mm long. Flowering period: February–March. A native to C. and SE. Europe but naturalized in some localities, occurring in thickets and other scrub, or among woodland. It is cultivated for its edible fruit and showy winter flowers. Al Au Be Bu FC Fr FS FY GB Ge Gr Hu It Ro Tu Sz. A related species, *C. sanguinea*, the **Dogwood**, is usually a deciduous shrub, found throughout Europe except in some parts of the extreme north and south.

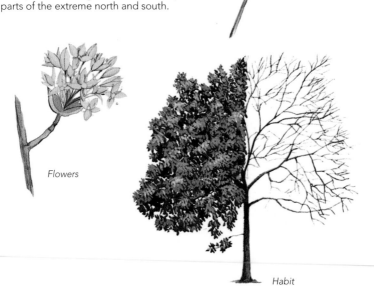

Fruit

Flowers

Habit

HEATHER FAMILY ERICACEAE

Arbutus unedo L.
Strawberry Tree

A small tree or shrub up to 9m high with a dense rounded crown and usually a short bole. The bark is at first red, later shredding and obscured by brown, hanging strips. The branches are numerous, ascending and sinuous, the young twigs glandular-hairy and pink or red. The leaves are 4–11cm long, 1.5–4cm wide, oblong-lanceolate, 2–3 times as long as broad, the margins with sharp forward-projecting teeth or almost entire, hairy only at the base, dark glossy green above, paler beneath and with a prominent midrib; the petiole is up to 1cm long, hairy and often red. The drooping panicle is 4–5cm long, the flowers appearing in autumn together with the ripening fruits from the previous year. The calyx is green, 1.5mm long with suborbicular lobes; the corolla 9mm long, white or tinged with pink or green, The berry is 2cm in diameter, globose and covered with conical papillae, yellow, becoming scarlet or deep red when ripe, the flesh rather acid. Flowering period: October–November. A species of evergreen thickets, wood margins and dry slopes in the Mediterranean region but occurring locally as far north as NW. Ireland. It is sometimes planted in gardens. Al Bl Co Cr Fr FY Gr Ir It Sa Si Sp Tu.

Flowering twig

Fruit

Bark

Habit

Arbutus andrachne L.
Cyprus or Eastern Strawberry Tree

Similar to *A. unedo* but sometimes reaching 12m in height. The bark is smooth and orange-red, peeling in sheets to reveal the yellowish or cinnamon-coloured underbark. The young twigs are glabrous, initially yellowish-green, later becoming brown. The leaves are 5–10cm long, 3–6cm wide, less than twice as long as broad, the young ones sometimes toothed, old ones entire, the midrib pale and prominent above; the petiole is 1.5–2.5cm long. The panicles are erect, the flowers appearing in spring. The calyx is 2.5mm long with ovate, acute lobes. The berry is 0.8–1.2cm in diameter, almost smooth or with a slight raised network, orange when ripe. Flowering period: March–April. An endemic of the Aegean region and S. Crimea. Al Cr Gr Ro Tu.

Flowering twig

Fruit

Bark

Habit

Arbutus x andrachnoides
Link
Hybrid Strawberry Tree

A vigorous fertile hybrid between *A. unedo* and *A. andrachne* with the brightly coloured bark of *A. andrachne*, peeling to reveal paler areas. There are at least some glandular hairs on the young twigs and the leaves have toothed margins and red petioles as in *A. unedo*. The flowers may appear in autumn or early spring and the fruits are smaller and smoother than those of *A. unedo*. Common when the parents grow together and sometimes raised in cultivation. The N. American **A. menziesii**, the **Madrona**, is sometimes grown in gardens in W. and S. Europe.

PERSIMMON FAMILY EBENACEAE

Diospyros lotus L.
Date Plum

A small tree up to 14m high with a rounded crown. The bark is furrowed and fissured into small plates, dark grey or sometimes pink-tinged. The leaves are 6–12cm (sometimes up to 18cm) long, elliptic to oblong, rounded at the base, pointed at the tip, the margins entire but wavy, dark glossy green above, somewhat glaucous below, pubescent when young, becoming glabrous above and hairy only on the veins beneath; the petiole is about 1cm long, hairy. The flowers are urn-shaped, the males about 5mm long, 2–3 in a cluster, the females 0.8–1cm long, solitary; the calyx is hairy within and has 4 short fringed lobes; the corolla is reddish or greenish-white, the lobes fringed and recurved, about half as long as the tube. The fruit is about 1.5cm in diameter, globose, yellow or bluish-black with a dew-like bloom, the flesh sweet but somewhat insipid. Flowering period: July. Native throughout Asia, it is cultivated in N. Europe for ornament and often becomes naturalized. In S. Europe it is cultivated for its edible fruits. Al Bl Bu Fr Gr It Ro Sp Sz.

Habit

Fruit

Leaf with female flower

Leaf with male flowers

Immature fruit

Diospyros kaki L. fil.
Chinese Persimmon
or **Kakee**

Similar to *D. lotus* but with a scaly bark and a larger fruit, 3.5–7.5cm in diameter, ovoid to more or less globose, yellowish or orange, the flesh sweet only when over ripe. Flowering period: June. A native of Japan and E. Asia, cultivated in S. Europe for its edible fruits. Al Bu Fr It Pl Ro.

Habit

STORAX FAMILY STYRACACEAE

Styrax officinale L.
Storax

A small deciduous tree or shrub 2–7m high with all parts stellate-hairy. The crown is rounded or somewhat flattened and the bark is smooth and grey. The leaves are alternate, simple, 3–7cm long, ovate to almost oblong, rounded at the base, obtuse at the apex, the margins entire, green above, paler or whitish beneath, both surfaces hairy but the lower one more densely so. The flowers number 3–6 in terminal or axillary, loose, drooping racemes; the calyx is bell-shaped, nearly entire, greenish and attached to the ovary; the corolla is *c.* 2cm in diameter, bell-shaped and deeply 5-lobed, white; there are 10 or occasionally 12 yellow stamens; the pedicels are 1–2cm long, densely hairy. The fruit is a dry drupe up to 1cm long, ovoid, greyish and densely hairy, crowned with the remains of the persistent style. Flowering period: April–May. A species of woods and thickets, often by streams in parts of the Mediterranean from Italy eastwards, and naturalized in France. The aromatic gum storax is obtained by making incisions in the bole and branches. Cr Fr FY Gr It Tu.

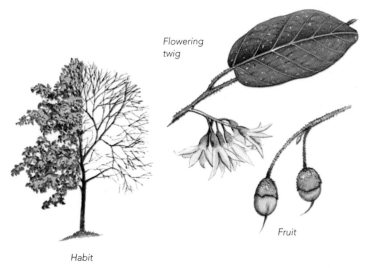

Flowering twig

Fruit

Habit

Styrax japonica
Siebold & Zucc.
Snowball Tree

A similar species to *S. officinale* but up to 11 m high. Flowering period: June–July. A native of China and Japan which produces numerous flowers and is often grown as an ornamental in N. Europe.

OLIVE FAMILY OLEACEAE

Fraxinus L.
Ashes

Fraxinus ornus L.
Manna Ash

A medium-sized tree up to 24m high with a domed or somewhat flattened crown. The bark is smooth and grey, sometimes dark grey or even black. The twigs are grey or yellowish, usually glabrous. The buds are greyish or brownish and covered with a whitish bloom. The leaves are pinnate with a terminal leaflet, up to 30cm long, each with a grooved rachis and bearing 5–9 leaflets; each leaflet is 3–10cm (rarely as little as 1.5cm) long, ovate or lanceolate with a pointed apex and irregularly sharp-toothed margin, pale beneath with downy brown or white hair on the veins, subsessile to distinctly stalked. The panicles are 15–20cm long, terminal or axillary, appearing after the leaves. The flowers are creamy-white and fragrant, the calyx small, deeply lobed and persistent, the corolla consisting of 4 linear petals, each 5–6cm long. The samara is 1.5–2.5cm long, oblong, widest above the middle or sometimes notched at the apex, with a slender wing, green at first, becoming brown when mature. Flowering period: May. A common species of woods, thickets and rocky parts of C. Europe and the Mediterranean area. It is frequently found in parks and gardens and sometimes as a street tree. Al Au Bu Co FC Fr FY Gr Hu It Ro Sa Si Sp Sz Tu.

Part of inflorescence

Flower

Leaf

Habit

Bark

Fruits

286

Fraxinus pennsylvanica
Marshall
Red Ash
A dioecious tree up to 25m high with a domed crown. The bark is slightly furrowed and reddish-brown. The leaves are 22cm (sometimes up to 30cm) long with a white, hairy rachis bearing 5–9 (usually 7) leaflets, the largest 8–15cm long, lanceolate to ovate-lanceolate or elliptic, pointed or blunt at the apex and often unequal at the base, irregularly toothed or entire, green and densely hairy beneath, rather thin in texture, subsessile or with the base of the blade decurrent on a short stalk. The flowers occur in axillary, densely hairy panicles appearing before the leaves; they have a persistent calyx but lack a corolla. The samara is 3–6cm long, the wing linear-oblong or widest above the middle, pointed, rounded or notched at the tip, decurrent to about the middle of the cylindrical body. A species of wet woods in E. N. America, planted for timber or to provide shelter in C. and SE. Europe, becoming naturalized in places. The **Green Ash**, var. *'subintegerrima'* is also cultivated in Europe and differs in its thicker leaves and glabrous young branches, rachis, panicles and lower leaf-surfaces. Au Bu FC FS Ge Ro.

Bark

Fruits

Leaf

Female flowers

Male flowers

Habit

Fraxinus americana L.
White Ash
A species similar to *F. pennsylvanica* but taller, up to 40m high, with longer petiolules and the bases of the leaflets not decurrent. A wet woodland species of E. N. America planted in E. Europe on a small scale.

Leaf

Fraxinus excelsior L.
Common Ash

A tall tree up to 40m high with an open, domed crown. The bark is pale grey, smooth on young trees, becoming ridged and fissured when old. The twigs are strongly flattened at the nodes. The buds are conical and black. The leaves are 20–35cm long with a glabrous or densely hairy rachis bearing 7–13 leaflets or occasionally a large single terminal leaflet; each leaflet is 5–12cm long, oblong-ovate to oblong-lanceolate, with a pointed apex and sharp-toothed margins, the number of teeth exceeding the number of lateral veins, dark green above, pale beneath with dense white hair on the midrib and towards the base. The axillary panicles are globose, on 2nd year twigs, appearing before the leaves. The flowers are purple. The numerous samaras form large pendent clusters, each samara 2.5–5cm long, oblong to lanceolate, notched and with a spine at the tip, bright green at first, becoming brown, Flowering period: April–May. Individual trees may be completely male, completely female, completely hermaphrodite, or have a mixture of male and female branches. A common species throughout Europe, and frequently cultivated, especially on damp base-rich soils. The grafted cv. *'Pendula'*, the **Weeping Ash**, is planted in towns and parks. Au Be Bu De FC Fr FS FY GB Ge Hu Ir It Ne No Po Ro Sz Sp Sw Tu.

Flowering twig

Male flower

Leaf

Habit

Fruits

Bark

Fraxinus angustifolia
Vahl
Narrow-leaved Ash
A medium-sized tree up to 25m high with a tall irregular crown. The bark has a network of narrow but deep fissures, dark grey and becoming warty in older trees. The branches are rather few and ascending, the twigs short, pendulous and glabrous. The buds are dark brown and hairy. The leaf is 15–25cm long, with a glabrous rachis bearing 5–13 leaflets; the petiole is glabrous; each leaflet is 3–9cm long, oblong-lanceolate to linear-lanceolate, long-pointed at the apex and with toothed margins, the number of teeth usually equalling the number of lateral veins, shiny green above, glabrous or hairy at the base of the midrib below. The axillary panicles appear before the leaves; the flowers are hermaphrodite. The samaras form small clusters; each samara 2–4.5cm long, oblong to lanceolate, glabrous, becoming brown when mature. Flowering period: May. A species of deciduous woods, banks and flood-plains of rivers in S. and E.C. Europe. Al Au Bl Bu Co FC Fr FS FY Gr Hu It Pl Ro Sa Si Sp Tu.

Flowering twig

Fruits

Leaf

Bark

Habit

Fraxinus pallisiae
Wilmott
Similar to *F. angustifolia* but reaching 30m in height with twigs, petioles, rachis and young leaflets densely hairy. SE. Europe. Bu FS Ro Tu.

Ligustrum lucidum
Aiton fil. in Aiton
Glossy Privet

Usually a small evergreen tree up to 15m high, though some-times a large shrub with a broad, domed crown. The bark is smooth or very finely fissured, grey with pale brownish streaks. The branches are spreading, the twigs straight, glabrous and marked with white lenticels. The leaves are opposite, simple, 8–12cm long, ovate, long-pointed, entire, thick, dark and very glossy green above, much paler and matt beneath; the young leaves are rather reddish. The inflo-rescence is a loosely-branched conical panicle, 12–20cm long with numerous small fragrant white flowers. The flower has a bell-shaped 4-toothed calyx and a corolla with a long tube expanding into 4 flat lobes. The fruit is an oval berry *c.* 1cm long, black but with a whitish bloom. Flowering period: August–January. It is a Chinese species grown in S. Europe for ornament and shade, particularly as a street tree, but also for hedging. Its native relative **L. vulgare**, the **Common Privet**, is a widespread shrub of European woods, also frequently used as a hedging plant and as an ornamental in gardens.

Flower

Flowering twig

Fruit

Habit

Olea europaea L.
Olive

A long-lived evergreen tree up to 15m high with a broad crown and a thick, gnarled and often very short bole, sometimes dividing into several boles or producing suckers, and often with numerous holes or cavities in the bole and main branches. The bark is finely fissured and grey or silvery. The twigs are terete or 4-angled and covered with small silvery scales. The leaves are opposite, 2–8cm long, lanceolate to widest below the middle, shortly pointed at the tip, entire, leathery, glabrous and dark grey-green above, paler and densely scaly below, more or less sessile or with a very short petiole. The flowers are bisexual or polygamous, fragrant, and borne in axillary many-flowered panicles; the calyx has 4 short teeth or shallow lobes; the corolla is white with 4 rather broad lobes. The fruit is a succulent oily drupe, 1–3.5cm long, ovoid or somewhat globose, green at first, taking a year to become brownish, black or occasionally ivory-white when mature. Flowering period: July–August. Fruiting period: September–October. It grows in open woods and scrub in dry rocky areas. The **Cultivated Olive** var. *europaea* is an important source of oil and is widely grown for its fruit. The **Wild Olive** var. *sylvestris* differs from the common cultivar in having an often bushy habit with spiny 4-angled stems and lower branches, much smaller oval leaves and smaller drupes. Al BI Co Cr Fr FY Gr It Pl Ro Sa Si Sp Sz Tu.

Flower

Flowering twig

Fruit

Habit

Phillyrea latifolia L.

A small evergreen tree or shrub up to 15m high with a dense rounded crown. The bark is smooth and grey, eventually with a raised network of ridges. The branches are rather erect when young but become spreading later; the twigs are slender, grey or brownish and densely hairy. The leaves are opposite, simple, making a wide angle with the midrib and forking towards the margin; the juvenile leaves are 2–7 x 1–4cm, ovate-cordate to ovate-lanceolate, sometimes lanceolate, with sharply toothed margins; the adult leaves are 1–6 x 0.4–2cm, lanceolate to elliptical, the margins entire or very finely toothed, very dark glossy green above, paler and dull beneath, with 7–11 pairs of close lateral veins. The flowers are bisexual, borne in short axillary racemes; the thin, yellowish calyx is divided to three-quarters of its length into 4 triangular lobes; the corolla is greenish-white, 4-lobed with a very short but distinct tube. The fruit is a dry drupe, 0.7–1 cm in diameter, globose, bluish-black when ripe. Flowering period: June. A native of evergreen woods in the Mediterranean region, and occasionally planted in gardens near the coast. Al Bl Bu Co Cr Fr FY Gr It Pl Sa Si Sp Tu.

Fruit

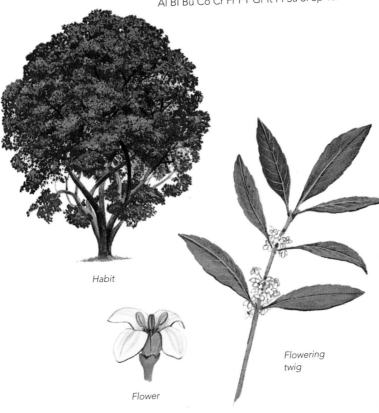

Habit

Flower

Flowering twig

Syringa vulgaris L.
Common Lilac

A small deciduous tree or shrub 3–7m high, with a rounded or oval crown, and suckering easily. The spirally fissured bark is greyish or sometimes russet. The branches are terete and shiny brownish-green. The shortly petiolate leaves are opposite, simple, 4–8cm (sometimes up to 12cm) long, ovate or shallowly heart-shaped, the margins entire, glabrous, yellowish-green and slightly leathery. The inflorescences are usually paired, axillary, leafless, conical panicles 10–20cm long, arising from the apical axillary buds. The flowers are fragrant; the calyx is small, shallowly 4-lobed; the corolla is tubular, lilac or occasionally white, 0.8–1.2cm long with 4 valvate, hooded and spreading lobes. The fruit is an ovoid, pointed capsule, 0.8–1cm long. Flowering period: May or June. A scrubland species native to the rocky hillsides of the Balkan Peninsula, but widely cultivated for centuries throughout the rest of Europe. *Syringa josikaea*, **Hungarian Lilac**, differs from *S. vulgaris* in its elliptical leaves, which are wedge-shaped at the base, and its solitary leafy terminal inflorescences. It is confined to mountains in N. Rumania and the Carpathians but is now naturalized in Germany. FS Ge Ro.

Fruit

Habit

Flowering twig

Flower

BIGNONIA FAMILY BIGNONIACEAE

Catalpa bignonioides
Walter
Indian Bean Tree

A broadly domed deciduous tree up to 20m high. The bark is dull grey-brown, usually smooth, finely scaling or sometimes becoming fissured. The twigs are stout, smooth, grey-brown. The buds are minute, orange-brown, the terminal bud not developing. The leaves are opposite, or in whorls of 3, 10–25 x 7–22cm, broadly ovate with short tapering tip, the base rounded or shallowly heart-shaped, the margin sometimes shallowly lobed, light green or occasionally purplish when young, densely pubescent beneath; the petiole is 10–18cm long, flattened, smooth. The flowers are in broadly conical paniculate heads, 15–25cm long; each flower up to 5cm in diameter, bell-shaped with 5 spreading frilled lobes, white with yellow and purple spots in the throat and on the lower lip. The fruit is a cylindrical capsule, 15–40 x 0.6–0.8cm, pendulous. The seeds are c. 2.5cm long, flat, papery, with a fringe of long hairs at each end, white. Flowering period: June–August. A native of SE. United States, frequently planted for ornament in parks and gardens or occasionally as a street tree in W. C. and S. Europe.

Bark

Fruit

Habit

Leaf

Flower head

Catalpa x erubescens
Carr.
Hybrid Catalpa
Like *C. bignontoides* but the bark with coarser ridges and fissures; the leaves up to 38cm (rarely to 60cm) long, often broader than long, broadly ovate to somewhat pentagonal, each corner with a short tapering point, heart-shaped at the base, opening purple, becoming bright green; the flowers are in heads up to 32cm in diameter, each flower fragrant, 4cm long; the seeds are sterile. Flowering period: July-September. A hybrid between *C. ovata* and *C. bignonioides* frequently planted for ornament in S. and W. Europe.

Flower

Leaf

Catalpa speciosa
Engelm.
Western Catalpa
Like *C. bignonioides,* but sometimes up to 30m high, the bark with scaling, ridges and fissures; the leaves are 12–32 x 7–23cm, ovate-lanceolate or occasionally with 3 shallow lobes, the tip long and tapering, the base usually deeply heart-shaped, glossy, dark green above, the underside with pale brown pubescence. The flowers are in heads up to 20cm long, each flower up to 6cm in diameter; the capsule is up to 50 x 1.5cm. Flowering period: June–July. A native of the C. United State occasionally cultivated for ornament.

Flower

Catalpa ovata
G. Don fil.
Yellow Catalpa
Like *C. bignonioides* but the leaves up to 25 x 25cm, more or less pentagonal with short tapering points on the corners, heart–shaped at the base, dark green; the flowers in heads up to 25cm long; each flower c. 2.5cm in diameter, dull white suffused with yellow, spotted red inside; the capsule up to 30 x 0.8cm. Flowering period: July–August. A native of China, planted for ornament.

Flower

FIGWORT FAMILY SCROPHULARIACEAE

Paulownia tomentosa (Thunb.) Steudel
Foxglove Tree

A deciduous tree up to 12m (rarely to 26m) high with a domed crown. The bark is smooth and grey. The branches are rather few, widely spreading. The twigs are rather stout, purplish-brown, with numerous lenticels. The buds are minute, purplish. The leaves are opposite, up to 45 x 25cm, broadly ovate with a long tapering tip, the base deeply heart-shaped, the margin entire or with up to 3 lobes on young trees, the lobes with tapering tips on either side of the base, pale green and softly pubescent above, densely grey-pubescent beneath, especially around the prominent veins; the petiole is 10–15cm, occasionally up to 45cm, densely pubescent. The flowers are in upright paniculate heads, 20–30cm long; each flower densely brown-pubescent in bud, becoming pale to deep violet, suffused yellowish inside the tube, up to 6cm long, tubular, with 5 widely spreading lobes. The fruit is a capsule, up to 5 x 2cm long, ovoid with a beak-like tapering tip, glossy and glutinous, splitting to release numerous seeds; the pedicel is *c.* 1.5cm long, stout, pubescent. The seeds are *c.* 8mm long, winged, whitish. Flowering period: May. A native of China, commonly planted for ornament in gardens, or occasionally as a street tree, especially in S. Europe.

Fruit

Flower head

Leaf from a young tree

Habit

MYOPORUM FAMILY MYOPORACEAE

Myoporum tenuifolium
G. Forster

An evergreen glabrous tree or shrub up to 8m high, but very variable in size, with a rounded crown. The bark is very finely fissured, greyish-brown. The leaves are alternate, 4.5–10cm (rarely 17cm) long; the narrow leaves are 1.5–3cm wide, elliptic-oblong to lanceolate or even linear, sharply contracted at the base and pointed at the apex; the leaves are broad, up to 5cm wide, widest below the middle and rather blunt at the apex, the margins usually entire but sometimes with a few teeth, glossy green above, with numerous translucent glands, the petiole is 0.5–1cm long. The flowers are clustered in small dense axillary cymes of 5–9, or occasionally solitary, on slender pedicels up to 1cm long; the calyx is 2–3mm long, divided to halfway into 5 narrow, acute, rather rigid lobes; the corolla is white, spotted with purple and bearded on the inside, nearly bell-shaped, the tube 4–5mm long, the limb 1–1.2cm in diameter, with equal spreading lobes shorter than the tube; the 4 functional stamens protrude shortly from the corolla. The fruit is a small, slightly fleshy drupe, 7–9mm in diameter, almost globose or ovoid, becoming purple when ripe. Flowering period: April. A native of Australia and New Caledonia, planted for shelter in W. Europe and becoming naturalized in some places. BI Pl Sp.

Habit

Leaves

Flowering twig

HONEYSUCKLE FAMILY CAPRIFOLIACEAE

Sambucus nigra L.
Elder

A small deciduous, much-branched tree up to 10m high, though frequently a shrub. The bark is extensively grooved and furrowed, brown or greyish, and becoming corky in older specimens. Vigorous erect shoots often grow from the base of the bole. The branches are arching and have a large white central pith. The leaves are opposite, pinnately compound, with 5–7 or sometimes 9 leaflets; the leaflets are 4.5–12cm long, more or less ovate, pointed, sharply toothed on the margins and sparsely hairy beneath. The inflorescence is a flat-topped corymbose cluster, 10–24cm in diameter, with 4–5 primary branches; the heavily scented flowers are in 3–5 parts with white petals and anthers. The fruit is a globose drupe with 3–5 stone-cells; the young fruits are green, ripening to black or occasionally red, the clusters drooping when mature. Flowering period: June–July. A species of damp woods, hedges and waste places, widely cultivated for its fruit in S. Europe. All except Cr Fi Ic Ro Sw. The **Alpine Elder,** *S. racemosa* L. is similar in appearance but distinguished by its scarlet fruits.

Flowering twig

Habit

Bark

Fruit

Fruit

Viburnum opulus L.
Guelder Rose

A spreading deciduous tree up to 4m high, with angled, greyish, hairless twigs and buds with scales. The leaves are 3–8cm long with 3 or sometimes 5 irregularly toothed lobes, and filiform stipules. The inflorescence is 4.5–10.5cm in diameter, the outer flowers sterile and much larger than the inner, fertile ones. The fruit is red, almost globose, often persisting after the leaves have fallen. Flowering period: June–July. It grows in damp woods, hedges and thickets throughout much of Europe. Al Au Be Bu De FC Fi Fr FS FY GB Ge Hu Ir It Ne No Po Ro Sw Sz.

Flowering twig

Viburnum lantana L.
Wayfaring Tree

A deciduous tree up to 6m high with terete, greyish, stellate, hairy twigs and naked buds. The leaves are 4–14cm long, ovate or widest above the middle, rough, toothed on the margins, densely stellate-hairy beneath; stipules are absent. The inflorescence is 6–10cm in diameter, the flowers are fertile and uniform. The fruit is ovoid and slightly flattened, red at first but turning black. Flowering period: May–June. A species of hedges, thickets, edges of woods and rocky places, especially on chalky soils. Al Au Be Bu Cr FC Fr FS FY GB Ge Gr Hu It No Sp Sw Sz.

Flowering twig

Fruit

Viburnum tinus L.
Laurustinus

A dense evergreen tree up to 7m high with usually glabrous, weakly-angled twig. The leaves are 3–10cm long, ovate-lanceolate or ovate-orbicular, entire, globose and shiny above, sparsely hairy beneath; stipules are absent. The inflorescence is 4–9cm in diameter, the flowers are fertile and uniform. The fruit is more or less globose and dark blue. A species of woody and stony places in S. Europe, sometimes forming thickets and often grown for ornament or to provide shelter. Al Bl Co Fr FY GB Gr It Pl Sa Si Sz.

Flowering twig

Fruit

AGAVE FAMILY AGAVACEAE

Cordyline australis (G. Forster)
Hooker fil.
Cabbage Palm

A small evergreen tree up to 13m high with a cylindrical trunk, becoming forked after flowering, and frequently suckering at the base. The bark is pale brownish-grey. The leaves are 30–90 x 2.5–8cm, linear to linear-lanceolate, gradually tapering to a sharp point, dark green or yellowish-tinged, usually in a single rounded cluster on top of each stem, erect, the lowermost drooping to hide the trunk, sessile, with numerous parallel veins. The flowers are in large terminal panicles, 60–120 x 30–60cm; each flower fragrant, *c.* 1cm in diameter with 6 narrowly oblong lobes, creamy-white; there are 6 stamens. The fruit is a berry, *c.* 6mm long, globose, white or bluish-white, containing several black seeds. Flowering period: June–July. A native of New Zealand, commonly planted for ornament in streets, parks and gardens in coastal areas of W. and S. Europe.

Habit

Fruit

Flower

Yucca aloifolia L.,
Spanish Bayonet

Similar to *Cordyline australis* but up to 10m high, forming a stoutish, smooth trunk, much branched above; the leaves are 50–100cm long, the margins with small teeth, bluish-green; the flowers are 4–6cm in diameter, white, tinged with purple at the tips of the lobes; the fruit is elongated, blackish-purple when ripe, succulent, pedicellate. A native of SW. United States grown for ornament in S. Europe and occasionally escaping from cultivation.

Habit

Dracaena draco L.
Dragon Tree

Also similar to *Cordyline australis* but gradually forming a stout, much fluted and convoluted trunk, dichotomously branched above to form a dense, broadly-domed canopy; the leaves are bluish-green, tinged reddish at the base; the flowers are greenish-white; the fruit is up to 1.5cm long, globose, reddish-orange, 1-seeded. A native of the Canary Islands and Madeira, commonly planted in streets, parks and gardens in the Mediterranean countries.

Habit

BANANA FAMILY MUSACEAE

Musa cavendishii
Lambert ex Paxton
Banana

A tree-like herb with shoots up to 3m high which fruit once and then die. The plant grows again every year by means of suckers from a stout tuberous stock. The leaves arise from the base; the sheaths are very long, fibrous, persistent, tubular, with free margins but tightly wrapped round the sheaths of younger leaves to form a rigid false stem; the blade is 120–200 x 40–60cm, oblong, blunt at the tip, the margin entire but readily splitting to the midrib. The inflorescence is a long drooping spike up to 1m long. The fruit (banana) is a berry, 12–18cm long. The seeds are numerous but sterile. Flowering period: March–September. A native of tropical Asia but cultivated in small orchards and gardens along the Mediterranean coast. Cr Gr Si Sp.

Inflorescence

Habit

PALM TREE FAMILY PALMAE

Arecastrum romanzoffianum (Cham.) Bell
Queen Palm
A monoecious tree with a single slender trunk up to 10m high and 70cm in diameter. The bole is smooth and distinctly ringed. The leaves are pinnate and up to 5m long; the leaflets are narrow, less than 3cm wide, long, soft, drooping from the centre, green on both surfaces. The inflorescence is up to 1m long, hanging from the axils of the lower leaves, covered with cream-coloured flowers and yellow ovoid beaked fruits at maturity. A native of C. and S. Brazil, cultivated as a street tree in the Mediterranean region.

Leaf

Inflorescence

Habit

Howeia forsterana
(C. Moore & F. Mueller) Bell
Sentry Palm
A monoecious tree with a single slender trunk up to 15m in height. The bole is grey, smooth and covered with leaf-scars. The leaves are pinnate, up to 5m long, with a prominent midrib and widely-spaced flat leaflets; each leaflet is narrowly lanceolate, green on both surfaces although spotty and scaly below; the petiole is long, up to 1.5m,

Fruit

usually ascending and arching only slightly. The inflorescence is about 1m long, hanging, and branched. The fruit is ovoid, up to 6cm long, densely packed on the spadix. A native of Lord Howe Island and one of the more popular Mediterranean palms cultivated in parks and gardens.

Habit

Leaf

Habit

Jubaea chilensis (Molina) Baillon
Chilean Wine Palm

A monoecious tree with a single stout bole up to 30m tall and 2m in diameter. The bole is grey, smooth and covered with rhombic leaf-scars. The leaves are pinnatifid, up to 4m long with many leaflets; each leaflet can be up to 70cm long, 3cm in diameter and divided at the apex. The inflorescence emerges from the lower leaf axils and is a dense terminal panicle of yellowish flowers. The fruit is globose, ovoid and yellow. The Chilean Wine Palm is perhaps the hardiest of the southern hemisphere palms, growing further south of the equator than any other species. It endures drought and low temperatures and performs particularly well on the French Riviera. It is the largest palm to be widely planted in the Mediterranean region.

303

Chamaerops humilis L.
European Fan Palm

A small stemless or short-stemmed, dioecious or polygamous shrub or tree up to 2m high in the wild, or 3m high in
cultivation. The bole is grey and covered with grey or whitish
fibres and old leaf-bases. The leaves are palmate, up to 1m
in diameter, deeply divided and very stiff; the segments are
sword-shaped and split at the apex, green, grey-green or
powdery-blue, firm and not drooping. The inflorescence is
up to 35cm long, inconspicuous and often hidden in the
leaves. The fruits are up to 4.5cm in diameter, globose,
oblong, yellow or brown. The only native palm of Europe,
occurring on sandy ground mainly near the coast in the
W. Mediterranean region. Bl Fr It Pl Sa Si Sp.

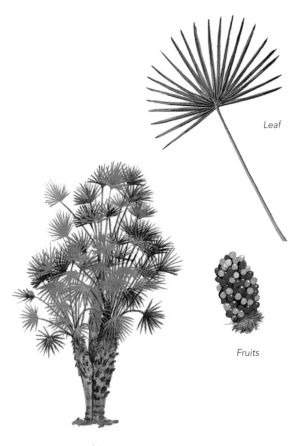

Leaf

Fruits

Habit

Livistona australis (R. Br.)
C. F. P. Mart.

A monoecious tree with a slender trunk attaining 20m or more in height. The bole is invariably covered with brown leaf-bases and untidy brown fibres until a considerable age. The leaves are palmate, up to 1.5m in diameter, circular in outline with a rib extending several centimetres into the centre of the leaf; the segments are glossy green, with a prominent yellow central nerve giving a golden-green appearance, soft, drooping at the tips and frequently with threads hanging from the segments; the petioles are long, slender, spiny and toothed. The inflorescence appears from amongst the leaves and is at first covered by a very woody spathe, later to become much branched, bearing long-branched fruit clusters. The fruit is spherical, about 2cm in diameter and reddish-brown. A distinctive native of E. Australia grown as a street and park tree in S. Europe.

Leaf

Inflorescence

Habit

Phoenix L.

Large dioecious trees with long stems. The leaves are pinnatifid with many induplicate, slender lanceolate lobes or
segments, the ones towards the base shorter than those
towards the tip; the petiole is stout, shorter than the blade
and unarmed. The spadices are stalked with a few simple
branches. The flowers are yellowish; the males have slender filaments, the females have ovaries with 3 carpels. The
fruit is a berry, usually developing from 1 carpel only. The
seeds are deeply grooved along the ventral side.

Phoenix canariensis
(hort. ex Chabaud)
Canary Island Date Palm

A stout tree up to 20m high, the persistent leaf-bases forming a massive bole up to 1–5m in diameter. The leaves are
pinnate, 5–6m long, forming a dense crown of up to 200,
strongly ascending but the lower ones hanging with age; the
leaflets are in 150–200 pairs, usually in several ranks leaving
the stem at various angles, short and narrow, long–pointed,
light green, induplicate, straight; the spines at the base of
each leaf-stalk gradually become longer and are followed by
small leaflets which eventually become full-sized; the petiole
is short, spiny and strongly ascending. The much-branched
inflorescence grows up to 2m and emerges from the axils of
the leaves. The fruits occur in heavy clusters, each one glo-
bose-ovoid, up to 3cm in diameter, orange. The seed is wrinkled. A native of the Canary Islands frequently planted as an
ornamental in subtropical parts of the world, particularly
in the Mediterranean region and SW. Europe, as a street
and garden tree. It is sometimes
naturalized. A smaller, sever-
al-stemmed species with
non-succulent   fruits,
P. theophrastii, is
endemic to Crete.

Leaf

Habit

*Cluster
of fruits*

Phoenix dactylifera L.
Date Palm

A fairly tall dioecious tree up to 35m tall, suckering freely at the base; the bole is covered for years with old leaf-bases which later form a characteristic scarred pattern. The leaves are pinnate, up to 4m long, forming a lax sparse crown of about 20–40 leaves, the upper ones ascending, the lower ones curving downwards; the leaflets are up to 50cm long, induplicate, grey-green, glaucous, rigid, sharp-pointed, occurring in several ranks. The inflorescence is hanging in fruit. The fruit is 2.5–8cm in diameter, deep orange when ripe, edible and sweet. The true Date Palm provides the staple food of millions in the Middle-East and the S. Mediterranean region. It is planted on a small scale in S. Europe for ornament, and for dates in SE. Spain. Sp.

Cluster of fruits

Habit

Leaf

Single Fruit

Trachycarpus fortunei (Hooker)
H.A. Wendl.
Chinese Windmill Palm
A monoecious tree with a single slender trunk up to 14m high. The bole is covered for a long time with persistent, dense, long, brown, fibrous leaf-bases, giving a matted appearance. The leaves are palmate, up to 1m in diameter, divided almost to the base; the segments are pointed, stiff, glaucous below and dark green above; the petioles are up to 50cm long, toothed, and covered with dense long brown fibres at the base. The inflorescence is a pedunculate densely branched spadix, covered with many fragrant yellow flowers. The fruits are 3-lobed, kidney-shaped, about 2cm long, purplish-black when ripe. The seeds are grooved on the ventral side. A hardy native of C. and E. China, widely planted on roadsides and in parks in the Mediterranean region.

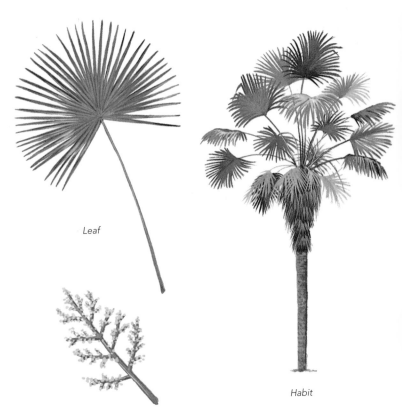

Leaf

Inflorescence

Habit

Washingtonia filifera (J.J Linden) H.A. Wendl.
Petticoat Palm

An hermaphrodite tree up to 20m tall and 1m in diameter with a single bole. The upper part and sometimes the whole of the bole is covered with the remains of dead leaves, forming a 'petticoat'; if the leaves are removed the leaf-bases form a compact but irregular covering and the surface of the bole is grey and marked with vertical chinks or ridges, more prominent than the growth rings. The leaves are up to 2m in diameter, fan-shaped in outline, divided more than halfway to the base, very persistent and covered with many long threads attached to the segments and sinuses; the petiole is up to 2m long and 15cm in diameter; each leaf consists of up to 50 grey-green segments. The inflorescence emerges from the axils of the lower leaves and is covered with numerous small white flowers, at first erect, the remains later hanging. The fruits are ovoid and lightly wrinkled. A native of S. California, W. Arizona and NW. Mexico, conspicuously planted in parks, gardens and roadsides throughout the Mediterranean region.

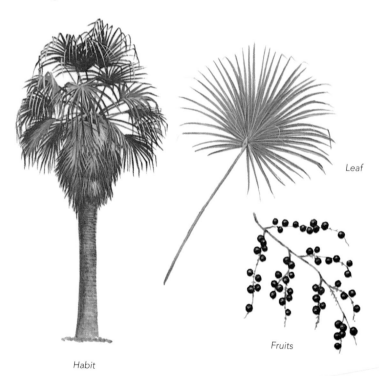

Leaf

Fruits

Habit

GLOSSARY

abortive imperfectly developed, not functional

acuminate gradually tapering into a slender point

acute sharply pointed

alternate staggered singly around the stem (usually leaf arrangement)

anther part of the stamen containing the pollen

apomict plant which reproduces by seed not formed as a result of sexual fusion

appressed parts pressed closely together but not joined

aril outer layer surroundihg a seed, usually fleshy, derived from the seed stalk

articulated jointed

ascending sloping or curving upwards

auricles rounded lobes at the base of a leaf

axil upper angle between a stem and a leaf or bract

basic soils rich in free basic ions, eg. calcium or magnesium

berry fleshy fruit without a stony layer surrounding the seeds

bifid split deeply into two

blade expanded, flattened part of a leaf

bloom whitish or bluish covering, very easily removed (as on the outside of some grapes)

bole lower branch-free part of a trunk

bract scale-like or leaf-like structure, from the axil of which an inflorescence or part of an inflorescence emerges

bracteole scale-like or leaf-like structure, from the axil of which a single flower emerges

bud developing shoot or flower, often protected by scales and the growth suspended during unfavourable conditions

burr lumpy outgrowth from a trunk, often covered with sprouting shoots

buttressed base of the trunk surrounded by tapering flanges or ridges

callus swelling, usually surrounding diseased or damaged tissue on a branch or trunk

calyx sepals of a flower considered as a whole

carpel functional unit of the female organ of a flower; may be separate or joined, resulting in a partitioned ovary

catkin elongated, crowded inflorescence of inconspicuous, wind-pollinated flowers

ciliate margin surrounded by regularly projecting hairs

clone group of individual plants arising from an original plant without sexual reproduction; many cultivars are clones

columnar narrow, almost parallel-sided crown

compound leaf made up of several distinct leaflets

cone inflorescence of a conifer, often woody and conical, composed of scales and bract

coniferous cone-bearing

contiguous parts touching at the margins but not fused

coppiced cut down regularly to the base, yielding long poles

cordate heart-shaped, often restricted to the base of a leaf with a rounded lobe either side of the stalk

coriaceous leathery textured, like the leaves of many evergreens

corolla petals of a flower considered as a whole

corymb short, broad and more or less flat-topped inflorescence, developing like a raceme

crenate margin with shallow, rounded teeth

cuneate wedge-shaped or tapering leaf-base

cupule cup-like structure at the base of a fruit, composed of bracts (eg. the acorn cup of oaks)

cyme more or less flat-topped inflorescence, each growing point terminated by a flower

deciduous dropping off; usually referring to leaves which fall in autumn

decurrent the base continued down the stem as a wing

decussate leaves in pairs on opposite sides of the stem, but each pair at right-angles to the next

deflexed bent sharply downwards

dehiscence process of opening of a dry fruit to shed its seed

dentate margin with sharp teeth

diadelphous stamen arrangement of some species of the Pea family: 9 fused in a bundle and 1 separate

digitate leaflets spreading like the fingers of a hand; palmate

dioecious with separate male and female flowers borne on different plants

dorsal back or outer surface of an organ

double-toothed margin with large teeth, each of which has smaller teeth

drupe fleshy fruit with the seed(s) surrounded by a stony layer

ellipsoid solid body, widest at the middle, elliptic in longitudinal section

elliptic outline, widest at the middle, rounded and narrowed towards each end

endemic native to a restricted region, usually a single country or smaller area

entire margin unbroken by teeth or lobes

fastigiate branches more or less upright (as in Lombardy Poplar)

filament part of the stamen, the stalk supporting the anther

filiform thread-like; long and very slender

fluted with deep vertical grooves

fruit ripe seeds and surrounding structures, either fleshy or dry

glabrous without hairs

gland a small vesicle containing oil or other liquid, within, on or protruding from the surface of a plant

glaucous covered with a bluish or whitish layer

globose globe-shaped body, more or less round in cross-section

hermaphrodite flowers possessing both functional male and female parts

hispid covered with rather long, stiff, bristly hairs

hybrid a plant originating from the fertilization of one species by another

incised deeply cut

indehiscent not releasing the seeds

indumentum general term for the hairy covering of any part of a plant

induplicate folded or rolled inwards or upwards

inflorescence flower cluster including the stem bearing flowers and bracts

involucre joined bracts, usually surrounding the base of a short dense inflorescence

juvenile (i) young (ii) first-formed

keeled having a raised ridge or sharp folded edge, resembling the keel of a boat

laciniate divided deeply into narrow segments

lanate woolly; densely covered with long, curly, intertwined hairs

lanceolate lance-shaped in outline; widest below the middle, about 3 times as long as wide

lateral at the side

legume a dry fruit splitting along its length above and below to release its seeds; typically, the fruit of a species of the Pea family

lenticel rounded or elliptical pore in bark, usually raised

linear narrow and more or less parallel-sided

locule division of an ovary that has internal walls

maquis thicket of tall shrubs and scattered trees, characteristic of countries bordering the Mediterranean

membranous thin, dry, somewhat papery

midrib central or main vein of a leaf

monodelphous stamens united into a bundle by the fusion of their filaments

monoecious with separate male and female flowers, both on the same plant

mucronate narrowing abruptly into a small, sharp point

nectary nectar-secreting gland, usually within a flower

node point on a stem where a leaf or leaves arise

ob- prefix meaning 'inverted', eg. obovate = ovate but broadest above the middle

obtuse blunt

operculum rounded cover or lid

opposite in pairs at the same level on the stem (usually leaf arrangment)

orbicular (in outline) rounded

outbreeding species in which the flowers are usually fertilized by pollen from a different plant

ovary female part of the flower immediately enclosing the ovule

ovate outline, widest below the middle, rounded towards each end

ovoid solid body, widest below the middle, ovate in cross-section

ovule structure which contains the egg and develops into a seed after fertilization

palmate leaf with more than 3 leaflets arising from the same point

panicle branched inflorescence with each branch developing like a raceme

papillae small slender projections from a surface

pedicel stalk of a flower

peduncle stalk of an inflorescence or group of flowers within an inflorescence

peltato organ with the stalk attached near the centre of a surface, rather than at the margin

perianth sepals and petals together

pericarp wall of a fruit

petiole stalk of a leaf

petiolule stalk of a leaflet

phyllode flattened, leaf-like petiole with no blade (as in *Acacia*)

pinnate compound leaf with many leaflets arranged either side of a central stalk (rachis)

pinnatifid leaf cut into lobes either side of a central intact region

pioneer amongst the first species to colonize open ground

pith (i) spongy tissue in the centre of most stems (ii) the whitish, inner skin of a Citrus fruit

placenta area in the ovary where the ovules are attached

pollard tree cut back repeatedly to 2–3m above the ground

polygamous with male, female and hermaphrodite flowers on the same or on different plants

pome fruit where the seeds are enclosed first by a tough cartilage-like layer, then by the fleshy receptacle (eg. apple)

procumbent trailing; lying near to the ground

pubescent covered with short, rather soft hairs

pyramidal crown which is widest at the base, gradually tapering above

raceme an inflorescence, usually elongated, which continually adds new, stalked flowers to the tip; the oldest flowers are thus at the base

rachilla stem-like axis bearing leaflets or flowers, arising from a main rachis

rachis stem-like axis bearing leaflets or flowers

receptacle enlarged upper part of flower stem from which the parts of a flower arise

recurved curved backwards

reflexed bent sharply backwards

remote widely spaced

reticulate marked with a network of ridges; netted

revolute curved underneath (usually leaf-margins)

rhomboid lozenge-shaped; shaped like the diamond of playing cards

samara indehiscent dry fruit with a wing formed from part of the wall

scabrid covered with short stiff hairs

scarious thin, dry and membranous

seed fertilized, ripened ovule, sometimes including the outer layers of a small dry fruit; the dispersed reproductive unit

sessile stalkless

simple leaf not divided into leaflets

sinuate margin wavy when viewed from above

sinus depression in a margin, between two teeth or lobes

spadix spike-like inflorescence, sometimes branched, surrounded by one or more sheaths, at least while young

spathe bract-like or petal-like sheath enclosing an inflorescence

spathulate spoon-shaped; expanded suddenly towards the tip

spike raceme-like inflorescence with stalkless flowers

spired narrowly conical; shaped like a church spire

sprout young shoot, sometimes clustered around the base of trunks or from burrs

stamen male reproductive organ of a flower, consisting of anther and filament

staminodes sterile stamen, often much reduced

sterile (i) (stamens) not producing viable pollen (ii) (plant) not producing seed capable of germination

stigma surface receptive to pollen; part of the female reproductive organs of a flower

stipule appendage at base of petiole, either scale-like or leaf-like

stomata pores, usually in a leaf or stem surface, through which gas exchange takes place

stomatiferous area bearing stomata

stone seed enclosed by a hard layer formed from the inner layers of fruit wall

stone-cell hard, gritty enclosures in a fleshy fruit (eg. pear)

strobilus cone-like structure bearing male or female reproductive organs

style part of the female reproductive organs of a flower, connecting the stigma to the ovary

sub- prefix meaning 'almost'

subalpine at the limits of the tree-line

sucker shoot arising directly from a root, often away from the main trunk

suture junction, often a line where splitting open occurs

terete circular in cross-section; without grooves or ridges

terminal at the end or tip, usually of a branch

tomentose densely covered with rather short, soft hairs

tripinnate (leaf) pinnate with 3 levels of division; the main stalk bears 2 rows of secondary stalks, each bearing 2 rows of tertiary stalks with 2 rows of leaflets

truncate with a squarish, transverse tip

tubercle a short, blunt, smooth projection

tuberculate with tubercles

twice-pinnate (leaf) pinnate with 2 levels of division; the main stalk bears 2 rows of secondary stalks with 2 rows of leaflets

umbel inflorescence with all the pedicels or peduncles arising from the same point

undulate margin wavy when viewed from the edge

valve segment, usually of a fruit, that separates during dehiscence

ventral front or inner face of an organ

villous covered with long shaggy hairs

viscid sticky, glutinous

whorl arrangement with more than two organs arising at the same level around a stem

wing (i) thin, expanded portion of a seed, fruit or other organ (ii) side petals of a flower of the Pea family

zygomorphic divisible into equal halves in one plane only

Bean, W.J. 1970–1976 *Trees and Shrubs Hardy in the British Isles* (8th edition) vols I–III. John Murray, London.

Chittenden, F.J. 1951 *The Royal Horticultural Society Dictionary of Gardening.* Clarendon Press, London.

Corner, E.J.H. 1966 *The Natural History of Palms.* Weidenfeld & Nicholson, London.

Dallimore, W. & Jackson, A.B. 1966 *A Handbook of Coniferae and Ginkgoaceae,* ed. 4. Arnold, London.

Lancaster, R. 1974 *Trees for your Garden.* Floraprint, Nottingham.

McCurrach, J.C. 1960 *Palms of the World.* Harper & Brothers, New York.

Miller Gault, S. 1976 *The Dictionary of Shrubs.* Rainbird/Ebury Press, London.

Penfold, A,R. & Willis, J.L. 1961 *The Eucalypts.* Leonard Hill/Interscience, London & New York.

Phillips, R. 1978 *Trees in Britain, Europe and North America.* Pan, London.

Polunin, O. & Everard, B. 1976 *Trees and Bushes of Europe.* Oxford University Press, London.

Stafleu, F.A. *et al.* (editors) 1978 *International Code of Botanical Nomenclature.* Bohn, Scheltema & Holkema, Utrecht.

Tutin, T.G. *et al.* (editors) 1964–1980 *Flora Europaea,* vols 1 –5. Cambridge University Press, Cambridge.

Vicomte de Noailles & Lancaster, R. 1977 *Mediterranean Plants and Gardens.* Floraprint, Nottingham.

Wilkinson, G. 1978 *Epitaph for the Elm.* Hutchinson, London.

ACKNOWLEDGEMENTS

The authors and publishers would like to thank Mr Keith Rushforth for reading the manuscript and Dr John Dransfield for supplying valuable reference material for the section on palm trees. We should also like to thank Mrs M. Humphries for typing the manuscript, and Mrs H. Press for the illustrations of the Eucalyptus fruits. Finally, special thanks are due to Ian Garrard, whose cooperation and unflagging ability to produce plates of a uniformly excellent standard have contributed so much to this book.

INDEX

Page numbers in *italic* type
refer to illustrations

Abies 10, 54
  alba 54, *54*
  cephalonica 55, *55*
  concolor 56
  delavayi 55, *55*
    var. *forrestii* 55
  grandis 56, *56*
  x *insignis* 58
  lasiocarpa 57, *57*
  nordmanniana 57, *57*, 58
  pinsapo 58, *58*
  procera 59, *59*
  sibirica 59, *59*
Acacia 212
  cyanophylla 212, *212*
  cyclops 217
  dealbata 213, *213*, 214
  farnesiana 217, *217*
  karoo 217, *217*
  longifolia 214, *214*
  mearnsii 214, *215*
  melanoxylon 215, *215*
  pycnantha 216, *216*
  retinodes 217, *217*
Acer 230
  campestre 230, *230*
  cappodocicum 231
  davidii 231, *231*
  granatense 232, *232*
  griseum 231, *231*
  heldreichii 231, *231*
  hersii 231
  hyrcanum 232, *232*
  japonicum 232, *237*
    cv. 'Vitifolium' 237
  lobelii 238
  macrophyllum 231
  monspessulanum 233, *233*
  negundo 234, *234*
    cv. 'Variegatum' 234
  obtusatum 235, *235*
  opalus 235, *235*
  palmatum 236, *236*
    cv. 'Atropurpureum' 236, *236*
    cv. 'Osakazuki' 236
  platanoides 238, *238*
  pseudoplatanus 239, *239*
  rubrum 240, 241, *241*
  rufinerve 231
  saccharinum 240, *240*
    cv. 'Laciniatum' 240
  saccharum 231
  sempervirens 233, *233*
  tataricum 241, *241*
Aceraceae 230
Aesculus
  x *carnea* 243, *243*
  hippocastanum 6, 243, *243*
  pavia 243
Agavaceae 300

Ailanthus attissina 224, *224*
Albizia 208
  julibrissin 209, *209*
  lophantha 208, *208*
Albizia, Plume 208, *208*
Alder 116
  Common 13, 117, *117*
  Green 116, *116*
  Grey 117
  Italian 117
  Smooth 117
Almond 193, *193*
Alnus 13, 116
  cordata 117
  glutinosa 13, 117, *117*
  incana 117
  rugosa 117
  viridis 116, *116*
Amelanchier 180
  canadensis 182
  grandiflora 181, *181*
  laevis 182, *182*
  ovalis 181, *181*
  spicata 181, 182
Anacardiaceae 226
Apple 166
  Chinese Crab 169
  Crab 166, *166*
  Cultivated 168, *168*
  Hall's Crab 169
  Hupeh Crab 169
  Magdeburg 168
  Purple Crab 169
  Siberian Crab 169
Apricot 194, *194*
Aquifoliaceae 11, 244
Araucaria araucana 36, *36*
Araucariaceae 36
Arbutus
  andrachne 283, *283*
  x *andrachnoides* 283
  menziesii 283
  unedo 282, *282*, 283
Arecastrum romanzoffianum 302, *302*
Ash 11
  Common 288, *288*
  Green 287
  Manna 286, *286*
  Mountain 172, *172*
  Narrow-leaved 289, *289*
  Red 287, *287*
  Weeping 288
  White 287
Aspen 14, 106, *106*
  Trembling 106
Avocado 151, *151*
Azarole 191, *191*

Balm of Gilead 108
Banana 301, *301*
Bangalay 270, *270*
Bay, Sweet 150, *150*
Beech 11, 122
  Common 122, *122*

Oriental 123, *123*
Roble 123, *123*
Betula 11, 13, 114
  papyrifera 115, *115*
  pendula 114, *114*
  pubescens 115, *115*
Betulaceae 114
Bignoniaceae 294
Birch 10, 114
  Downy 115, *115*
  Paper-bark 115, *115*
  Silver 13, 114, *114*, 115
Bitternut 111, *111*
Blackthorn 196, *196*
Blackwood 215, *215*
Box 248, *248*
  Balearic 249
Box-elder 234, *234*
Broussonetia papyrifera 145, *145*
Buckthorn 252, *252*
  Alder 253, *253*
  Sea 262, *262*
Bullace 197, *197*
Bull Bay 149, *149*
Butter-nut 113
Buxaceae 248
Buxus
  balearica 249
  sempervirens 248, *248*

Californian Big Tree 51, *51*
Calocedrus decurrens 41, *41*
Caprifoliaceae 298
Carob 210, *210*
Carpinus 118
  betulus 118, *118*
    cv. 'Fastigiata' 118
  orientalis 119, *119*
Carya 110, *110*
  alba 111, *111*
  cordiformis 111, *111*
Castanea 11, 124
  sativa 124, *124*
Catalpa
  bignonioides 294, *294*, 295
  x *erubescens* 295, *295*
  ovata 295, *295*
  speciosa 295, *295*
Catalpa
  Hybrid 295, *295*
  Western 295, *295*
  Yellow 295, *295*
Caucasian Wing-nut 112, *112*
Cedar 60
  Atlantic 60, *61*
  Atlas 12, 60, *61*
  Blue Atlas 12, *61*
  Himalayan 60, *60*
  Incense 41, *41*
  Indian 60, *60*
  Japanese Red 52, *52*
  of Goa 39, *39*
  of Lebanon 61, *61*
  Pencil 46, *46*
  Western Red 48, *48*

314

Cedrus 7, 60
  atlantica 12, 60, 61
    cv. 'Glauca' 12, 61
  deodara 60, 60
  libani 61, 61
Celastraceae 246
Celtis 140
  australis 140, 140
  tournefortii 141, 141
Cephalotaxaceae 35
Cephalotaxus 10
  harringtonia 35, 35
Ceratonia siliqua 210, 210
Cercidiphyllaceae 147
Cercidiphyllum japonicum
  147, 147
Cercis siliquastrum 210, 210
Chamaecyparis
  lawsoniana 37, 37, 38
  nootkatensis 14, 38, 38
  obtusa 37, 37
  pisifera 38, 38
Chamaerops humilis 304, 304
Cherry 192
  Autumn 202
  Bird 204, 204
  Black 204, 205
  Choke 205
  Cornelian 281, 281
  Japanese 201, 201
  Morello 199
  Oshima 201
  Rum 204, 205
  Saint Lucie 203, 203
  Sargent's 200, 200
  Sour 199, 199
  Spring 202, 202
  Tibetan 202, 202
  Yoshino 201, 201
Chestnut 124
  Horse 243, 243
  Spanish 124, 124
  Sweet 124, 124
Chilean Firebush 146, 146
Citron 223, 222
Citrus 222, 222
  aurantium, 222, 222
  bergamia 223, 222
  deliciosa 223, 222
  grandis 223, 222
  limetta 223, 222
  limon 223, 222
  medica 223, 222
  paradisi 223, 222
  sinensis 223, 223
Cordyline australis 300, 300,
  301
Cornaceae 281
Cornus
  mas 281, 281
  sanguinea 281
Corylaceae 118
Corylus 120
  avellana 120, 120, 121
  colurna 121, 121

  maxima 121, 121
    cv. atropurpureus 121
Corynabutilon vitifolium 249,
  249
Cotoneaster 12
  frigidus 182, 183, 183
  salicifolius 183
Cotoneaster, Himalayan Tree
  182, 183
Crataegus 184
  azarolus 191, 191
  calycina 185, 187, 187
  crus-galli 184, 184
  heldreichii 186
  laevigata 185, 185
  x lavallei 184
  monogyna 6, 185, 186, 186,
    187, 190
  nigra 186, 189, 189
  orientalis 186, 190, 190
  pentagyna 186, 188, 188, 190
  x prunifolia 184
Cryptomeria japonica 52, 52
Cupressaceae 37
Cupressocyparis leylandii 14,
  38, 38
  cv. 'Haggerston Grey' 38
  cv. 'Leighton Green' 39
Cupressus 10
  glabra 40, 40
  lusitanica 39, 39
  macrocarpa 14, 39, 39, 40
  sempervirens 40, 40
Cydonia oblonga 158, 158
Cypress
  Hinoki 37, 37
  Italian 40, 40
  Lawson 37, 37
  Leyland 14, 14, 38, 38
  Mexican 39, 39
  Monterey 14, 38, 39, 39
  Nootka 14, 38, 38
  Sawara 38, 38
  Smooth Arizona 40, 40
  Swamp 52, 52

Davidia involucrata 261, 261
Deodar, 60, 60
Diospyros
  kaki 284, 284
  lotus 284, 284
Dogwood 281
Dove Tree 261, 261
Dracaena draco 301, 301
Dragon Tree 301, 301
Drimys winteri 149, 149

Ebenaceae 284
Eleagnaceae 262
Eleagnus
  angustifolia 263, 263
  commutata 263
Elder 298, 298
  Alpine 298

Elm 9, 134
  Caucasian 138, 139
  Coritanian 137, 137
  Cornish 137, 137
  Dutch 135, 135
  English 135, 135
  European White 138, 138
  Plot's 137, 137
  Smooth 136, 136
  Wych 134, 134
Embothrium coccineum 146,
  146
Ericaceae 282
Eriobotrya japonica 180, 180
Eucalyptus 11, 270
  amygdalina 276
  botryoides 270, 270
  camaldulensis 275, 275
  citriodora 271, 271
  cladocalyx 276
  coccifera 276
  diversicolor 276
  globulus 276, 276
  gomphocephala 274, 274
  gunnii 279, 279
  maculata 276
  maidenii 277, 277
  pauciflora 276
  punctata 276
  resinifera 273, 273
  robusta 272, 272
  rudis 276
  sideroxylon 276
  tereticornis 276
  x trabutii 273
  urnigera 276
  viminalis 278, 278
Eucryphia 261
  cordifolia 261
  glutinosa 261
  x intermedia 261
  lucida 261
  x nymansensis 261
Eucryphiaceae 261
Euonymus 246
  europaeus 246, 246
  japonicus 247, 247
  latifolius 247, 247

Fagaceae 11, 122
Fagus 11
  orientalis 123, 123
  sylvatica 122, 122
Ficus
  carica 144, 145
  elastica 145
Fig 144, 145
Filbert 121, 121
Fir
  Alpine 57, 57
  Caucasian 57, 57
  Colorado White 56
  Common Silver 54, 54
  Delavay's Silver 55, 55
  Douglas 73, 73

Giant 56, *56*
Grecian 55, *55*
Noble 59, *59*
Siberian 59, *59*
Spanish 58, *58*
Foxglove Tree 296, *296*
Frangula alnus 253, *253*
Fraxinus 286
   americana 287, *287*
   angustifolia 289, *289*
   excelsior 288, *288*
      cv. *'Pendula'* 288
   ornus 286, *286*
   pallisiae 289
   pennsylvanica 287, *287*
      var. *subintegerrima* 287

Gean 198, *198*
Ghost Tree 261, *261*
Ginkgoaceae 34
Ginkgo biloba 34, *34*
Gleditsia triacanthos 211, *211*
Golden Rain Tree 242, *242*
Golden Wreath 212, *212*
Grapefruit 223, *222*
Guelder Rose 298, *298*, 299
Gum 270
   Black 260, *260*
   Cider 279, *279*
   Lemon-scented Spotted 271, *271*
   Maiden's 277, *277*
   Murray Red 275, *275*
   Red 275, *275*
   Ribbon 278, *278*
   Tasmanian Blue 276, *276*

Hamamelidaceae 152
Hamamelis 153, *153*
   x *intermedia* 153
   japonica 153
   mollis 153
   virginiana 153
Hawthorn 184
   Common 6, 186, *186*
   Midland 185, *185*
Hazel 11, 120
   Common 120, *120*
   Turkish 121, *121*
Hemlock
   Eastern 72, *72*
   Western 72, *72*
Hiba 49, *49*
Hickory 110, *110*
   Shagbark 111, *111*
Hippocastanaceae 243
Hippophäe rhamnoides 262, *262*
Holly 244
   Canary 245
   Common 244, *244*
   Highclere 245, *245*
   White 155, *155*
Hornbeam 118, *118*

Eastern 119, *119*
Hop 119, *119*
Horse Chestnut
   Common 6, 243, *243*
   Red 243, *243*
Howeia forsterana 302, *303*

Ilex 244
   x *altaclarensis* 245, *245*
   aquifolium 244, *244*
   perado 245
Indian Bead Tree 225, *225*
Indian Bean Tree 294, *294*
Iron Bark 272, *272*

Jubaea chilensis 303, *303*
Judas Tree 210, *210*
Juglandaceae 110
Juglans 112
   cinerea 113
   nigra 113, *113*
   regia 112, *113*
Jujube, Common 251, *251*
Juniper 42
   Chinese 47, *47*
   Common 12, 42, *42*
   Grecian 44, *44*
   Phoenician 44, *44*
   Prickly 43, *43*
Juniperus 10, 42
   chinensis 47, *47*
   communis 12, 42, *42*
      subsp. *hemisphaerica* 43
      subsp. *nana* 42
   excelsa 44, *44*
   foetidissima 45, *45*, 46
   oxycedrus 43, *43*
      subsp. *macrocarpa* 43
      subsp. *oxycedrus* 42
      subsp. *transtagana* 43
   phoenicea 44, *44*
   thurifera 46
   virginiana 46, *46*

Kakee 284, *284*
Katsura Tree 147, *147*
Keaki 139, **139**
Koelreuteria paniculata 242, *242*

Laburnum 12, 218
   alpinum 218, *218*, 219
   anagyroides 219, *219*
   x *watereri* 219
Laburnum 218
   Alpine 218, *218*
   Common 219, *219*
   Scotch 218, *218*
   Voss's 219
Larch 62
   Common 62, *62*, 64
   Dahurian 64, *65*
   Dunkeld 64, *64*
   Golden 65, *65*
   Japanese 63, *63*, 64
   Polish 63

Larix 62
   decidua 62, *62*, 64
      subsp. *polonica* 63
   x *eurolepis* 64, *64*
   gmelinii 64, *65*
   kaempferi 63, *63*, 64
Lauraceae 150
Laurel
   Cherry 207, *207*
   Portugal 206, *206*
Laurus nobilis 150, *150*
Laurustinus 299, *299*
Leguminosae 208
Lemon 223, *223*
Ligustrum
   lucidum 290, *290*
   vulgare 290
Lilac
   Common 293, *293*
   Hungarian 293
Lime
   Caucasian 259, *259*
   Common 258, *258*
   Large-leaved 256, *256*
   Silver 254, *254*
   Small-leaved 257, *257*
   Sweet 222, 223
   Weeping Silver 255, *255*
Liquidambar
   orientalis 152, *153*
   styraciflua 152
Liriodendron
   chinense 148
   tulipifera 148, *148*
Livistona australis 305, *305*
Locust
   Clammy 221, *221*
   Honey 211, *211*
Locust Tree 210, *210*, 220, *221*
Loquat 180, *180*

Maclura pomifera 144, *144*
Madrona 283
Magnoliaceae 148
Magnolia, Evergreen 149, *149*
Magnolia grandiflora 149, *149*
Mahogany
   Red 273, *273*
   Swamp 272, *272*
Maidenhair Tree 34, *34*
Malus 166
   baccata 169
   dasyphylla 167, *167*
   domestica 168, *168*
   florentina 166
   x *floribunda* 169, *169*
   halliana 169
   hupehensis 169
   x *magdeburgensis* 168
   praecox 168
   x *purpurea* 169
   spectabilis 169
      x *pumila* 168
   sylvestris 166, *166*
Malvaceae 249

Maple 9, 230
  Balkan 232, *232*
  Cretan 233, *233*
  Downy Japanese 237, *237*
  Field 230, *230*
  Flowering 249, *249*
  Heldreich's 231, *231*
  Italian 235, *235*
  Lobel's 238
  Montpelier 233, *233*
  Norway 238, *238*
  Paper-bark 231, *231*
  Père David's 231, *231*
  Red 241, *241*
  Silver 240, *240*
  Smooth Japanese 236, *236*
  Tartar 241, *241*
Mastic Tree 228, *229*
Medlar 183, *183*
Melia azedarach 225, *225*
Meliaceae 225
Mespil, Snowy 180, 181, *181*
Mespilus germanica 183, *183*
Metasequoia glyptostraboides 53, *53*
Mimosa 212, 213, *213*
Mock Orange 155, *155*
Monkey Puzzle 36, *36*
Moraceae 142
Morus 142
  alba 142, *142*
  nigra 143, *143*
Mountain Ash 172, *172*, 173
Mulberry 142
  Black 143, *143*
  Common 143, *143*
  White 142, *142*
Musa cavendishii 301, *301*
Musaceae 301
Myoporaceae 297
Myoporum tenuifolium 297, *297*
Myricaceae 110
Myrica faya 110, *110*
Myrobalan 194, *195*
Myrtaceae 270
Myrtle, Orange-bark 279, *279*
Myrtus apiculata 279, *279*

Nettle-tree 140
  Southern 140, *140*
Nothofagus 11
  obliqua 123, *123*
  procera 123, *123*
Nyssaceae 260
Nyssa sylvatica 260, *260*

Oak 7, 9, 11, 13, 125
  Algerian 133, *133*
  Cork 128, *128*
  Downy 132, *132*
  Durmast 130, *130*
  English 131, *131*
  Holm 13, 127, *127*
  Hungarian 132, *132*

Macedonian 129, *129*
  Mirbeck's 133, *133*
  Pin 126, *126*
  Pyrenean 133, *133*
  Red 125, *125*
  Scarlet 126, *126*
  Sessile 130, *130*
  Turkey 128, *128*
Oleaceae 286
Olea europaea 291, *291*
  var. *europaea* 291
  var. *sylvestris* 291
Oleaster 263, *263*
Olive 291, *291*
  Cultivated 291
  Wild 291
Orange
  Osage 144, *144*
  Seville 222, *222*
  Sweet 223, *223*
Osier, Common 101, *101*
Ostrya carpinifolia 119, *119*

Pagoda Tree 220, *220*
Paliurus spina-christi 250, *250*, 251
Palm 9
  Cabbage 300, *300*
  Canary Island Date 306, *306*
  Chilean Wine 303, *303*
  Chinese Windmill 308, *308*
  Date 307, *307*
  European Fan 304, *304*
  Petticoat 309, *309*
  Queen 302, *302*
  Sentry 302, *303*
Palmae 302
Parrotia persica 153, *153*
Paulownia tomentosa 296, *296*
Peach 192, *192*
Pear 158
  Almond-leaved 163, *163*
  Aurelian 162, *162*
  Common 165, *165*
  Sage-leaved 162, *162*
  Willow-leaved 159, *159*
Pepperidge 260, *260*
Pepper Tree 227, *227*
  Brazilian 227
Persea americana 151, *151*
Persian Ironwood 153, *153*
Persian Lilac 225, *225*
Persimmon, Chinese 284, *284*
Phillyrea latifolia 292, *292*
Phoenix 306
  canariensis 306, *306*
  dactylifera 307, *307*
  theophrastii 306
Phytolacca 146, *147*
Phytolaccaceae 146
Phytolacca dioica 146, *147*
Picea 66
  abies 66, *66*
    subsp. *abies* 66
    subsp. *obovata* 66

breweriana 67, *67*
  engelmanii 69, *69*
  glauca 68, *68*
  omorika 71, *71*
  orientalis 68, *68*
  pungens 67, *67*
  sitchensis 70, *70*
Pinaceae 54
Pine 74
  Aleppo 84, *84*
  Arolla 86, *86*
  Austrian 79, *79*
  Bhutan 87, *87*
  Bosnian 82, *82*
  Bristle-cone 89, *89*
  Calabrian 84
  Canary Island 84
  Corsican 79, *79*
  Cow Tail 35, *35*
  Digger 78
  Jack 77, 77
  Jeffrey 78
  Lodgepole 75, *74*
  Macedonian 88, *88*
  Maritime 75, *75*
  Monterey 76, *76*
  Mountain 80, *81*
  Northern Pitch 76, *76*
  Red 81
  Scots 7, 80, *80*
  Stone 85, *85*
  Umbrella 85, *85*
  Western Yellow 78, *78*
  Weymouth 88, *89*
  White 88, *89*
Pinus 74
  aristata 89, *89*
  banksiana 77, 77
  brutia 84, *84*
  canariensis 84, *84*
  cembra 86, *86*
  contorta 74, *74*
    var. *latifolia* 75, *74*
  halepensis 84, *84*
  heldreichii 83, *83*
  jeffreyi 78
  leucodermis 82, *83*
  mugo 81, *81*
  nigra 79, *79*, 82
    subsp. *laricio* 79, *79*
    subsp. *nigra* 79, *79*
  peuce 88, *88*
  pinaster 75, *75*
  pinea 85, *85*
  ponderosa 78, *78*, 81
  radiata 76, *76*
  resinosa 81
  rigida 76, *76*
  sabiniana 78
  strobus 88, *89*
  sylvestris 7, 80, *80*, 81
  uncinata 81
  wallichiana 87, *87*
Pistacia
  atlantica 228

lentiscus 228, *229*
x *raportae* 229
terebinthus 228, *228*
vera 229, *229*
Pistachio 229, *229*
Pittosporaceae 154
Pittosporum 154, *154*
colensoi 154
crassifolium 154, *155*
eugenioides 154
ralphii 154
tenuifolium 154, *154*
cv. 'Silver Queen' 154
cv. 'Variegatum' 154
tobira 155, *155*
undlatum 155, *155*
Plane 156
London 12, 157, *157*
Oriental (Eastern) 12, 156, *156*
Western 12, 157
Platanaceae 156
Platanus 156
x *hispanica* 12, 157, *157*
occidentalis 12, 157
orientalis 12, 156, *156*, 157
Plum 192, 196, *197*
Cherry 194, *195*
Date 284, *284*
Pocket-handkerchief Tree 261, *261*
Pomegranate 280, *280*
Pomelo 223, *222*
Poplar 104
Balsam 107, *107*, 108
Berlin 109
Black 108, *108*
Grey 14, 105, *105*
Hybrid 14, 105
Hybrid Black 109, *109*
Lombardy 108
Western Balsam 107, *107*
White 104, *104*
Populus 104
alba 104, *104*, 105
balsamifera 107, *107*, 108
x *berolinensis* 109
x *canadensis* 109, *109*
candicans 108
canescens 14, 105, *105*
x *tremula* 105
deltoides 109, *109*
gileadensis 106
x *hybrida* 14, *105*
laurifolia 108
nigra 108, *108*
cv. 'Italica' 108
simonii 106
tremula 14, 105, 106, *106*
x *tremuloides* 106
trichocarpa 107, *107*
Pride of India 242, *242*
Privet
Common 290
Glossy 290, *290*
Proteaceae 146

Prunus 192
armeniaca 194, *194*
avium 198, *198*, 200, 202
brigantina 195, *195*
cerasifera 194, *194*
var. *pissardii* 195, *195*
cerasus 199, *199*
cocomilia 197
domestica 196, *197*
subsp. *institia* 196, *197*
dulcis 193, *193*
laurocerasus 207, *207*
lusitanica 206, *206*
mahaleb 203, *203*
padus 204, *204*
persica 192, *192*
sargentii 200, *200*
serotina 204, *205*
serrula 202, *202*
serrulata 201, *201*
speciosa 201
spinosa 196, *196*
subhirtella 200, 201, 202, *203*
cv. 'Autumnalis' 202
virginiana 205
x *yedoensis* 201, *201*
Pseudolarix amabilis 65, *65*
Pseudotsuga menziesii 73, *73*
Pterocarya 104
fraxinifolia 112, *112*
Punicaceae 280
Punica granatum 280, *280*
Pyrus 158
amygdaliformis 163, *163*
austriaca 164, 165
bourgaeana 161, *161*
communis 163, 164, 165, *165*
var. *culta* 165
cordata 160, *160*
elaeagrifolia 162, *162*
nivalis 162, 164, *164*, 165
pyraster 160, *161*, 165
salicifolia 159, *159*
cv. 'Pendula' 159
salvifolia 162, *162*, 165

Quercus 11, 13, 125
canariensis 133, *133*
cerris 128, *129*
x *suber* 124
coccifera 126, *126*
coccinea 126, *126*
dalechampii 130, *130*
frainetto 132, *132*
x *hispanica* 124
ilex 13, 127, *127*
macrolepis 129, *129*
palustris 126, *126*
pedunculiflora 131, *131*
petraea 130, *130*
pubescens 132, *132*, 133
pyrenaica 133, *133*
robur 131, *131*
rubra 125, *125*, 126

suber 128, *128*
trojana 129, *129*
virgiliana 133, *133*
Quickthorn 186, *186*
Quince 158, *158*

Rauli 123, *123*
Redwood
Coast 50, *50*
Dawn 53, *53*
Giant 51, *51*
Rhamnaceae 250
Rhamnus catharticus 252, *252*
Rhus coriaria 226, *226*
typhina 226, *226*
vernicifluar 226
Robinia 220
pseudacacia 221, *221*
viscosa 221, *221*
Rosaceae 158
Rowan 170, 172, *172*
Hupeh 173, *173*
Japanese 171, *171*
Sargent's 173, *173*
Vilmorin's 171, *171*
Rutaceae 222, *222*

Salicaceae 90
Salix 90
alba 92, *92*
subsp. *coerulea* 93
subsp. *vitellina* x *babylonica* 93
appendiculata 97, *97*
atrocinerea 98, *98*
aurita 98, 101
babylonica 93, *93*
borealis 95, *95*
caprea 97, 98, 99, 101
x *chrysocoma* 93
cinerea 97, *97*, 98, 101, 102
coeatanea 99
daphnoides 103, *103*
elaeagnos 102, *102*
fragilis 90, *90*
x *alba* 90
x *triandra* 94
x *leiophylla* 94
x *macrophylla* 97
x *mollissima* 94
nigricans 95, 102
pedicellata 96, *96*
pentandra 91, *91*
purpurea x *triandra* 94
rossica 101
x *rubens* 90
x *speciosa* 94
triandra 94, *94*
x *viminalis* 94
viminalis 101, *101*, 102
xerophila 100, *100*
Sallow
Common 97, 98, *98*
Eared 98
Great 98, *99*

Sambucus
nigra 298, *298*
racemosa 298
Sapindaceae 242
Schinus
molle 227, *227*
terebinthifolia 227
Scrophulariaceae 296
Sequoiadendron giganteum
51, *51*
Sequoia sempervirens 50, *50*
Serviceberry, Allegheny 182, *182*
Service Tree 170
Bastard 179, *179*
of Fontainebleau 178, *178*
True 170, *170*
Wild 174, *174*
Shaddock *222*, 223
Silver Berry 263
Silver Fir 54, *54*
Simaroubaceae 224
Siris 208
Pink 209, *209*
Sloe 196, *196*
Snowbell Tree 285
Sophora japonica 220, *220*
Sorbus 170
aria 170, 174, *175*, 178
cv. *'Decaisneana'* 175
cv. *'Lutescens'* 175
aucuparia 172, *172*, 176
austriaca 176, *176*
subsp. *austriaca* 176
commixta 171, *171*
domestica 170, *170*
graeca 175, *175*, 176
hupehensis 173, *173*
hybrida 179, *179*
cv. *'Fastigiata'* 179
intermedia 177, *177*
latifolia 178, *178*
meinchii 179, *179*
mougeotii 176, *176*
rupicola 175
sargentiana 173, *173*
torminalis 170, 174, *174*, 178
umbellata 176, *176*
vilmorinii 171, *171*
Spanish Bayonet 300, *300*
Spindle Tree 246
Broad-leaved 247, *247*
Common 246, *246*
Japanese 247, *247*
Spruce 66
Brewer's Weeping 67, *67*
Colorado 67, *67*
Engelmann 69, *69*
Norway 66, *66*
Oriental 68, *68*
Serbian 71, *71*
Siberian 66
Sitka 70, *70*
White 68, *68*
Storax 285, *285*

Strawberry Tree 282, *282*
Cyprus 283, *283*
Eastern 283, *283*
Hybrid 283
Styracaceae 285
Styrax
japonica 285
officinale 285, *285*
Sumach 226, *226*
Stag's Horn 226, *226*
Swamp Messmate 272, *272*
Sweet Gum 152
Oriental 152, *152*
Sycamore 230, 239, *239*
Syringa
josikaea 293
vulgaris 293, *293*

Tamaricaceae 264
Tamarisk 264
African 264, *264*
Chinese 269
French 266, *266*
Tamarix 264
africana 264, *264*
canariensis 265, *265*
chinensis 269
dalmatica 268, *268*
gallica 266, *266*
parviflora 267, *267*
smyrnensis 269, *269*
tetrandra 267, *267*
Tangerine 223, *222*
Taxaceae 35
Taxodiaceae 50
Taxodium distichum 52, *52*
Taxus 10
baccata 35, *35*
Tetraclinis articulata 48, *48*
Thorn
Broad-leaved Cockspur 184
Christ's 250, *250*
Cockspur 184, *184*
Hybrid Cockspur 184
Oriental 190, *190*
Thuja plicata 48, *48*
Thujopsis dolabrata 49, *49*
Tilia
cordata 257, *257*, 258, 259
dasystyla 259
x euchlora 259, *259*
petiolaris 255, *255*
platyphyllos 256, *256*, 258
rubra 257, *257*
tomentosa 254, *254*, 255
x vulgaris 258, *258*
Tiliaceae 254
Trachycarpus fortunei 308, *308*
Tree of Heaven 224, *224*
Tsuga
canadensis 72, *72*
heterophylla 72, *72*
Tuart 274, *274*
Tulip Tree 148, *148*
Chinese 148

Tupelo 260, *260*
Turpentine Tree 228, *228*

Ulmaceae 11, 134
Ulmus 134
angustifolia 137, *137*
canescens 137, *137*
carpinifolia 136, *136*
coritana 137, *137*
glabra 134, *134*, 135, 136
x hollandica 135, *135*
cv. 'Hollandica' 135
cv. 'Vegeta' 135
laevis 138, *138*
minor 136, *136*, 137
plotii 137, *137*
procera 135, *135*

Varnish Tree 226
Viburnum
lantana 299, *299*
opulus 298, *298*
tinus 299, *299*

Walnut 112
Black 113, *113*
Common 112, *113*
Washingtonia filifera 309, *309*
Wattle 212
Golden 216, *216*
Green 214, *215*
Silver 213, *213*
Swamp 217, *217*
Sydney Golden 214, *215*
Willow 212, *212*
Wayfaring Tree 299, *299*
Wellingtonia 51, *51*
Whitebeam 170, 174, *175*
Swedish 177, *177*
Willow 11, 90
Almond 94, *94*
Bay 91, *91*
Chinese Weeping 93, *93*
Crack 90, *90*
Dark-leaved 95
Goat 98, *99*
Grey 97
Hoary 102, *102*
Pussy 98, *99*
Violet 103, *103*
Weeping 93
White 92, *92*
Winter's Bark 149, *149*
Witch Hazel 153, *153*
Chinese 153
Japanese 153
Virginian 153

Yew, Common 35, *35*
Yucca aloifolia 300, *300*

Zelkova 138
carpinifolia 138, 139, *139*
serrata 139, *139*
Zizyphus jujuba 251, *251*

More titles from the Philip's 'Guide to' range

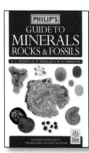

0 540 07429 2
£9.99

Philip's Guide to Minerals, Rocks & Fossils

A. C. Bishop, A. R. Woolley & W. R. Hamilton

Published in association with The Natural History Museum, London, this is a practical and authoritative guide to identifying all minerals, rocks and fossils. This edition has been completely revised, updated and redesigned, with extended introductory sections and appendices.

0 540 08389 5
£9.99

Philip's Guide to Gems

Cally Oldershaw

A practical guide to the identification and use of precious and semi-precious stones, novelty stones, agates and crystals. The substantial introductory section describes all aspects of gemmology in clear and accessible terms. The main part of the book examines stones, concentrating especially on the semi-precious stones used by professional and amateur jewellers.

0 540 08747 5
£9.99

Philip's Guide to Seashores and Shallow Seas

Andrew C. Campbell

An identification guide to the fascinating plant and animal life found in the shallow seas and on the seashores of Britain and northern Europe. More than 1,000 species are described and illustrated, with details of form, size, habitat and distribution.

Philip's Guide to Seashells of the World

A.P.H. Oliver

A fascinating book providing an easy-to-use identification guide that covers a wide range of shells, from the commonest to the most beautiful and coveted. The identification section describes some 1,200 species in great detail, with more than 1,000 illustrations.

0 540 08566 9   £9.99

Also available...

Philip's Guide to Fossils of the World
A.P.H. Oliver • 0 540 08374 7 • £9.99

Philip's Guide to the State of the World
0 540 08578 2 • £9.99

Philip's World Factbook
Keith Lye • 0 540 08696 7 • £9.99

Philip's Guide to Oceans
Dr John Pernetta
0 540 08559 6 • £9.99

Philip's Guide to Wetlands
Dr Patrick Dugan
0 540 08793 9 • £9.99

Philip's Guide to Mountains
General Editor Doug Scott
• 0 540 08579 0 • £9.99

Philip's Guide to Weather
0 540 08704 1 • £9.99

☎ **How to order** The Philip's range of reference titles is available from bookshops o directly from the publisher by phoning 01903 828503 or online at www.philips-maps.co.uk.

Prices are correct at time of going to press but are subject to change without notification.